M. Gunasekaran

DISCARDED

Principles of Plant Physiology

Principles of Plant Physiology

by James Bonner
California Institute of Technology

Arthur W. Galston
Yale University

Illustrations by Evan L. Gillespie

W. H. FREEMAN AND COMPANY · SAN FRANCISCO

PREFACE

A FORMIDABLE task confronting the teacher of plant physiology is that of deciding what information to present to his students. The difficulty lies not in gathering sufficient data, but rather in discarding certain less important details in favor of those facts and concepts which are central to our understanding of the functioning plant. The same task confronts the writer of a textbook of plant physiology. The nature of the selection and the degree of condensation and crystallization achieved depend, of course, on the viewpoint of the authors. We should like, therefore, to outline the principles which have guided us in the preparation of this book.

An elementary textbook must be sufficiently brief and decisive to permit the student to visualize and grasp clearly its basic principles. For this reason, the presentation of extensive data in tabular form has been minimized in the present volume. Similarly, detailed discussions of contradictory views have been avoided, as far as possible, in favor of synthesis of existing knowledge into a single working hypothesis. Thus in Chapter 7, we have chosen, in the interests of clarity, to emphasize one view of phloem transport over other views. This has been done in the hope that a clear conception of translocation will aid the student in organizing and remembering the facts relative to this subject. It may be objected that such a selective treatment tends to become dogmatic. This is true. We have, however, tried diligently to avoid dogmatism and to indicate uncertainties and controversy where they exist.

The developments of modern biology have tended more and more to obscure whatever dividing line may once have existed between physiology and biochemistry. The growth of our knowledge in plant physiology is no exception to this pattern. Indeed, by taking advantage of the discoveries and unifying principles of modern biochemistry, we can today discuss certain aspects of plant physiology more concretely and in simpler terms than was possible a few years ago. This is particularly true of respiration, of nitrogen metabolism, and of photosynthesis. We hope that in presenting these subjects in biochemical terms we have achieved a simplification as well as a deeper insight into each.

This book is presented as an elementary text, and as such it will, we trust, be used by many students whose interests lie in the applied fields of plant science as well as by those interested in plant physiology itself. For students of both categories, however, we have tried to link the principles of plant physiology to actual agricultural problems and to suggest ways in which plant physiology is related to practical affairs.

In writing this book, the authors have necessarily assumed that the student possesses a certain minimum background in basic science. This background is taken to be an introductory course in chemistry and an elementary course in general botany. Certain matters often discussed in textbooks of plant physiology, such as the principles of pH and buffer action, are omitted from this book, since they are now adequately treated in such introductory chemistry texts as Pauling's *College Chemistry*. Detailed anatomical discussions presented in many textbooks of general botany have been avoided for the same reason. As our knowledge of plant physiology increases in bulk, our textbooks would similarly increase, were it not for the possibility of reorganizing our facts into more compact and closely integrated units.

The lists of suggested reading material appended to each chapter include certain classical papers, monographs, review articles, and other texts. They have been chosen, with few exceptions, on the basis of general availability, and are in the main limited to works in the English language. The original researches upon which the material in this text is ultimately based will usually be found in the literature citations in these general references.

This book is planned for a one-semester or a two-quarter course in elementary plant physiology. It can also serve, with suitable pruning, for a one-quarter course in the subject. We suggest that, where necessary, Chapters 6, 9, 12, 13, and 19, and portions of Chapters 10 and 11 may be omitted.

The writing of a textbook is a process which is arduous and painful not only to the authors but to a host of other people as well. Those upon whom we have most depended for detailed criticism of all of the manuscript through its successive incarnations have been Ralph Emerson and Leonard Machlis. Rosamond S. Baker has participated in various aspects of our work from beginning to end and has lightened our burden in many ways. The staff of W. H. Freeman and Company has, by its good judgment, boundless enthusiasm, and sense of humor, helped us over one rough spot after another. Various portions of the text have been read and criticized by Adriance S. Foster, Dale J. Galston, David R. Goddard, Leonard L. Jansen, Anton Lang, George G. Laties, James L. Liverman, Adele Millerd, John G. Torrey, and Betty Jean Wood. Kay Asakawa, Mrs. Logan Clendening, and Andrée Crehan have typed the manuscript, and Mary E. Durrell and D. Harold McRae have aided in the reading of the proof. To all of these friends, we express our deep thanks. In acknowledging our indebtedness to them, we do not wish to minimize our complete responsibility for any errors of fact or interpretation which may have crept into this book.

Finally, it is a pleasure to pay tribute to the splendid artistic collaboration of Evan Gillespie.

September 1951　　　　　　　　　　JAMES BONNER
Pasadena　　　　　　　　　　　　ARTHUR W. GALSTON

CONTENTS

Part III: Growth and Development

CHAPTER 1

Plants and Plant Physiology

The Subject Matter of Plant Physiology

The living creatures of the earth all depend for their sustenance directly or indirectly on the plants that cover the surface of the land and dwell in the waters of the oceans. The biblical statement that "all flesh is grass" applies, of course, not only to the animals that devour plants but also to the organisms that subsist on these animals, and to the microorganisms that produce their substance as they decompose the remains of other plant or animal life.

The thin mantle of plants which covers the globe is an ever-changing one; plant substance removed by human, animal, and microbial activity is continuously replenished by fresh plant growth; and this plant growth represents the world's most exuberant and extensive chemical activity. Each year some 200 billion tons of carbon are removed from the air as carbon dioxide and incorporated into plant material through photosynthesis. Each year, also, roughly an equivalent amount of carbon is transformed from plant material to other forms of life, whence it is returned, ultimately, to the carbon dioxide of the air. The plant cover of the earth is hence in a constantly dynamic state, constantly being added to by photosynthesis and plant growth—constantly being utilized by other forms of life. It is with this dynamic state of the plant world that the present book is concerned.

Plants occupy the most varied habitats. The dense, storied vegetation of the tropical rain forest; the cool, dark, coniferous forests of the temperate regions; the sweeping grasslands of the prairie or veld; the sparse, creeping vegetation of the wind-swept tundra; and the algae of the lakes and oceans are as dissimilar in outward appearance as are the climates of these varied regions. Yet the principles of plant growth and metabolism—the principles of plant physiology—are remarkably

1

uniform and apply equally throughout this wide range of plant forms.

Plant physiology is the study of how plants function. Very broadly speaking, it is the study of the processes involved in plant growth and plant behavior. It includes the examination of the internal mechanisms by which the plant carries on its many complex synthetic chemical processes and the way in which these processes are integrated. The climatic factors of the environment and the interactions of the plant with its fellow organisms, insofar as they influence and modify the course of plant development, are also of concern to plant physiology.

The Activities of the Plant

The apparent ease with which a seed planted in the garden or field sprouts and grows into a mature plant shows us that plants are well adjusted to the circumstances under which they must complete their life cycle, but it gives us no hint of the complexity and delicate balance between the many processes which, by their simultaneous progression, result in plant development. While the green leaves take up and fix carbon dioxide through the process of photosynthesis, the roots at the same time absorb from the soil the mineral elements and water which are so essential to plant growth.

The CO_2 absorbed by the leaves and the water and minerals taken up by the roots constitute the raw materials of plant growth. Our first consideration will be devoted to these raw materials—their nature, the ways in which they enter into the plant, and their effect on the plant's economy. Plants grow in soil, and the water and minerals consumed by plants must be extracted from this ubiquitous but complex medium. We shall need therefore to consider the soil in its relation to plant welfare.

Although the separate organs of the plant are highly specialized in their activities, harmonious and integrated growth is achieved through mutual cooperation and continuous interchange of materials. Minerals and water taken up by the roots are transported and made available to the leaves, while simultaneously the photosynthetic products of the leaves are moved downward to the roots. Translocation, the transport of materials within the plant, is then another important aspect of the plant's economy.

Raw materials do not make a plant; they are merely the essential ingredients from which a plant augments itself by subsequent processes of plant metabolism. It is the unique and wonderful property of plants that from the simplest starting materials they manufacture the magnificent array of complex chemical compounds which together make up plant tissue. Sugars, fats, proteins, vitamins, and a host of other substances are formed through the processes of plant metabolism. These same materials, so important to the life of the growing plant, form the raw materials of our own economy—our source of food, clothing, heat, and so on. Plant metabolism, the synthesis and interconversion of complex molecules from the simple raw materials of plant nutrition, is the subject of an important section of this book.

The principal events in the life of the plant—seed germination, growth, flower formation, fruit production, and seed formation—follow one another in orderly progression through the changing seasons and through the years. During the successive stages of plant development, the growth of each organ is attuned to, and kept in step with, the growth of other organs. How is this harmonization of plant growth in time and space achieved? We know today that the synchronization and integration of the growth of the separate plant organs, as well as the control of flower and fruit production, are achieved through particular chemical substances, substances which, like the hormones of animals, move from organ to organ and from tissue to tissue, evoking or suppressing growth in size or changes in form. The work of these messenger substances is complex and is intermeshed with the relations between the various plant parts which result from the interchange of the basic raw materials of plant growth. Our knowledge of these substances, incomplete as it is, has given us much insight into, and control over, plant growth. Plant growth and its integration by the chemical messenger substances make up another important part of the study of plant physiology.

Finally, we must consider the plant in relation to its environment. Such climatic influences as temperature, light, and rainfall, together with the factors of the soil, determine not only the nature of the agricultural enterprises that may be successfully undertaken in a given region, but also in a large measure the way in which the different vegetational types are distributed over the earth's surface. Although most of our discussion will necessarily be focused on the individual processes which constitute plant growth, we shall in the final chapter enter the field of plant ecology to consider the plant as a whole in relation to its environment.

Plant Physiology and Agriculture

Agriculture is still the world's biggest business, a business to which more people are devoted, and which yields a greater volume of product, than any of man's other activities. Agriculture is based on the ability of plants to grow and thereby transform simple raw materials into complex substances suitable to man's needs. These are the very properties of plants which form the subject matter of plant physiology. It is not surprising, therefore, that the information gained by study of plant physiology finds its principal application in the improvement of agricultural procedures. Agricultural research is, in fact, primarily a matter of the application of certain sciences, including plant physiology, to the specific problems of crop production. Research in the plant sciences is carried forward on a wide scale both in the United States and elsewhere. Prior to the second world war, the U. S. Department of Agriculture was one of the largest scientific research organizations in the world. The contributions of this research have made it possible to increase both the amount of crop produced per unit of human effort invested and the amount of produce per unit of land area utilized. The benefits of these increases in agricultural efficiency have resulted in an economy in which the majority of individuals no longer need to concern themselves directly with food production but can, rather, rely on the agricultural labors of a relative few.

Important advances in agricultural productivity have been derived from plant improvement through the application of the principles of genetics and plant breeding. Important contributions have been made also through the control of the insect, bacterial, and fungal pests which formerly did so much to lower crop production. One of plant physiology's major contributions to agriculture is the improvement of fertilizer practice. We now know a great deal about what minerals and how much of each should be added to a soil for maximal productivity of a given crop. We possess relatively satisfactory methods for the diagnosis and assessment of fertilizer needs. The knowledge of what constitutes proper fertilizer practice, which has been of the greatest importance in enabling us to achieve and maintain high crop yields over the years, has been purely a matter of the application of principles of plant physiology to the practical problem of crop production. Similarly, the study of the water relations of plants has found its application in irrigation practice, while the study of plant metabolism has been of value in developing methods for the storage and transport of fruits and vegetables.

New methods for the control of plant growth and development through the use of specific chemical substances constitute one of the most spectacular agricultural applications of plant physiology in recent years. Flowering, fruit set, fruit drop, dormancy, root formation, and even the suppression of undesirable plants can all be controlled to advantage in certain crops through the use of specific chemical materials. These applications are based on the information which plant physiology has amassed concerning the chemical messenger substances which plants themselves use in the regulation of their activities. The success of these practical developments is in fact a good example of the relation between basic research, which is concerned with the discovery of new principles, and technological research, which is concerned with the application of these principles to practical problems. The investigation into the chemical nature of the substances used in growth regulation by plants themselves was true discovery research—discovery of new principles. The development of chemical crop control in the years since 1935 has been based on these principles.

Although plant physiology itself is concerned with the principles which govern plant growth and development, we should not lose sight of the fact that the ultimate usefulness of these principles lies in their application—in agriculture, in forestry, or in other fields in which the production of plant products for man's welfare is concerned. And we should keep in mind that it is through unbiased research into principles, through discovery research, that new practical applications are made possible.

Plant Physiology and World Affairs

The world is confronted by an ever-deepening food crisis. We live in an age of chronic food shortage, a shortage which is intensified as the population of the world increases faster than our current production of food. Considering the globe as a whole, the available food supply in 1949 approximated that of 1939, but in these ten years the world's population had increased by 15 per cent. A few areas of the earth, including the Americas, are fortunately regions of food surplus. These areas of plenty are more than offset, however, by great areas of food deficiency. Although many economic factors bear on this problem, it is evident that food production over the world as a whole must be increased if everyone is to be adequately fed.

Large increases in agricultural production cannot be immediately achieved by the subjugation of additional land, since the bulk of the fertile soils of the world are already in use. Further research may indicate methods for the successful and stable utilization of certain of the vast tropical regions which cannot now be exploited effectively. More important at present are the increases in agricultural productivity which may be achieved through a better understanding of plants and through the application of existing knowledge to a larger portion of the world's agriculture. The application of our knowledge of genetics, chemical pest control, and proper fertilizer practices would perhaps most rapidly and significantly increase agricultural output in the food-deficient areas of the world.

Many problems of food production still await solution in the hands of plant physiologists. Not only is it desirable to achieve still further control and guidance over crop development, but we need also entirely new approaches. One might, for example, conceive of new crop plants or of new ways for production of edible fats or proteins from existing crop plants, and one might foresee also the more intensive utilization in various ways of aquatic plants. The soils of the world present their own problems, problems which are in urgent need of more study. Soil fertility shows a downward trend over the world as a whole—a trend which we cannot afford in the face of the world's food requirements. We need more information on how to create and maintain soils at maximum fertility. It is clear, therefore, that a satisfactory future for the world's food supply will depend on the development of our knowledge of plant physiology.

Plant physiologists work to obtain a better understanding of, and better control over, the growth of plants. They have the satisfaction of seeing their findings translated into practice in the world's largest industry. And the ability of the world to support its growing population depends on the future developments of plant physiology and the application of these developments.

The Place of Plant Physiology in the Plant Sciences

The field of experimental plant science is frequently divided into several categories, based on the objectives and methods of investigation pertaining to each. The organic chemistry of plants has to do with the isolation and identification of the chemical compounds present in plants. Plant biochemistry is concerned with the chemical transformations carried on within the plant. Genetics deals with the manner in which the organism passes on its particular and unique characteristics from generation to generation. Ecology encompasses the relations between the plant and its environment. Plant physiology, as the study of the processes involved in plant growth and plant behavior, impinges on and merges with all of these varied branches of plant science. It is not possible to draw hard and fast lines between the varied aspects of botanical science, for they are merely different ways of looking at, and different methods of studying, the plant. An understanding of plant physiology is, however, essential to the study of the other aspects of plant science, just as some understanding of biochemistry, genetics, and ecology is essential for the study of plant physiology. The descriptive branches of plant science—systematics, morphology, anatomy and cytology—constitute the basis for experimental plant study. It is necessary that the plant physiologist know, for example, what kinds of plants there are and with what plant he happens to be working. Morphology, anatomy, and cytology describe the complex systems with which experimental plant science is concerned. Conversely, plant physiology contributes to the descriptive plant sciences by aiding in the interpretation of the form of plants and plant parts in terms of function. Study of the relation of form to function is, then, the subject of the physiological aspects of morphology, anatomy, and cytology.

Plant Physiology as a Career

In plant physiology, as in other fields of science, the professional is generally the holder of a Ph.D. degree, and has therefore received training in a graduate school. This training includes course work in plant physiology and supporting sciences, independent research, and the preparation of a thesis based on this research. Undergraduate course work lays the foundation for, and gives the future plant physiologist the tools he will use in, advanced work. The advance of biological science is based to a considerable degree on the application of principles taken from chemistry and physics to biological problems. The future plant physiologist's undergraduate training must, then, be a broad one, including the fundamentals not only of plant science but of chemistry, physics, and mathematics as well.

There are roughly 2500 professional plant physiologists in the United States, and this number is rapidly growing. These plant physiologists are employed in universities, agricultural colleges, agricultural experiment stations, the U. S. Department of Agriculture, other Federal agencies such as the National Laboratories of the Atomic Energy Commission and the Department of Defense, and in industry, particularly in chemical and agricultural industries. A majority of the plant physiologists of the United States are concerned with the application of plant physiology to agricultural problems, and only relatively few are concerned with increasing our basic information. New fields for the application of physiological principles are continually being recognized, however, and this often brings new demands for basic information. The future success of plant physiology will depend upon a proper balance between basic and applied research. It is the plan of this book to present those principles which underlie both the study and the application of plant physiology.

GENERAL READING

American Society of Plant Physiologists, Committee for Professional Status and Training, "The Status of Plant Physiology in the United States: The Number, Interests and Rate of Training of Plant Physiologists." *Plant Physiol.*, **25:** 529, 1950.

Crops in Peace and War. U. S. Dept. of Agriculture Yearbook, 1950–1951. A survey of agriculture and world affairs.

De Turk, E. E., ed., *Freedom From Want.* Waltham: Chronica Botanica, 1948. An appraisal of our chances for feeding mankind.

Reed, H. S., *A Short History of the Plant Sciences.* Waltham: Chronica Botanica, 1942. A lively account of the development of botany written by a plant physiologist.

Weevers, Th., *Fifty Years of Plant Physiology.* Amsterdam: Scheltema & Holkema's Boekhandel, 1949. The main trends of plant physiology in the 20th Century as seen by an elder Dutch physiologist.

PART ONE

———————————————————————————————————————

Nutrition

CHAPTER 2

Photosynthesis

The Process of Photosynthesis

The energy which supports the activities of most living creatures on earth is derived directly or indirectly from the energy of sunlight through the process of *photosynthesis*. This process consists of the transformation of the carbon dioxide (CO_2) of the air into the carbon-containing organic materials of plants. The conversion of CO_2 to organic compounds is a transformation which requires energy. It is one of the unique and characteristic features of green plants that they are so constituted as to be able to utilize light as a source of this energy. From the standpoint of energetics we may conceive of photosynthesis as a process in which light energy is taken up by the plant, transformed, and stored in the form of energy-rich carbon compounds. These carbon compounds are then available as sources of energy both to the plant itself and to other organisms incapable of using the energy of light to synthesize their substance from carbon dioxide, but able to utilize plant materials as food.

$$CO_2 + \text{Light energy} \xrightarrow{\text{Green plant}} \text{Carbon-containing compounds of plants}$$

THE GENERAL COURSE OF PHOTOSYNTHESIS.

The carbon compounds of plants have less oxygen per carbon than does CO_2, and in the photosynthetic transformation of CO_2, excess oxygen is given off as molecular oxygen (O_2). When carbon-containing organic compounds are burned, oxygen is consumed, and the carbon is again transformed to CO_2. In this combustion process, organic materials release their stored energy. Living organisms that use plant material as a source of energy do so by burning the organic compounds in

11

the biological process of *respiration*. The energy released by the combustion is then used by the organism for the execution of the varied kinds of biological and chemical work characteristic of living things.

$$\text{Carbon-containing compounds of plants} + O_2 \xrightarrow{\text{Living organisms}} CO_2 + \text{Energy}$$

THE GENERAL COURSE OF RESPIRATION.

The CO_2 of the atmosphere is thus being continuously consumed in the photosynthesis of plants and at the same time is being continuously replenished by the CO_2 liberated during plant, microbial, and animal respiration (Fig. 2-1). The relationship between photosynthesis and

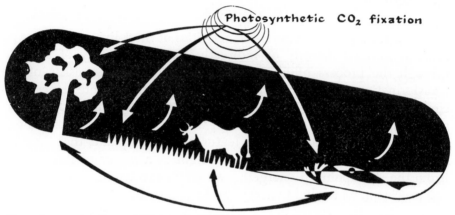

Photosynthetic CO_2 fixation

Respiratory formation of CO_2

Figure 2-1. *The carbon dioxide which is photosynthetically transformed in living plants is ultimately restored to the atmosphere through the respiratory processes of animals, plants, and microorganisms.*

respiration is summed up in the expression below, an expression which includes the fact that water also is involved in both reactions, being consumed in photosynthesis and liberated in respiration.

$$CO_2 + H_2O \underset{\text{Respiration}}{\overset{\text{Photosynthesis}}{\rightleftarrows}} \text{Carbon-containing compounds of plants} + O_2$$

THE INVERSE RELATIONSHIP BETWEEN PHOTOSYNTHESIS AND RESPIRATION.

Life on our earth has been going on sufficiently long so that photosynthesis and respiration are now nicely balanced. CO_2 uptake by photosynthesis is so precisely offset by respiratory CO_2 liberation that the CO_2 concentration of the atmosphere remains nearly constant from day to day and from year to year. In ages past, photosynthesis has, however, very considerably outstripped the respiratory utilization of photosynthetically produced organic carbon compounds, and the excess photosynthate is now stored in the earth in modified form as coal and petroleum. Both of these materials owe their origin to photosynthetic transformation of atmospheric CO_2. Today, as we burn our coal and petroleum reserves to CO_2, we are compensating for the exuberant photosynthesis of the carboniferous era.

Photosynthesis vs. Respiration

Our first clear understanding of the role of light in photosynthesis was contributed by the Dutch physician Jan Ingenhousz. In his book *Experiments on Vegetables,* published in 1779, Ingenhousz showed that the green leaves of plants evolve oxygen when they are placed in the light. In the dark, however, green leaves consume oxygen, just as animal organisms were already known to do. That the evolution of oxygen is accompanied by the uptake of CO_2, and that both occur only in the light was next established by the Swiss physicist and botanist Nicolas Th. de Saussure in 1804. These facts have an important bearing on all of our discussions of photosynthesis, for they show that photosynthesis is accompanied by the reverse process, respiration, which can also take place in green leaves. Thus respiration of green leaves continues both in the light and in the dark, but in the light it is masked by the photosynthetic process, which is ordinarily of the greater magnitude.

Further evidence of the intimate relationship between photosynthesis and respiration is the similarity of the organic material produced in photosynthesis to that consumed in respiration. In the process of photosynthesis, CO_2 is transformed to sugars, compounds of the general formula $(CH_2O)_n$, which accumulate in the plant. These same sugars, such as glucose, $C_6H_{12}O_6$, serve as substrates for respiration. Photosynthesis then follows the over-all reaction:

$$CO_2 + H_2O + \text{Light energy} \xrightarrow{\text{Green plant}} \underset{\text{Sugars}}{(CH_2O)} + O_2$$

SUGARS AS THE DIRECT PRODUCT OF PHOTOSYNTHETIC CO_2 FIXATION.

In the biological degradation of plant organic material during respiration it is the sugars which most frequently serve as the starting material.

Respiration is therefore the exact reverse of photosynthesis and follows the course:

$$(CH_2O) + O_2 \xrightarrow{\text{Respiration of living organisms}} CO_2 + H_2O + Energy$$

SUGARS AS THE SUBSTRATE OF RESPIRATION.

The respiratory breakdown of sugars takes place not only in leaves but also in the nonphotosynthetic portions of the plant—in roots, in flowers and fruit, and in stems. The daily photosynthetic increment of carbon compounds is therefore the amount by which photosynthetic CO_2 fixation in the leaves exceeds the respiratory losses contributed by all of the organs of the plant.

How Much Photosynthesis Goes On in the World?

We usually think of such enterprises as the steel or the cement industry as activities which deal on a large scale with vast tonnages of material. These industries, as well as all of man's other chemical activities, are dwarfed into insignificance by comparison with the magnitude of the photosynthetic process. It has been mentioned in Chapter 1 that each year over the earth as a whole, on the order of 2×10^{11}, 200 billion, tons of carbon are transformed photosynthetically from CO_2 into plant materials. This corresponds to the uptake by plants of roughly 7×10^{11} tons of CO_2 and the production of roughly 5×10^{11} tons of solid plant material. Approximately 90 per cent of the world's photosynthesis is carried out by marine and fresh-water algae. The remaining 10 per cent, 2×10^{10} tons of carbon per year, is fixed by the activity of land plants, both cultivated and wild. The various species and vegetations of the earth's land surface contribute very different amounts to this total, however. It has been estimated that an average acre of corn stores about one ton of carbon per year. A thrifty acre of sugar cane may store twenty times this amount, whereas an acre of desert shrubs may contribute a yield as little as one-twentieth that of an acre of corn. The greatest single contribution to terrestrial photosynthesis is that of forests. As shown in Table 2-1, forests are not only relatively efficient photosynthetically but they also cover a wide area. The cultivated areas of the world contribute a smaller, though substantial, fraction of the world's total photosynthesis, and grassy steppes and desert lands contribute still smaller amounts.

How does the amount of CO_2 utilized by the plant life of the world compare with the amount of CO_2 present in the air and dissolved in the waters of the oceans? Although air contains only 0.03 per cent CO_2 by volume, the atmosphere has been estimated to contain roughly 6×10^{11} tons of carbon as CO_2. The oceans contain even more, roughly 5×10^{13}

Table 2-1. *The Magnitude of Photosynthesis on the Earth's Surface. (Based on Riley, Am. Scientist, 32, 1944, p. 132; and Noddack, Angew. Chem., 50, 1937, p. 505.)*

HABITAT	AREA COVERED, KM²	AVERAGE C FIXED/YR/KM², TONS	ANNUAL TOTAL C FIXED, TONS	ANNUAL TOTAL C FIXED (CORRECTED FOR RESPIRATORY CO₂ LOSS), TONS
Oceans	361×10^6	375	13.5×10^{10}	
Land	149×10^6	130	1.6×10^{10}	
Total			15.1×10^{10}	18.8×10^{10}
Forests	44×10^6	250	11.0×10^9	
Cultivated	27×10^6	160	4.0×10^9	
Steppes	31×10^6	36	1.1×10^9	
Desert	34×10^6	7	0.2×10^9	
Polar	13×10^6	0	· · · · · · · · ·	
Total	149×10^6		16.3×10^9	1.9×10^{10}

tons of carbon as CO_2 and as carbonates. Using our earlier figure of 2×10^{11} tons of carbon fixed each year in photosynthesis, it is apparent that this represents about 0.4 per cent of the world's readily available CO_2. To put it another way, the earth's surface contains enough readily available CO_2 to support photosynthesis for about 250 years. Each 250 years, on the average, all of the CO_2 of the earth's surface must be cycled through photosynthesis to plant material and returned to CO_2 by respiration.

The Leaf as a Photosynthetic Apparatus

The bulk of the photosynthesis of higher plants takes place in the green leaves, which are particularly adapted to the efficient performance of the process. The leaf blade, whose structure is shown in Figure 2-2, consists of three general types of tissue. It is covered by a protective layer of epidermal cells, which often develops a thick, waxy, relatively water-impervious external surface. Beneath the epidermis lies the photosynthetic mesophyll, which may, in turn, frequently be subdivided into a layer or layers of elongated palisade parenchyma cells arranged perpendicularly to the leaf surface, and the more loosely arranged spongy parenchyma. Interspersed through the mesophyll are

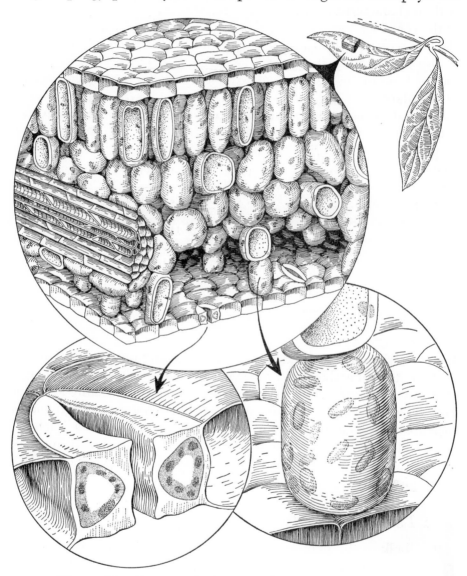

Figure 2-2. *Between the upper and lower epidermis of the leaf lie the cells of the mesophyll and the vascular tissues. Interspersed between the parenchymatous cells of the mesophyll are intercellular air spaces which lead, through the stomata, to the exterior.*

intercellular air passages, which open to the outside through the stomatal pores. This network of air passages constitutes the pathway by which CO_2 gains access to the photosynthetic cells and by which the O_2 liberated in photosynthesis is returned to the external atmosphere. A third characteristic structural feature of the leaf is the vascular tissue of the veins. The network of conductive tissue not only serves to supply the leaf with water and nutrient elements derived from the soil, but it is also the pathway by which the products of photosynthesis are removed from the leaf and transported to the nonphotosynthetic organs of the plant.

The light energy used in the photosynthetic transformation of CO_2 is taken up (absorbed) by *chlorophyll,* the characteristic green pigment of plants. All of the chlorophyll of the leaf is present in the saucer-shaped *chloroplasts,* one hundred or more of which may be present in the protoplasm of a single photosynthetic mesophyll cell. The mature chloroplast, which is typically about 2–20 microns in diameter, is made up of still smaller bodies, the *grana,* which are enclosed within the limiting or boundary membrane of the chloroplast. On the order of 50 grana, each 0.3–2.0 microns in diameter, may be present in a single chloroplast.

The Measurement of Photosynthesis

The quantitative measurement of photosynthesis may be based on the determination of either the CO_2 taken up by the photosynthesizing plant or the resulting products—the O_2 evolved or the organic matter synthesized. A simple method, one introduced by Julius Sachs in 1860 and depicted in Figure 2-3, depends merely on determination of the increase in organic material in plant tissue during a period of photo-

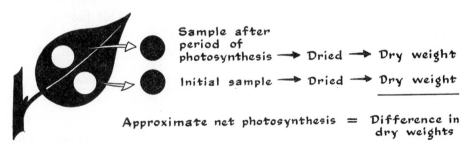

Sample after period of photosynthesis → Dried → Dry weight

Initial sample → Dried → Dry weight

Approximate net photosynthesis = Difference in dry weights

Figure 2-3. *The net photosynthetic rate may be roughly determined from the dry weight increase of a measured area of leaf surface during a period of CO_2 assimilation.*

synthesis. The increase in dry or solid weight of leaves or measured areas of leaf surface during the experimental period gives a measure of the amount of organic material added to the leaf by photosynthesis. This method is at best an approximation, since a portion of the organic material formed in photosynthesis may be lost through respiration or translocated out of the leaf during the experimental period. Solid material, such as minerals, may also be added to the leaf as a result of upward movement from the roots. Despite these limitations, the measurement of increase in solid organic material per unit area of leaf is a convenient method for the semiquantitative measurement of photosynthetic rate over short periods.

Since sugars are the immediate products of the transformation of CO_2 in green leaves, it is possible in certain instances to follow the progress of photosynthesis by determination of the sugar increase. This is easily accomplished in plants in which the simple sugars are immediately transformed to, and accumulated as, the complex sugar derivative, starch. That starch is produced in leaves and accumulated in the chloroplasts as a result of photosynthesis was another of the early discoveries of Julius Sachs. The presence of starch within the leaf can be readily detected by its reaction with iodine to form the intensely blue starch-iodine complex. This color reaction is therefore often applied for the qualitative determination of whether or not a leaf has been carrying on active photosynthesis. This method suffers, just as does that of organic matter accumulation, from the fact that a portion of the sugars, as they are formed, may be translocated from the leaf to other organs.

Most of the precise and useful measurements of photosynthesis are made by the study of gas exchange, by measurement of CO_2 taken up by the leaf or the O_2 evolved. These two measurements should be identical, since, as we have seen, in normal photosynthesis one molecule of O_2 is evolved for each molecule of CO_2 taken up. This fact is often expressed in terms of the *photosynthetic quotient*, or ratio of O_2 liberated to CO_2 taken up by the photosynthesizing organism. Meth-

$$\text{Photosynthetic quotient} = \text{P. Q.} = \frac{\text{Volume of } O_2 \text{ liberated}}{\text{Volume of } CO_2 \text{ absorbed}} = 1$$

THE PHOTOSYNTHETIC QUOTIENT.

ods for the measurement of photosynthetic gas exchange are most frequently based on the determination of CO_2 absorbed rather than O_2 evolved. This is because normal air contains but little CO_2 (0.03

per cent by volume), whereas it contains much O_2 (20 per cent by volume). Even if all of the CO_2 were taken up from a sample of air by a photosynthesizing plant, only a small increase in the already large percentage of O_2 in the air would result, and accurate measurement of this small increase would be difficult.

In the measurement of photosynthetic CO_2 uptake, the general arrangement is to pass a stream of air over the photosynthesizing plant

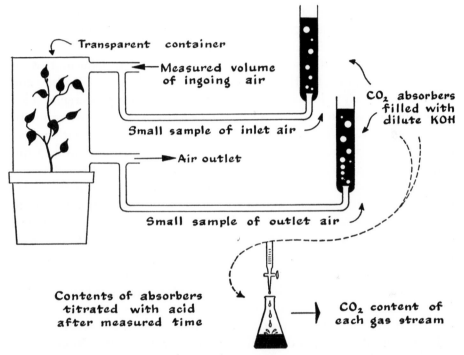

Figure 2-4. *Determinations of photosynthetic rate, based on measurement of CO_2 uptake from a moving gas stream, depend on analyses of the CO_2 content of small samples of the inlet and outlet air.*

or plant tissue, as shown in Figure 2-4. A small, measured proportion of the inflowing air is removed, and the CO_2 concentration in it determined. A similar sample is removed from the air stream after it has passed over the photosynthesizing plant, and the CO_2 concentration is again measured. The difference between these two concentrations tells us then the decrease in concentration of CO_2 which is being brought about by the plant tissue. If we also measure the volume of air which passes over the plant per unit time, we can compute the total amount of CO_2 consumed. For this type of experiment the entire plant or leaf is confined in a transparent container through which it can be illuminated. The volume of air passed over the plant may be measured with a gas flow meter similar to a household gas meter, while measurement of the CO_2 concentration in the ingoing and outgoing gas can be accomplished by passing small portions of each stream through tubes or towers containing measured volumes of KOH or NaOH of known concentration. As air samples bubble up through the alkaline solution, the CO_2 is consumed in neutralization of the alkali, and by titration of the residual alkali after a measured period of time, one may determine the CO_2 content of each gas sample.

A great many variants of the procedure outlined above have been applied to the measurement of CO_2 uptake in photosynthesis. Perhaps the most important are those in which changes in CO_2 concentration are translated into electrical changes, which may then be recorded to give continuous automatic records of CO_2 uptake. The American plant physiologist M. D. Thomas has designed and developed a widely used apparatus for such automatic registration of photosynthetic CO_2 uptake. This machine measures the increase in electrical conductivity of an alkaline solution as air containing CO_2 is bubbled through it. The conductivity of the solution can in turn be amplified by appropriate electrical methods and received on a recording galvanometer, the record of which can be calibrated to yield CO_2 concentration of the original gas sample.

A great deal of the study of photosynthesis has been done not with higher plants but with cultures of unicellular green algae, especially with the alga Chlorella. These algae have the advantage that they can be grown in flasks under standard and reproducible conditions, and a culture can then be subdivided into smaller portions which closely resemble each other. Measurement of photosynthesis with such algae has in general been carried out in closed vessels rather than in a flowing air stream such as is used with larger plants. In a closed system it is possible to measure gas exchange by study of the pressure changes in the vessel due to CO_2 uptake and O_2 evolution rather than by chemical measurement of the changes in the concentrations of the gases themselves. Manometric, or pressure change, measurements are even more frequently used in the study of plant respiration, and we will therefore defer discussion of the principles involved to Chapter 10.

The methods for the measurement of photosynthesis outlined above give the net photosynthetic rate, the rate at which CO_2 uptake in photosynthesis exceeds the simultaneous evolution of CO_2 in respiration. It is commonly assumed that the true photosynthetic rate exceeds the net rate by an amount equal to the rate at which CO_2 is evolved in respiration, and that the rate of respiration of photosynthesizing cells is equal to the rate of respiration of the same cells in darkness. The determination of true photosynthesis must therefore be carried out somewhat as shown in Figure 2-5. The respiratory rate of the cells or tissues is first

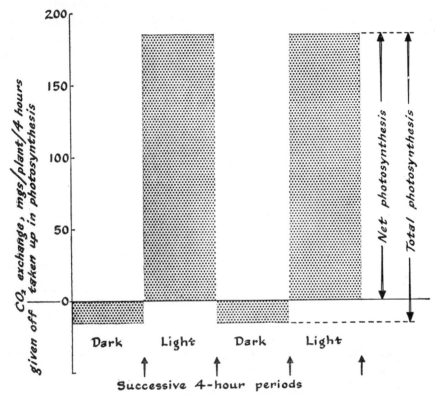

Figure 2-5. *Net or apparent photosynthetic CO_2 uptake is less than the total uptake by the amount of CO_2 produced in respiration. (Data after Hamner, Botan. Gaz., 97, 1936, p. 755.)*

determined in darkness. Light is allowed to fall on the experimental object, and the net photosynthetic rate is then measured. As a check on the original measurement, a final measurement of respiration in darkness may be made. The true photosynthetic rate is the sum of the net rate and the respiration rates.

Limiting Factors in Photosynthesis

When a green plant is kept in total darkness, it takes up oxygen and evolves CO_2, that is, it respires. If light of low intensity is now permitted to fall on the plant, a certain amount of photosynthetic CO_2

fixation and O_2 evolution will result. At very low light intensities, the photosynthetic gas exchange may still be smaller than the respiratory gas exchange, so that the only apparent effect of light will be a decrease in both O_2 uptake and CO_2 evolution. As the intensity of light increases, a point is reached at which, as shown in Figure 2-6, the photosynthetic and respiratory gas exchanges exactly balance one another. This point of zero net gas exchange is called the *compensation point*. As the light intensity is raised above the compensation point, CO_2 is absorbed and

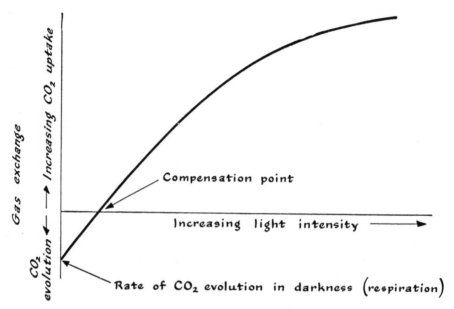

Figure 2-6. *Photosynthetic rate increases as light intensity is increased from 0 (darkness). At the compensation point, photosynthesis just balances respiration.*

O_2 evolved. Over a considerable range, the rate of photosynthetic gas exchange is nearly proportional to light intensity. At sufficiently high light intensities, however, the rate no longer increases with increasing light. The plant is now *light saturated* and, as was first clearly brought out by the studies of the British plant physiologist F. F. Blackman at the beginning of the 20th Century, factors other than available light now limit the photosynthetic rate. As a result of the work of Blackman and others we recognize today that three external factors—light intensity, CO_2 concentration, and temperature—together with internal factors due to the constitution of the plant itself, determine the ultimate

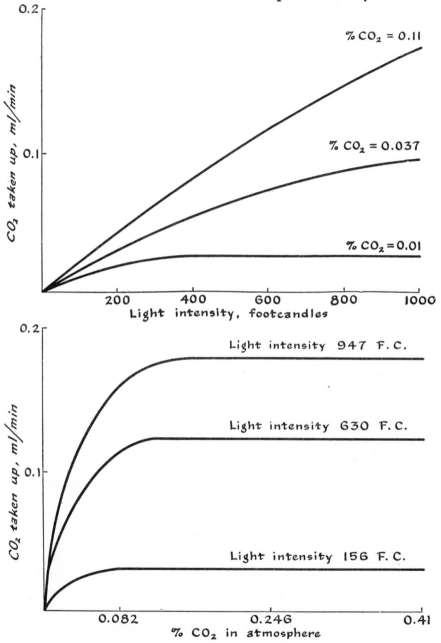

Figure 2-7. *Photosynthetic rate of wheat as a function of light intensity and CO₂ concentration. Top, at low CO₂ pressures. Bottom, at low light intensities. (Adapted from Hoover, Johnston, and Brackett,* Smithsonian Inst. Misc. Collections, **87**, 1933, pp. 16 and 17.)

rate of photosynthesis. Let us first consider the interaction of the three principal external factors.

The maximum rate of photosynthetic CO_2 fixation of which a plant is capable varies both with light intensity and with the CO_2 concentration in the surrounding air. Figure 2-7 (*top*) shows how photosynthetic rate increases with increase in light intensity at three different CO_2 concentrations. At very low concentrations of atmospheric CO_2, a maxi-

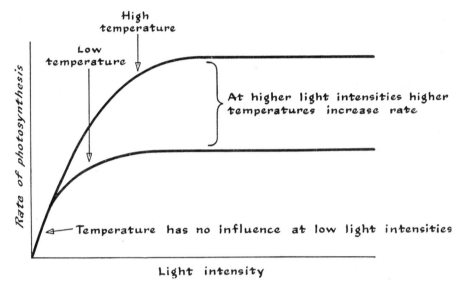

Figure 2-8. *At low light intensities (where light is rate limiting), photosynthetic rate is independent of temperature. At higher light intensities (where CO_2 is rate limiting), photosynthetic rate is increased as temperature increases. (Adapted from Manning, J. Phys. Chem., 42, 1938, p. 822.)*

mum photosynthetic rate is achieved by a relatively low light intensity. Higher light intensities do not further increase the rate of CO_2 uptake, since CO_2 concentration is now the limiting factor. Each higher CO_2 concentration requires a higher light intensity in order for light saturation to be achieved. Photosynthetic rate can also be described as a function of CO_2 concentration at different light intensities (Fig. 2-7, *bottom*). It is again clear that at relatively low CO_2 concentrations the system becomes light saturated at relatively low light intensities. As light intensity is increased, higher CO_2 concentrations are required to saturate the system.

The influence of temperature on photosynthetic rate depends in turn on whether the photosynthetic system is light or CO_2 limited. Thus, as shown in Figure 2-8, photosynthetic rate does not increase appreciably with increase in temperature in a system maintained at low light intensity and high CO_2 concentration (light is rate limiting). Under conditions of high light intensity and low CO_2 concentration (CO_2 is rate limiting) on the contrary, the rate of CO_2 uptake is greatly increased with increasing temperature. It may be concluded, therefore, that photosynthesis consists of at least two different steps, one requiring

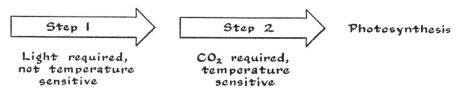

THE COMPONENT REACTIONS OF PHOTOSYNTHESIS.

light and one requiring CO_2. These two steps differ in the way in which they are affected by temperature. The rate of the first step is not increased by temperature, which is not surprising in view of the fact that most photochemical reactions (reactions requiring light) are known to be relatively insensitive to temperature changes. The rate of the second, or CO_2-requiring, step, however, is greatly influenced by temperature, a behavior which is generally characteristic of chemical reactions which do not specifically require light.

This brief survey has then shown that either light intensity or CO_2 concentration may limit photosynthetic rate, and that the further effect of temperature on this rate depends on whether light intensity or CO_2 concentration is the limiting factor. Our discussion has also indicated that photosynthesis may be separated into two component processes, one requiring light and one requiring CO_2, and that the two steps differ in their response to temperature changes.

The Role of Chlorophyll in Photosynthesis

That chlorophyll is an essential component of the photosynthetic machinery has been established from such simple facts as the absence of photosynthesis in the nongreen portions of variegated leaves. It is even possible to show that the oxygen liberated in photosynthesis is evolved directly from the chlorophyll-containing chloroplasts, an experiment first done by the German plant physiologist Engelmann in 1882. Engelmann's experiment consisted in allowing a very narrow beam of light to fall on different portions of a cell of the green alga Spirogyra. Only when the beam impinged on the bandlike chloroplast was oxygen given off by the cell.

Chlorophyll is essential to photosynthesis as the agent which, by absorbing light energy, drives the entire process. Like other pigments, chlorophyll is characterized by the fact that whereas it absorbs certain wave lengths or colors of light, it permits others to pass through unaffected. Since chlorophyll is present in the chloroplast in an insoluble, combined form, it must be extracted into, and dissolved in, such sol-

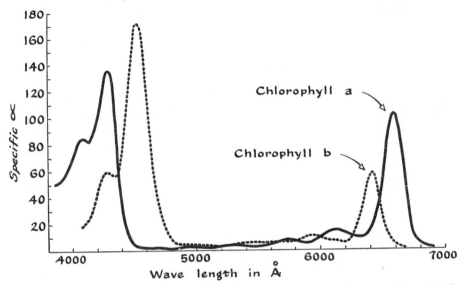

Figure 2-9. *The absorption spectra of extracted plant chlorophylls in ether solution. (After Zscheile and Comar,* Botan. Gaz., **102**, *1941, p. 468.)*

vents as ether or acetone for study of its light absorption. When a chlorophyll solution is irradiated with white light, containing all of the visible wave lengths, it absorbs the red and blue portions of the spectrum but permits the green portion to pass through largely unabsorbed. Chlorophyll therefore appears green. The relative absorption of different wave lengths of light by a pigment is ordinarily represented by means of an absorption spectrum in which the fraction of incident light absorbed is plotted (generally logarithmically) against the incident wave length. Such an absorption spectrum for extracted chlorophyll is reproduced in Figure 2-9.

These facts provide a basis for the demonstration of the role of chlorophyll as the effective light-absorbing agent in photosynthesis. Suppose we permit equal amounts of light energy of different wave lengths to fall on a green leaf and measure the rate of photosynthesis which results from light of each wave length. The photosynthetic activity of each quality of light may then be plotted against wave length to yield what is referred to as an action spectrum (Fig. 2-10). It is clear that maximum photosynthetic activity is exhibited by light of the same wave

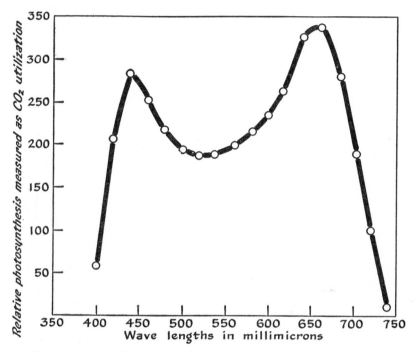

Figure 2-10. *The action spectrum of wheat leaf photosynthesis. The amount of CO_2 fixed photosynthetically is given as a function of equal amounts of total incident light energy of varying wave lengths. (After Hoover, Smithsonian Inst. Misc. Collections,* **95,** *1937, p. 11.)*

lengths as those maximally absorbed by chlorophyll. The close correspondence between the absorption spectrum of chlorophyll and the action spectrum of photosynthesis provides one of the principal grounds for the belief that the light active in photosynthesis is actually taken up by chlorophyll within the chloroplast.

Although chlorophyll plays the role of the light-absorbing agent in green plant photosynthesis, this role may be taken over in part by other pigments in certain of the lower plant groups. Thus the pigments phycoerythrin and phycocyanin act as light-absorbing agents in some red algae, while particular carotenoid pigments (Chap. 13) may absorb light for the photosynthetic process in other algae. In many of these instances, however, the light energy appears to be ultimately passed on to chlorophyll before photosynthesis actually takes place.

Even though the chlorophyll molecule is a complex one, its chemical nature has been established in detail, primarily by the work of the German chemists Willstätter and Fischer, in the early 20th Century, and more recently by American chemists, particularly Conant. The basic unit of chlorophyll is the *porphyrin* ring system, a structure made up of four simpler pyrrole nuclei joined by carbon linkages, as shown in Figure

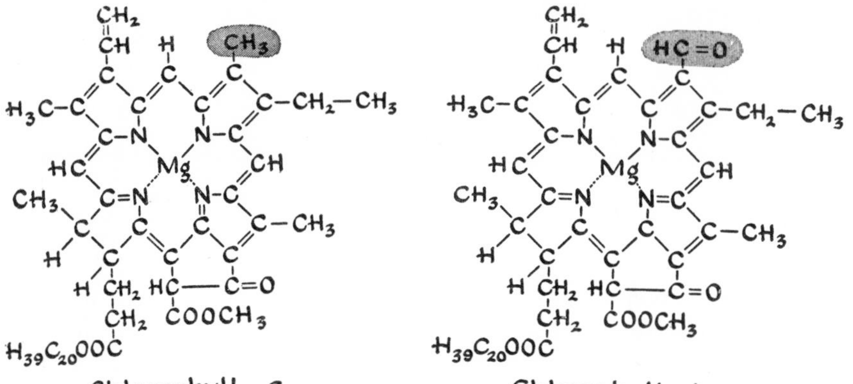

Chlorophyll a   Chlorophyll b

Figure 2-11. *The chemical structure of chlorophylls* a *and* b. (*Adapted from Fischer and Stern,* Die Chemie des Pyrrols, II., *Akademische Verlagsgesellschaft [Leipzig], 1940, p. 23*).

2-11. The center of the porphyrin is occupied by a single atom of magnesium. The pyrrole nucleus possesses characteristic side chains, or appendages, to one of which is bonded the long-chain alcohol phytol. Strictly speaking, higher green plants possess two molecular species of chlorophyll, which differ from one another in the nature of a particular side chain. Chlorophyll *a*, the more abundant of the two forms, possesses a —CH_3, or methyl, group, which, as shown in Figure 2-11, is replaced by a —CHO, or aldehyde, group, in chlorophyll *b*. Chlorophyll *a* is capable of mediating photosynthesis in the absence of chlorophyll *b*, and the significance of the presence of the two forms is therefore quite obscure.

Chlorophyll is by no means the only porphyrin found in living organisms or even in green leaves. Thus the porphyrin ring is the fundamental unit of heme, the red pigment of blood hemoglobin. Porphyrin-containing materials are also essential components of the biological systems involved in the respiratory oxidations. The porphyrins of heme and of the respiratory mediators differ from chlorophyll in two important ways. Chlorophyll, as we have seen, contains magnesium bonded in the center of the porphyrin ring, whereas heme and the other respiratory pigments all contain iron bound in this position. Chlorophyll is characterized too by the nature of its side chains and particularly by the presence of the phytol residue as an essential component. It is of interest, however, that the reaction effected by the magnesium porphyrin (chlorophyll) is similar, although opposite in direction, to the reaction effected by iron-containing porphyrins which mediate respiration.

$$CO_2 \; + \; H_2O \quad \underset{\substack{Fe \; porphyrins \\ (respiratory \; mediators)}}{\overset{\substack{Mg \; porphyrin \\ (chlorophyll)}}{\rightleftharpoons}} \quad Sugars \; + \; O_2$$

BOTH PHOTOSYNTHESIS AND RESPIRATION ARE MEDIATED BY PORPHYRINS.

Chlorophyll makes up roughly 8 per cent of the dry weight of the chloroplast. The remaining 92 per cent is shared by a great number of other materials which together constitute the structure of the chloroplast or, more properly, of the grana into which the chloroplast is subdivided. Some 40–50 per cent of the granum is made up of proteins (Chap. 11), which constitute the structural framework of the particle and which include the many enzymes (Chap. 8) responsible for the conduct of photosynthesis. Another 30 per cent is composed of fatty materials, possibly phospholipids (Chap. 12). The yellow carotenoid pigments (Chap. 13) are always found together with chlorophyll in the grana, where they make up perhaps 1–2 per cent of the granum weight. We do not know how these various components are assembled to make up the photosynthetically active units of the plant. We do know that the structure of the particle is of importance to its function, and that any drastic mechanical disturbance of the chloroplast causes it to lose entirely the ability to carry on photosynthesis.

The Formation of Chlorophyll

The production of chlorophyll by angiosperms is a process which is dependent on light. Seedlings germinated in total darkness (*etiolated seedlings*) do not produce chlorophyll, and are white or yellow (due to the presence of carotenoids) rather than green. Etiolated seedlings do, however, produce and contain small amounts of *protochlorophyll,* a substance closely related to chlorophyll, but differing from it by the absence of two hydrogen atoms in one of its pyrrole rings. When an etiolated seedling containing protochlorophyll is illuminated, the protochlorophyll is quantitatively converted to chlorophyll *a* within the space of a few minutes. Additional protochlorophyll is then formed; this is converted to chlorophyll, and within a short space of time the plant becomes visibly green. Normal green leaves also contain a small proportion of protochlorophyll, and it is thought that in general chlorophyll synthesis involves protochlorophyll as an intermediate product.

Although light is required for the production of chlorophyll by angiosperms, gymnosperm seedlings have the ability to produce chlorophyll even in darkness. In this case, the final conversion of protochlorophyll to chlorophyll would appear to be a chemical, rather than a photochemical, reaction.

Many steps all of which can take place either in dark or light ⟶ Protochlorophyll — Light ⟶ Chlorophyll

GENERAL SEQUENCE OF STEPS INVOLVED IN FORMATION OF CHLOROPHYLL.

Chlorophyll formation is influenced by nutritional and genetic factors as well as by light. A simple example is that of the relation of magnesium to chlorophyll formation. Magnesium is, as we have seen, a component of the chlorophyll molecule. If a plant is grown in a soil or nutrient medium deficient in magnesium, chlorophyll fails to form or is formed in only small amounts. The leaves are yellow rather than green, and the plant is said to be *chlorotic.* A deficiency of nitrogen, another essential component of the chlorophyll molecule, also leads to the production of yellow leaves of low chlorophyll content, although the exact pattern of the chlorosis differs from, and is readily distinguished from, the chlorosis induced by magnesium deficiency. Elements which are not themselves constituents of the chlorophyll molecule may, however, be required for chlorophyll synthesis by the plant. This is true of iron, and iron deficiency leads to immediate and striking chlorosis, particularly of the young developing leaves. The elements manganese and copper are similarly essential to chlorophyll formation in some unknown manner.

The production of chlorophyll is controlled by a great number of different genes. Mutation or loss of a gene essential to chlorophyll formation results in the production of albino plants, which can survive only so long as they can grow at the expense of the seed reserve ma-

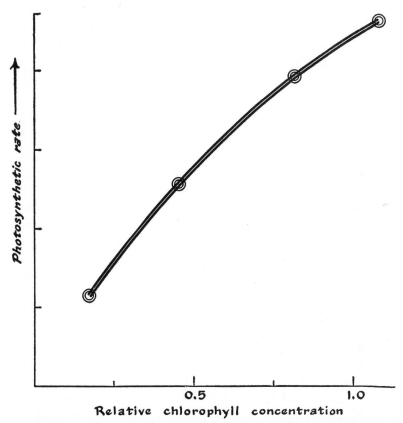

Figure 2-12. *Photosynthetic rate as influenced by chlorophyll concentration in cells of the alga Chlorella. The varying chlorophyll contents were obtained by varying the iron concentration in the medium. (After Emerson, J. Gen. Physiol., 12, 1929, p. 619.)*

terials. Variegation, in which a portion or portions of the leaf area are devoid of chlorophyll, is also often genetically controlled.

The chlorophyll content of the cell is perhaps more closely associated with photosynthetic performance than is any other internal factor. Photosynthetic rate is in fact proportional to cell chlorophyll concentration over a wide range, as is shown in Figure 2-12. Since even healthy leaves of the same species may vary in chlorophyll content by a factor of two or more, depending particularly on the available nitrogen supply, we can sense that wide variation in photosynthetic rate of leaves is to be expected, particularly in nature or under field conditions.

Photosynthesis in the Out-of-Doors

With plants growing in the out-of-doors under natural or field conditions, light intensity and CO_2 concentration influence photosynthetic rate just as in laboratory experiments. These environmental factors vary widely from hour to hour and from place to place, however, and it is interesting to consider the circumstances under which a particular factor becomes the crucial or limiting one.

Plants may be divided roughly into two classes, *sun plants* and *shade plants*, the division being based on the fraction of the normal maximum intensity of sunlight required to saturate their photosynthetic system. The shade plants, species which normally grow under the canopy or shade of other taller plant species, are often saturated by light of one-tenth the intensity of full sunlight, and do not respond to higher intensities by increased photosynthetic rate. The sun plants, species which cannot tolerate shade, are light saturated only at intensities of one-third or even more of full sunlight. The individual leaves of any species, whether sun or shade, become light saturated at intensities lower than those needed to saturate the plant as a whole. Thus in the apple tree or in corn, both of which are sun plants, individual leaves are saturated at one-fourth to one-third of full sunlight. This is because of the shading of the lower and inner leaves by the outer leaves. As higher and higher intensities fall on the plant, more and more of its leaves attain light saturation. The fact that plants with many layers of leaves do in fact remove more of the incident light energy than do species with few layers of leaves is evident from comparison of the relatively dark floor of a coniferous forest with the sunlit state of the ground under a field of corn.

Since sun plants, which include most of our crop species, are light saturated only at relatively high intensities, it is not surprising that the photosynthesis of the plant or of a growing crop of plants follows closely the prevailing light intensity, as is shown in Figure 2-13 for a field of alfalfa. On a bright cloudless day, photosynthesis increases and falls with the rising and setting of the sun. On an intermittently cloudy day, photosynthetic rate drops abruptly as the sun is obscured by clouds and rises again when the sun reappears.

The amount of CO_2 removed from the air by a photosynthesizing plant or crop is tremendous, and since normal air contains very little CO_2, large volumes of air must be exploited. Thus an eight-year-old apple tree fixes approximately 50 gm of carbon per day in August, the

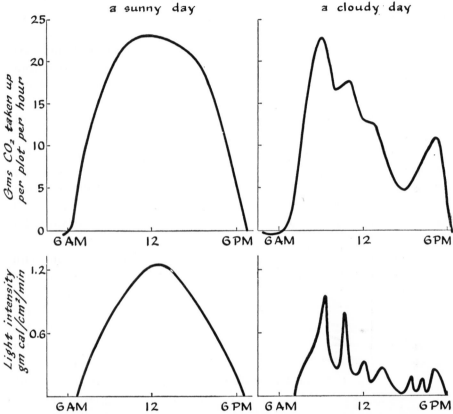

Figure 2-13. *The daily course of photosynthesis of an alfalfa plot in relation to prevailing light intensity. The upper curves record photosynthetic rate, the lower curves the light energy incident on a horizontal surface during the course of a clear day and during an intermittently cloudy day. (After Thomas and Hill, Plant Physiol., 12, 1937, p. 300.)*

month of its greatest photosynthetic rate (in Geneva, New York). This amount of carbon is contained in the CO_2 of 300,000 liters (300 cubic meters) of air. Since photosynthetic activity of the apple tree only partially depletes the CO_2 from the air about it, the volume of air actually used is greater than 300,000 liters. It is not surprising that the air surrounding or above a rapidly photosynthesizing crop or forest contains less CO_2 than the 0.03 per cent of normal air. The CO_2 content of the air in a field of corn may drop to 0.01 per cent on windless days. On windy days, when the atmosphere about the crop is continuously and rapidly renewed, CO_2 depletion of this sort does not occur.

The foregoing facts indicate that available CO_2 may become the factor limiting photosynthetic rate under field conditions, provided that light intensity is high. It has, in fact, been well established that photosynthetic rate can be increased under field or natural conditions

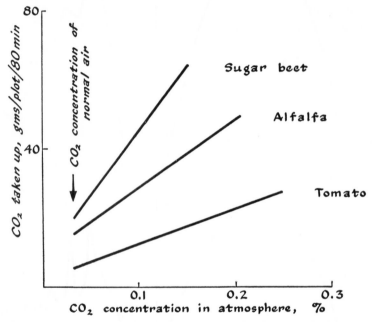

Figure 2-14. *Increased photosynthetic rates in small plots of various crops as a result of enrichment of the air with additional CO_2. (After Thomas and Hill, in* Photosynthesis in Plants, *Iowa State College Press, 1949, p. 49.)*

by increasing the CO_2 concentration of the air even above the normal 0.03 per cent. Figure 2-14 gives data on the increased yield of sugar beets, alfalfa, and tomato brought about by increasing the air CO_2 concentrations to as high as 0.2 per cent. These results do not mean, however, that the addition of CO_2 to the air would bring about increased yields of crops over any practicable range of conditions. In the first place, light is too often the limiting factor, particularly in regions with appreciable amounts of cloudy weather. In the second place, many plants do not tolerate increased levels of CO_2 concentration over any prolonged period of time. Thus with the tomatoes of Figure 2-14, injured and dead areas of leaf developed within two weeks in air containing 0.3 per cent of CO_2. Increase of photosynthetic yield by addition of CO_2 to the air can probably be applied in the future at most to particular crops in particular regions of high light intensities.

The Component Processes of Photosynthesis

We have already seen that photosynthesis may be resolved into component reactions or processes which differ in their response to

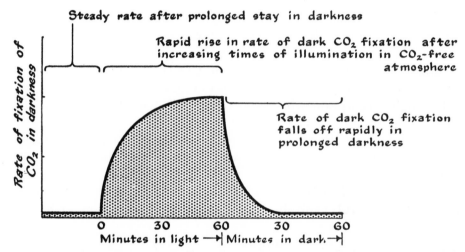

Figure 2-15. *Fixation of CO_2 in the dark following pre-illumination of algal cells in the absence of CO_2. (Adapted from Benson et al., in* Photosynthesis in Plants, *Iowa State College Press, 1949, p. 389.)*

temperature. The first reaction, a process which requires light energy, is scarcely influenced in its rate by temperature. The second process, one which involves CO_2 and becomes rate limiting at low CO_2 concentrations, is one whose rate depends greatly on temperature. These early observations have been supplemented in recent years by more elegant experiments which enable us more fully to resolve and study the component processes of photosynthesis.

In measurements of photosynthesis as ordinarily carried out, light and CO_2 are simultaneously provided to the plant. The absorption of light energy, the evolution of oxygen, and the transformation of CO_2

to sugars are all carried on during the experimental period. Suppose, however, that we first provide the plant with light energy in the absence of CO_2. If the light energy can be stored in the plant in any form, then this energy should be available for CO_2 transformation if CO_2 is provided after the light is turned off. This experiment has been done, and it has been shown that light energy can be stored in green cells in the absence of CO_2 and used for subsequent CO_2 transformation in the dark. Data from such an experiment are given in Figure 2-15, which shows that the ability to transform CO_2 in the dark at the expense of light energy previously absorbed and stored persists for only a few minutes after the light has been turned off. CO_2 fixation in the dark at the expense of light received earlier is therefore not of any great importance from the standpoint of the plant, but it is of importance to our understanding of photosynthesis because it shows us that the processes of light absorption and CO_2 transformation are separable from one another, and that CO_2 transformation depends not on the action of light itself on CO_2 but on the action of some product of light absorption which can then react with CO_2 even in the dark.

A second observation basic to our understanding of photosynthesis concerns the source of the oxygen which is evolved. The over-all representation of photosynthesis, as we have seen before, involves the uptake of one molecule each of CO_2 and H_2O for each molecule of O_2 released. The O_2 evolved might then be contributed either by the

$$CO_2 + H_2O \xrightarrow[\text{Green plant}]{\text{Light}} (CH_2O) + O_2$$

(1)

ONE MOLECULE OF OXYGEN IS EVOLVED FOR EACH MOLECULE OF CO_2 REDUCED IN PHOTOSYNTHESIS.

oxygen of the CO_2 or by the oxygen of the water. A decision between these two alternatives has been made possible by the use of isotopic oxygen, which has an atomic weight of 18 rather than the 16 of the usual oxygen. Experiments of this kind were first undertaken by the American chemists Ruben and Kamen in 1941. When green plants were allowed to photosynthesize in the presence of H_2O containing the O^{18} isotope, it was found that the O_2 evolved contained the isotopic marker. When O^{18} was supplied to the plant in the CO_2 molecule, essentially no O^{18} was found in the O_2 evolved. We must therefore rewrite Equation 1 above to account for the fact that all of the O_2

arises from water. The revised equation, given below, requires the decomposition of two molecules of water per molecule of O_2 evolved.

$$CO_2 + 2H_2O^* \xrightarrow[\text{Green plant}]{\text{Light}} (CH_2O) + O_2^* + H_2O$$
$$\text{Sugar}$$

(2)

THE OXYGEN EVOLVED FROM PHOTOSYNTHESIS COMES FROM WATER.

The hydrogen of these two water molecules is then available for two purposes: (1) for removal of one oxygen atom from the CO_2 molecule as H_2O, and (2) for combination with the resultant molecule to form (CH_2O), the basic unit of the sugars. It will be shown below that the decomposition of water is the partial process of photosynthesis which requires light. The transformation of CO_2 to sugar depends, then, on the hydrogen atoms made available by the decomposition of water, and is the part of photosynthesis which can take place even in the dark.

The Role of Light in Photosynthesis

Green plants do not ordinarily evolve detectable quantities of oxygen if they are illuminated in the absence of CO_2. Some oxygen may be given off, but the small amounts involved are obscured by the rapid uptake of O_2 in respiration. It is of interest, however, that oxygen can be evolved by illuminated plants in relatively large amounts even in the absence of CO_2, provided that the cells are furnished with some material other than CO_2 which can act as an acceptor for the hydrogen atoms produced by the light-induced cleavage of water. Such a material is the organic molecule benzoquinone, which can accept hydrogen atoms to become hydroquinone. The fact that the reduction of

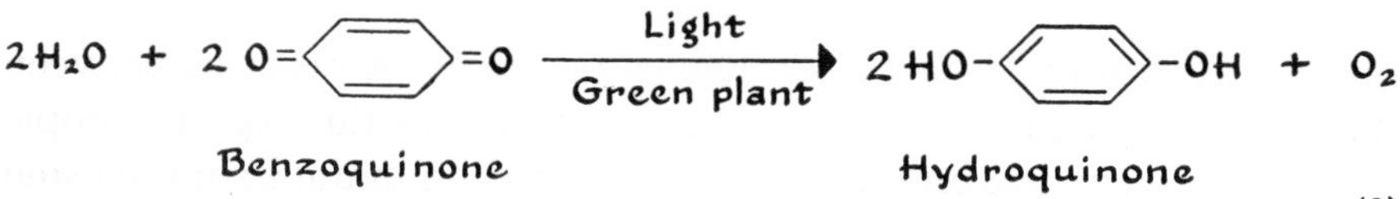

$$2H_2O + 2O=\langle\!\!\!\rangle=O \xrightarrow[\text{Green plant}]{\text{Light}} 2HO-\langle\!\!\!\rangle-OH + O_2$$

Benzoquinone　　　　　　　　　　　　Hydroquinone

(3)

THE PHOTOSYNTHETIC REDUCTION OF BENZOQUINONE BY ALGAL CELLS.

benzoquinone to hydroquinone can be accomplished by green algal cells in the light with the evolution of oxygen is consistent with the view that the light reaction of photosynthesis consists of the decomposition of water with the production of hydrogen atoms. These hydrogen atoms can then be utilized in various ways, as in the transformation of benzoquinone or, more usually, in the transformation of CO_2.

The photochemical reduction described above is but one variant of a more general reaction, commonly studied with isolated chloroplasts. Although it has so far been impossible to obtain photosynthetic transformation of CO_2 to sugars with isolated chloroplasts or grana, it was found by the English biochemist Robin Hill, in 1937, that isolated chloroplasts or chloroplast fragments are capable of evolving oxygen on illumination, provided again that they are supplied with some suitable reagent for the acceptance of hydrogen atoms (or electrons, Chap. 10). Thus the reaction of Equation 3 can be carried out by illuminated suspensions of chloroplasts. That all of the oxygen evolved in this reaction has its source in the oxygen atoms of water has been established by experiments with isotopically marked water molecules similar to the experiments outlined earlier for photosynthesis proper. It is today generally agreed that the primary act of photosynthesis is that of the decomposition of water with the aid of light energy absorbed by the chlorophyll of the chloroplast. The oxygen resulting from the cleavage of water is evolved as molecular oxygen. The hydrogen atoms made available in this way are stored in the chloroplast in small amounts, presumably through combination with some native substance or carrier capable of accepting hydrogen atoms. The hydrogen atoms stored in this natural way may then be used by the plant for the transformation of CO_2 or for other types of chemical transformation involving hydrogen transfer.

The Transformation of CO_2

The transformation of CO_2 to sugar in photosynthesis is a process which requires energy. We have already learned in a general way how the energy is supplied by light. Let us now consider the pathway by which the carbon atoms of CO_2 are transformed to the carbon atoms present in plant materials. It has already been brought out in the course of this discussion that sugars are the ultimate product of the photosynthetic transformation of CO_2. Although this has been known in a qualitative way for many years, it has been only relatively recently that good quantitative information has been obtained. The American chemist J. H. C. Smith has shown that as much as 97 per cent of the carbon taken up in photosynthesis of sunflower leaves over experimental periods of 30 minutes or more can be recovered from the leaves as sugars and sugar derivatives, including particularly sucrose and starch. There is then no doubt that sugars constitute the ultimate product of photosynthesis over relatively extended periods of time. The sugars are, however, relatively complex materials (Chap. 9), and it is now evident that their formation is accomplished stepwise through a number of reactions.

The study of the reactions leading to sugar formation has been made possible only by the application of the isotope technique. In this technique the plant is supplied with CO_2 which contains isotopic carbon of atomic weight 14, rather than the usual atomic weight of 12. Carbon 14 is radioactive and hence easily identified. The utility of this tool in the study of photosynthesis may be illustrated by the following example. Suppose we ask ourselves: What is the very first chemical compound to which CO_2 is converted on its pathway to the ultimate sugar? We can attempt to answer this question by an experiment in which cells are first allowed to photosynthesize in ordinary unmarked CO_2. When photosynthesis is proceeding steadily, the unmarked CO_2 may suddenly be replaced by labelled, isotopic CO_2. The carbon of the isotopic CO_2 will be converted to the first photosynthetic intermediate, then to the next intermediate, and so on, ultimately to sugar. If we allow the cells to photosynthesize the labelled CO_2 for a long enough period of time, say half an hour, then essentially all of the CO_2 assimilated will be found in the form of sugars. If, on the other hand, we allow the cells to photosynthesize the labelled CO_2 for a sufficiently short period of time, then we should find the bulk of the carbon of this CO_2 combined in the first of the intermediate compounds which intervene between CO_2 and sugar.

Such experiments have been carried out in great detail at the University of California by Calvin and Benson, who have shown that when the photosynthetic period is shortened to 2 seconds, roughly 90 per cent of the carbon fixed can be recovered in the form of a particular 3-carbon compound, *phosphoglyceric acid*. Phosphoglyceric acid is, then, the first stable intermediate in the photosynthetic transformation of CO_2 to sugars. The radioactive isotopic carbon, given as CO_2, appears first in a terminal position of the phosphoglyceric acid, indicating that this carbon atom has been added to some 2-carbon molecule already present in the cell. This 2-carbon molecule must itself ultimately be formed from CO_2, since with periods of photosynthesis longer than 2 seconds, isotopic carbon is gradually incorporated in increasing amounts into the two remaining carbon atoms of the phosphoglycerate molecule. The early stages of photosynthesis must, therefore, be some·

what as depicted in Figure 2-16. CO_2 is taken up, and incorporated into a pre-existing 2-carbon compound, which is itself reformed from CO_2 by some other pathway as yet unknown.

Phosphoglyceric acid is known to physiology and biochemistry as an intermediate not only in the photosynthetic production of sugars from CO_2 but also in the respiratory conversion of sugars to CO_2. The

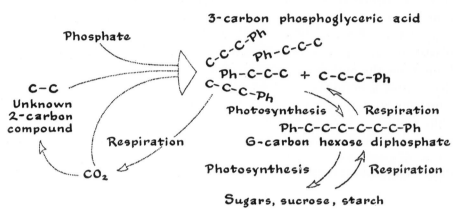

Figure 2-16. *The generalized pathway of carbon atoms from CO_2 to sugars through phosphoglyceric acid as an intermediate.*

pathway between sugar and phosphoglyceric acid, which appears, then, to be common to these two processes, will be further discussed in Chapter 10. So far as photosynthesis is concerned, however, we may view the sugars as being formed by the coupling of two 3-carbon compounds, both of which are derivatives of phosphoglyceric acid. The union of these 3-carbon units produces the 6-carbon-atom chain characteristic of the principal plant sugars, a process indicated in general outline in Figure 2-16.

Efficiency of Energy Utilization in Photosynthesis

The efficiency with which plants convert light energy into the chemical energy stored in plant products can be determined by measuring the total light energy which falls on a plant or field of plants during an experimental period and comparing this with the total increase in energy represented by the plant material formed during the same period. The light energy might be measured by appropriately housed thermocouples, in an instrument known as a *bolometer*. Evaluation of the chemical energy stored in the plant material might be carried out by combustion of initial and final samples of the crop in a *calo-rimeter*, an instrument for measuring the heat released when a sample of organic material is burned again to CO_2 and water. In any case, many determinations of the efficiency with which field-grown plants utilize light energy have shown that not more than 0.5 to 2 per cent of the total available light energy is actually stored by the plant in chemical form. A portion of the energy not stored as photosynthate is used in other processes relevant to the plant's economy, particularly in the evaporation of water (Chap. 5). By far the largest amount is either wasted or not absorbed by the leaf. This wastage is in part due to the limitations the environment places on the rate of growth and hence of dry matter accumulation of the plant. Field crops rarely grow under continuously optimal conditions with respect to soil nutrients, available water, or temperature. It has in fact been demonstrated that tomato plants grown in the greenhouse under conditions selected to be as nearly optimal as possible are several times more efficient in their chemical storage of light energy than are ordinary field-grown tomatoes. There is still much to be done in practical agriculture to effect greater utilization and storage by the crop of available light energy.

What is the ultimate efficiency which might be achieved by plants in their utilization of light energy for the photosynthetic transformation of CO_2? This question has been studied in some detail, particularly by the German biochemist Otto Warburg, the Americans Robert Emerson, Farrington Daniels, and others. We can recall that, although light energy travels as an electromagnetic radiation embodying wave properties such as wave length and frequency, light is nevertheless emitted and absorbed in the form of discrete packets of energy called *quanta*. The energy content of a light quantum is greater the shorter the wave length (and the greater the frequency) of the light. Thus

$$E = h\nu$$

Energy per quantum = Planck's constant × Frequency

THE RELATION BETWEEN THE ENERGY CONTENT OF LIGHT QUANTA AND THE FREQUENCY OF THE LIGHT.

a quantum of blue light possesses a greater energy content than a quantum of red light, and in both cases the energy per quantum is given by the frequency of the light multiplied by Planck's constant, h. Most modern investigations agree in indicating that some 8 to 10 quanta of light energy are required for the photosynthetic transformation of a single CO_2 molecule to sugar, although fewer quanta may possibly suffice under some circumstances. The number of quanta required appears to be quite independent of the wave length of the incident light, as is true of other photochemical reactions. This is because light quanta, like other chemical reactants, enter into the reaction in a stoichiometric manner. From an energetic standpoint, then, photosynthesis is most efficiently carried out by red light, the lowest energy quanta absorbed by chlorophyll. The energy contained in 8–10 quanta can be shown to correspond to some three to four times the chemical energy stored by the transformation of CO_2 to sugar. The remaining two-thirds to three-

$$CO_2 + 2H_2O + 8\text{--}10 \text{ quanta} \xrightarrow{\text{Green plant}} \underset{\text{Sugars}}{(CH_2O)} + O_2 + H_2O$$

THE QUANTUM REQUIREMENT OF PHOTOSYNTHESIS.

fourths of the absorbed light energy, even though it is essential to the driving of the photosynthetic process, does not appear in the energy of the final products but is lost as heat along the way. Even under the most favorable photosynthetic conditions, therefore, it cannot be hoped that more than one-third to one-fourth of the incident light energy might be stored by photosynthesis in the form of plant material.

Summary

Photosynthesis is the process by which carbon dioxide of the air is transformed into the organic matter of green plants with the aid of the energy of light. Most of the animals and other nonphotosynthetic organisms of the world are dependent for their food directly or indirectly on the organic matter produced by green plants.

In the utilization of plant organic material as their source of energy, animals and nonphotosynthetic plants again transform the sugars and other photosynthetically produced organic materials to carbon dioxide. Thus the carbon dioxide of the air is in a perpetual state of flux or turnover, continuously being depleted by photosynthesis, continuously being added to by the degradative respiratory activities of plants and animals.

Photosynthesis is measured by the amount of carbon dioxide utilized or the amount of organic material or oxygen produced. Most quantitative work is based on measurements of carbon dioxide consumption, since the concentration of this material in air is low (0.03 per cent), and relatively large changes in its concentration may be brought about by photosynthesis.

The photosynthesis of higher plants is accomplished primarily in the cells of the green leaf. The basic units of photosynthesis are the chloroplasts, saucer-shaped bodies within the cytoplasm of the cells of the leaf parenchyma which contain the green pigment chlorophyll. This pigment acts as the light-absorbing agent, capturing the light energy which is used in the energy-requiring process of CO_2 transformation to sugar, the final photosynthetic product.

Three external or environmental factors—light intensity, atmospheric CO_2 concentration, and temperature—are of primary importance in the regulation of photosynthetic rate. Any of these three factors may become the rate-limiting one under appropiate circumstances. Thus photosynthetic rate is limited by available light at low light intensities. Under these circumstances the rate of photosynthesis cannot be increased by increases in CO_2 concentration or temperature. At high light intensities, photosynthetic rate may be limited by available CO_2 and may be increased by increases in CO_2 concentration above the 0.03 per cent present in normal air. Photosynthetic rate is appreciably increased by increases in temperature only where CO_2, rather than light, is limiting. Under field conditions, light intensity most often appears to limit photosynthetic rate. Only under conditions of high light intensity may available CO_2 become limiting for short periods of time.

The complex process of photosynthesis can be resolved into two simpler component processes, one having to do with the absorption of

$$2 H_2O + 2 \text{ acceptor molecules} \xrightarrow[\text{Green plant}]{\text{Light}} 2 \text{ acceptor molecules each containing } 2(H) + O_2$$

THE INITIAL PROCESS OF PHOTOSYNTHESIS IS THE LIGHT-DRIVEN DECOMPOSITION OF WATER.

$$2 \text{ acceptor molecules each containing } 2(H) + CO_2 \xrightarrow[\text{plant}]{\text{Green}} (CH_2O) + H_2O + 2 \text{ acceptor molecules}$$
$$\text{Sugars}$$

THE SECOND PROCESS OF PHOTOSYNTHESIS IS THE TRANSFORMATION OF CO_2 TO SUGARS.

light energy by chlorophyll and the second having to do with the utilization of this energy in the transformation of CO_2 to sugars. In the first process, the energy of light is used for the cleavage of water to molecular oxygen and hydrogen atoms. These hydrogen atoms may then combine with a suitable acceptor and may be stored in the plant over measurable periods of time. In the second process, the hydrogen of the acceptor molecules is used in the transformation of CO_2 to sugars. In this reaction the hydrogen acceptor molecules may be presumed to be regenerated and made available for recycling through the process.

The principal end products of photosynthesis are sugars containing 6 carbon atoms. These 6-carbon units may, however, be secondarily combined in various ways to form more complex derivatives, such as sucrose or starch. In any case, the basic 6-carbon sugar units are formed from CO_2 through the intermediary of simpler 2- and 3-carbon units. The final formation of sugar is achieved through the union of two 3-carbon units to form the 6-carbon atom chain characteristic of these materials. The 3-carbon atom compounds formed as intermediates in the photosynthetic transformation of CO_2 are also formed in nonphotosynthetic organisms and in nonphotosynthesizing green plants (in the dark) as intermediates in the respiratory degradation of the sugars to CO_2. Photosynthesis and respiration, then, share in part a common pathway, a pathway which operates in the direction of sugar formation in photosynthesis, in the direction of sugar breakdown in respiration.

QUESTIONS

1. By means of ultraviolet radiation, it is possible to produce strains of the alga Chlorella which cannot photosynthesize, but which can grow if fed sugar. How may such strains be of use in research on photosynthesis?

2. It has been found that the characteristic pigments of marine algae often differ with the depth at which they grow. Explain the possible advantages of this phenomenon to marine algae as a whole.

3. What evidence leads us to believe that photosynthesis is composed of a series of discrete reactions, rather than of one step?

4. Explain in detail how you would obtain an action spectrum for photosynthesis. To what use could this information be put?

5. Certain algae may be trained to use molecular hydrogen (H_2) instead of water to reduce the CO_2 assimilated in photosynthesis. What would be the products of such a reaction? Still other bacteria can use hydrogen sulfide (H_2S). What products would you expect here?

6. Why is chlorophyll believed to be essential for photosynthesis? How does it function?

7. What is the Hill reaction? What does this reaction teach us about the role of the light energy absorbed in photosynthesis? What is the source of the oxygen released in photosynthesis?

8. Emerson and Arnold found in 1932 that the photosynthetic yield per unit light could be increased if the light, instead of being administered continuously, were given as brief flashes interrupted by longer dark periods. How can this phenomenon be explained?

9. What has the use of isotopic carbon revealed about the intermediate steps in the reduction of CO_2 to the level of carbohydrate?

10. The drug phenylurethan can inhibit photosynthesis without measurably affecting respiration. Explain how this finding may be of use in photosynthesis research.

11. It is a common practice in hospitals to remove plants from the rooms of patients at night and to replace them in the morning. Is such a practice based on sound scientific fact? Explain.

12. If a green leaf is illuminated in the absence of CO_2, it may be observed to fluoresce. The admission of CO_2 to this leaf results in the immediate quenching of fluorescence. Present a possible explanation.

GENERAL READING

Benson, A. A., and Calvin, M., "Carbon Dioxide Fixation by Green Plants." *Ann. Rev. Plant Physiol.*, 1: 25, 1950. A detailed discussion of the path of radiocarbon in photosynthesis.

Franck, J., and Loomis, W. E., eds., *Photosynthesis in Plants*. Ames: Iowa State College Press, 1949. A symposium of the American Society of Plant Physiologists, with chapters by specialists in various fields.

Rabinowitch, E. I., *Photosynthesis and Related Processes*, Vol. I. New York: Interscience Publishers, 1945. An encyclopedic review of the literature of photosynthesis, including a delightful chapter on historical aspects.

CHAPTER 3

Mineral Nutrition

Introduction

The great bulk of the plant is composed of three elements: carbon, hydrogen, and oxygen. We have seen how the carbon of the plant is derived from that of the atmospheric carbon dioxide. The hydrogen contained in the organic material of the plant is derived from the water taken up by the roots, while the oxygen is derived both from this water and from the atmospheric sources, CO_2 and O_2. Plants cannot, however, live and grow on air and water alone. They contain and require a variety of inorganic mineral constituents, materials which are ordinarily supplied to the plant from the soil through the root system. Although these mineral elements make up only a small proportion, frequently on the order of 2 to 10 per cent, of the plant's dry weight, they are nonetheless essential to the plant's well-being and are therefore known as the essential elements of plant nutrition. The mineral elements known to be essential to the plant are twelve in number. They include nitrogen, phosphorus, sulfur, calcium, potassium, magnesium, iron, zinc, manganese, copper, boron, and molybdenum. Of these twelve elements, one, nitrogen, although it is taken up by most plants from the soil, is derived ultimately from the nitrogen of the atmosphere (Chap. 11). The remaining eleven elements are all contained in and derived from the parent minerals which make up the rocks of the earth's crust.

With but few and minor exceptions, the mineral elements essential to plant growth appear to be common to all higher plants. Indeed, requirements for many of these same elements are shared by all living organisms. In particular instances, however, mineral elements which do not appear to be essential to the higher plants are required by one or another group of organisms. This is true of the element cobalt, which, although essential to the higher animals and to certain microorganisms, is not recognized as essential to higher plants. Similarly, the calcium required by higher plants may apparently be dispensed with by certain fungi and algae.

The Background of Our Knowledge of Mineral Nutrition

We know a lot today about the mineral nutrition of plants, but the acquisition of this knowledge has been a long, slow, and difficult task. For only a little over one hundred years has the role of minerals in plant growth been generally recognized. A part of the early difficulties

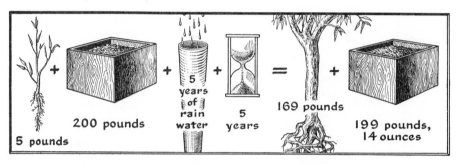

Figure 3-1. *Van Helmont's experiment on the growth of a willow tree in soil supplied with water.*

in the study of this subject are illustrated by the conclusions drawn from an experiment (Fig. 3-1) by van Helmont in the early 17th Century. This investigator planted a 5-pound willow branch in a container with a weighed amount of dried soil. Water was added as required, and the plant during a period of 5 years grew into a tree weighing 169 pounds. The soil itself had, however, lost only 2 ounces of its original 200 pounds. This loss in soil weight van Helmont ascribed to experimental error, and he concluded that the plant did not derive sustenance other than water from the soil. We know today that these two ounces of material which the plant did take up from the soil were of vital importance, and in fact essential to its growth.

The Swiss physicist de Saussure was the first to establish clearly the dependence of plants on minerals taken up by the roots, a fact brought out in his book published in 1804. Although he showed that the nitrogen of the plant, as well as the components of the ash which remain after the combustion of plant material, are obtained from soil, he was unable to establish in detail the exact elements required. That the soil supplies the growing plant with the elements calcium, potassium, sulfur, and phosphorus was generally accepted after the publication of Liebig's work on this subject in 1840.

The methods in use today for experimental determination of the mineral elements required by plants were devised and perfected in the years immediately before and after 1860 by Sachs and Knop. The basic and simple principle employed by these workers is illustrated in Figure 3-2. The plant is cultured in such a way that its roots are

Figure 3-2. *Sachs' method for the culture of plants in liquid nutrient. (Adapted from Sachs, Vorlesungen über Pflanzen-Physiologie, Wilhelm Engelmann [Leipzig], 1882, p. 341.)*

immersed in a nutrient solution. This nutrient solution consists of water in which is dissolved any desired inorganic salt or mixture of salts. The objective of Sachs and Knop was to discover the minimum number of elements or ions necessary to support indefinitely normal plant growth. Sachs found that plants could be grown satisfactorily in a nutrient solution containing the salts KNO_3, $Ca_3(PO_4)_2$, $MgSO_4$, $CaSO_4$, $NaCl$, and $FeSO_4$. Knop recognized that the $NaCl$ was not essential, and that the nutrient might be simplified to $Ca(NO_3)_2$, KNO_3, KH_2PO_4, $MgSO_4$, and $FePO_4$. These two nutrient solutions (Table 3-1), and in particular Knop's solution, have been used very extensively for the culture of higher plants.

It is clear today that Sachs and Knop correctly established the elements which are required by the plant in relatively large quantities. These elements, the so-called *major elements* of plant nutrition, are calcium, magnesium, potassium, nitrogen (as nitrate in the above cases), sulfur (as sulfate), and phosphorus (as phosphate). The salts containing these major elements are ordinarily supplied in concentrations varying between 200 mg and 1 gm per liter of nutrient solution.

Table 3-1. *The Composition of Two of the Earliest Solutions Used for the Nutrient Culture of Plants.*

SACH'S SOLUTION, 1860		KNOP'S SOLUTION, 1865	
SALT	GM/LITER	SALT	GM/LITER
KNO_3	1.0	$Ca(NO_3)_2 \cdot 4H_2O$	0.8
$Ca_3(PO_4)_2$	0.5	KNO_3	0.2
$MgSO_4 \cdot 7H_2O$	0.5	KH_2PO_4	0.2
$CaSO_4$	0.5	$MgSO_4 \cdot 7H_2O$	0.2
$NaCl$	0.25	$FePO_4$	trace
$FeSO_4$	trace		

Iron is required in much smaller concentrations than the major elements, concentrations of a few parts per million ordinarily being sufficient for optimal plant growth. The elements zinc, manganese, copper, boron, and molybdenum are required in still lower concentrations and are referred to, together with iron, as the *minor elements* of plant nutrition. The importance of the minor elements, with the exception of iron, entirely escaped the early workers, because the salts of the major elements available to them at that time contained adequate amounts of the minor elements as impurities.

Techniques for the Study of Plant Nutrition

There are three principal objectives in the study of the mineral nutrition of plants. The first objective considered by the early workers was the determination of those elements required by plants for their growth. The second is the study of the symptoms of malnutrition which are induced in the plant by the absence of particular elements. The third is the determination of optimal nutrient conditions, optimal concentrations of each nutrient element, and optimal balance among the several elements.

It might seem at first thought that the best way to approach these three problems would be to grow plants in soil and then to study their growth responses to specific added mineral elements. This is largely impractical, however, because it is often difficult to determine how much of any nutrient element is present in a given soil in a form available to the plant. For this and other reasons, which will be taken up in Chapter 6, most of the basic studies of mineral requirements have been conducted with plants grown with their roots in liquid nutrient solution, as in the work of Sachs, or with their roots in sand or gravel which is irrigated with nutrient solution. In either of these techniques, which are termed,

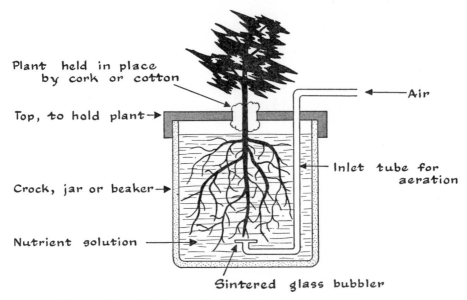

Plant held in place by cork or cotton

Top, to hold plant →

← Air

Crock, jar or beaker →

← Inlet tube for aeration

Nutrient solution

Sintered glass bubbler

Figure 3-3. *Modern solution culture.*

respectively, solution culture and sand or gravel culture, the composition of the nutrient solution may be exactly known and varied at will.

In solution culture the stem of the plant is held in place by a suitable support (Fig. 3-3), with its roots in a glass beaker, jar, or crock which in turn contains the nutrient solution. Since roots require oxygen for their respiratory activities, it is essential with most plants to aerate the nutrient solution by forcing a stream of small air bubbles up through it. The influence of such aeration on the growth of barley in solution culture is shown in Figure 3-4. The composition of the nutrient solution changes as the roots remove mineral elements from it, and it is therefore necessary to renew the solution periodically or to adjust the concentration of each element.

In sand or gravel culture the roots of the plant are allowed to grow in a suitable sand (generally quartz) or gravel contained in a crock provided with a bottom drainage hole. The sand or gravel is inert, that is, it provides the plant with mechanical support but does not supply

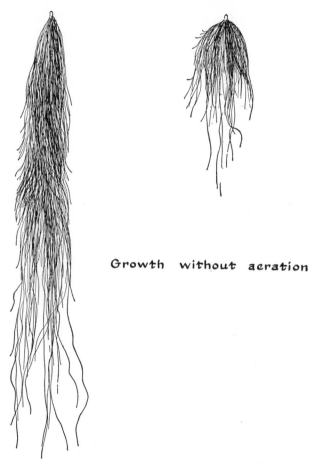

Growth without aeration

Growth with aeration

Figure 3-4. *The influence of aeration on the growth of barley roots in nutrient solution.* (*Adapted from Broyer, after Hoagland,* Inorganic Plant Nutrition, *Chronica Botanica, 1948, plate 24.*)

nutrient elements in any significant quantities. A nutrient solution is supplied in one of three ways. In the first variant of sand culture, a variant known as *slop culture* (Fig. 3-5A), nutrient is periodically supplied to the surface of the sand and allowed to drain out before fresh nutrient is added. Nutrient may be added once or several times daily. In the second variant, *drip culture* (Fig. 3-5B), nutrient solution is continuously dripped onto the sand. The rate of dripping and draining is arranged so that the sand is never completely saturated with solution. The third technique, *subirrigation* (Fig. 3-5C), is ordinarily used in large-scale experiments. In this technique the nutrient solution is pumped from a bottom reservoir up through the sand until it nears or reaches the surface. The pump is then turned off, and the nutrient is allowed to drain off again. The pump-drain cycle may be repeated several times daily, so that the plant is supplied with nutrient almost continuously.

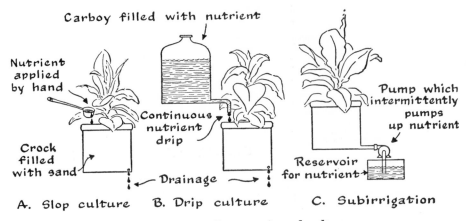

Figure 3-5. *The principal types of sand culture.*

Sand and gravel cultures are more widely used than solution cultures because they are simpler to arrange and easier to maintain. This is primarily because the aeration of roots in sand culture is taken care of by the normal diffusion of air through the spaces between the sand or gravel particles, and no special attention need be paid to this factor. Slop culture is the simplest way to grow plants under conditions of controlled nutrition, and it has been successfully applied to a wide range of nutritional studies. Sand or gravel culture is, however, of limited usefulness for the study of minor element nutrition, since most sands, no matter how carefully prepared, contain traces of many of the minor elements and can provide plants growing in them with sufficient amounts of these materials. Solution culture is therefore generally preferable to sand culture for study of the minor elements, but has been supplanted by sand or gravel culture for most routine plant physiological investigations.

The Balanced Nutrient Solution

The nutrient solutions of Sachs and Knop given in Table 3-1, while satisfactory for the growth of plants, are by no means the simplest, nor do they necessarily produce optimal growth. A great advance in the systematic study of the effects due to variation in composition of the nutrient solution was made by the American plant physiologists

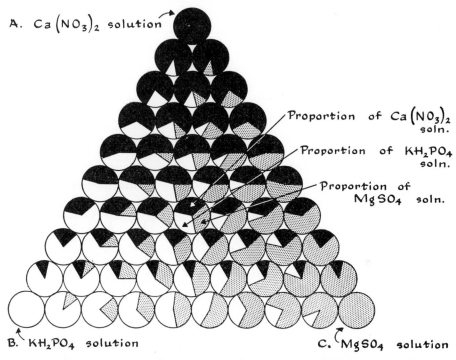

Figure 3-6. *Combination of three stock solutions to produce 55 different nutrient solutions of identical total concentration. (After Hamner, Lyon, and Hamner, Botan. Gaz., 103, 1942, p. 588.)*

Tottingham and Shive in the years after 1914. Three salts, KH_2PO_4, $MgSO_4$, and $Ca(NO_3)_2$, containing among them all of the essential major elements, may be combined in varying proportions in such a way that the total ionic concentration (total osmotic pressure, Chap. 4) is held constant. Thus, three stock solutions, each containing one of the salts, are combined in the varying proportions shown in Figure 3-6. The nutrient solution at point A of the triangle in Figure 3-6 consists solely of one stock solution, $Ca(NO_3)_2$. The nutrient solution represented by the exact center of the triangle of Figure 3-6 consists of the three stock solutions mixed with one another in equal proportions. Other nutrient solutions represented in the triangle are composed of different ratios of the three stock solutions. Plants are grown with nutrient solutions of these different compositions, and the nutrient solution which produces maximal growth can be selected. At the same time the symptoms of individual deficiencies may be observed in the plants grown in incomplete media.

One inadequacy of this system is that individual salts, rather than

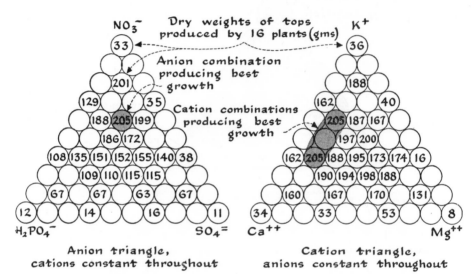

Anion triangle,
cations constant throughout

Cation triangle,
anions constant throughout

Figure 3-7. *Growth of tomato plants in a series of nutrient solutions in which either the anions or the cations are varied systematically. Numbers in circles represent the dry weight of the tops produced by the plants. (After Hamner, Lyon, and Hamner,* Botan. Gaz., **103,** *1942, p. 590.)*

individual ions or elements, are varied. An experimental method for the independent alteration of the negatively charged anions and the positively charged cations was suggested in 1940 by the American plant physiologist Hamner. In this method the stock solutions of Tottingham and Shive are replaced by stock solutions in which anions or cations are varied separately. The first stock solution contains the K, Mg, and Ca salts of nitrate; the second contains the same cations but as sulfate salts; whereas in the third the phosphate salts are used. The proportions of the cations are maintained constant in the stock solutions. These solutions are then combined as before to yield a series of nutrient solutions in which the K, Mg, and Ca concentrations are constant throughout but in which nitrate, sulfate, and phosphate are varied systematically. In this system, study of the effects of variation in concentration of K, Mg, and Ca is achieved by use of an additional series of stock solutions containing, respectively, the K salts of nitrate, sulfate, and $H_2PO_4^-$, the Ca salts of these anions, and the Mg salts of the same series. These three stock solutions may then be combined to yield a series of nutrient solutions in which the nutrient anions are constant throughout but in which the cations are varied systematically. An example of the growth of plants in a series of nutrient solutions varied according to the Hamner method is given in Figure 3-7. It can be seen

Table 3-2. *The Composition with Respect to Major Elements and Iron of Three Widely Used Nutrient Solutions. These Solutions to Be Complete Must Also Contain Salts of the Essential Minor Elements.* *

SHIVE'S SOLUTION		HOAGLAND'S SOLUTION		HOAGLAND'S #2 SOLUTION	
SALT	GM/LITER	SALT	GM/LITER	SALT	GM/LITER
$Ca(NO_3)_2 \cdot 4H_2O$	1.06	$Ca(NO_3)_2 \cdot 4H_2O$	1.18	$Ca(NO_3)_2 \cdot 4H_2O$	0.95
KH_2PO_4	0.31	KNO_3	0.51	KNO_3	0.61
$MgSO_4 \cdot 7H_2O$	0.55	KH_2PO_4	0.14	$MgSO_4 \cdot 7H_2O$	0.49
$(NH_4)_2SO_4$	0.09	$MgSO_4 \cdot 7H_2O$	0.49	$NH_4H_2PO_4$	0.12
$FeSO_4 \cdot 7H_2O$	0.005	Ferric tartrate	0.005	Ferric tartrate	0.005

* The minor elements are added by supplying 1 cc per liter of a solution containing 0.6 gm H_3BO_3 (boric acid), 0.4 gm $MnCl_2 \cdot 4H_2O$, 0.05 gm $ZnSO_4$, 0.05 gm $CuSO_4 \cdot 5H_2O$, and 0.02 gm $H_2MoO_4 \cdot 4H_2O$ (molybdic acid).

how it is possible, then, to select the optimal proportions of anions and cations from such an experiment.

A third method extensively used for the study of effects of nutrient composition is one in which two salts, for example $Ca(NO_3)_2$ and KH_2PO_4, are kept constant in concentration while the third, $MgSO_4$, is varied. This method has the disadvantage that the total salt concentration of the nutrient solution varies, which, as shown later in this chapter, is often of considerable consequence.

The methods above have been applied by many investigators to a great number of different plants. Although species differ somewhat among themselves as to the exact optima of concentration and proportion of the major nutrient elements, nutrient requirements of plants are, by and large, remarkably similar, and a single nutrient solution can be used for the successful culture of a great range of species. The compositions of three nutrient solutions now in wide use for the growing of plants in liquid or sand culture are given in Table 3-2.

The Minor Elements

The presence of the minor elements in a nutrient solution is, of course, necessary if the nutrient solution is to be a complete one, that is, a solution capable of supporting the complete growth cycle of a plant. Study of the major elements is, then, possible only in nutrient solutions which contain all of the essential minor elements. In the early investigations of mineral nutrition, the minor elements could not be recognized as essential, since they were contained as impurities in the salts

Table 3-3. *The Recognition of the Role of Minor Elements in Higher Plant Nutrition.*

ELEMENT	ESSENTIAL ROLE FIRST DEMONSTRATED			EXAMPLES OF WELL-KNOWN DISORDERS DUE TO DEFICIENCY
	FOR	BY	YEAR	
Manganese	Many species	McHargue	1922	Gray speck of oats
Boron	Broad bean	Warington	1923	Brown heart of vegetables, dry rot of sugar beets
Zinc	Sunflower, barley	Sommer and Lipman	1926	Mottle and little leaf of fruit trees
Copper	Barley	Lipman and MacKinney	1931	Frenching and dieback of fruit trees
	Various species	Sommer	1931	
Molybdenum	Tomato	Arnon and Stout	1939	Whiptail of cauliflower

of the major elements. As the purity of the salts available for nutrition studies increased, it became evident that the recognized major elements alone would not support plant growth. Iron was the first of the minor elements established as essential to plant growth, a discovery made by Gris in 1843–44. Definitive experiments on other minor elements required by higher plants were not carried out until the years following 1920. The recognition of the essential nature of manganese, boron, zinc, copper, and molybdenum in the years 1932–1939 has been an exciting chapter of modern plant physiology, made possible by the development of rigorous methods for the purification of the components of nutrient solutions and by recognition of the ease with which solutions may become contaminated with amounts of the minor elements sufficient to support plant growth. Thus the prolonged storage of water in a glass bottle may result in the solution of significant quantities of boron. Similarly, water, by flowing through a galvanized pipe or through a brass plumbing fixture, may dissolve sufficient zinc or copper to satisfy the plant's needs. Through scrupulous attention to such details has come our present knowledge of the role of the minor elements. Some of the historical details involved are given in Table 3-3, and further discussion of the economy of each element in relation to the plant is given in following sections.

Symptoms of Mineral Deficiency

When a plant lacks a particular essential element, symptoms of deficiency specific to this element develop. Some of these deficiency symptoms may be observed visually, whereas others are more subtle and may be detected only by more refined methods. Visually observable symptoms can frequently serve to diagnose plant ills of a nutritional nature. It should be remembered, too, that it was these visual symptoms which aided the early workers in determining those elements required for the growth of higher plants. Each of the essential elements participates in the formation of one or more chemical compounds which play indispensable roles in plant growth. In the absence of any essential element, then, one characteristic symptom is poor growth. Superimposed on this general symptom are other more specific symptoms more or less characteristic of each element.

With the notable exception of the legumes, plants are dependent upon soil nitrogen, principally in the form of nitrate ions, NO_3^-, but also as ammonium ions, NH_4^+. Legumes, in association with a particular bacterium, possess the ability to utilize the molecular nitrogen, N_2, of the air. The usual symptom of nitrogen deficiency is a lack of green color in the leaves, a symptom which increases to a complete yellowing and loss of the lower leaves (Fig. 3-8A) as the severity of the deficiency increases. Many species, as the tomato, exhibit purple or red coloration of leaf veins due to anthocyanin pigments (Chap. 13), which are produced in abnormal quantities under conditions of nitrogen deficiency. Plants supplied with a superabundance of nitrogen tend to form dark green, succulent leaves and weak stems and exhibit abundant vegetative growth. Nitrogen tends perhaps more than any other element to be limiting in the soil, and, together with phosphorus, is the element most abundantly supplied to soil in fertilizers.

Phosphorus is taken up by plants principally in the form of the ions

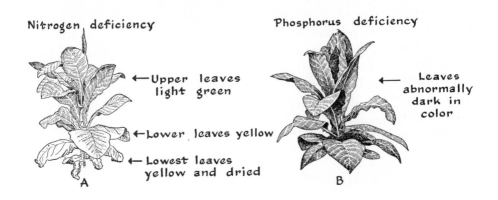

Nitrogen deficiency

←Upper leaves light green

←Lower leaves yellow

← Lowest leaves yellow and dried

A

Phosphorus deficiency

← Leaves abnormally dark in color

B

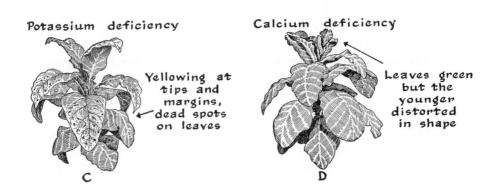

Potassium deficiency

Yellowing at tips and margins, dead spots on leaves

C

Calcium deficiency

Leaves green but the younger distorted in shape

D

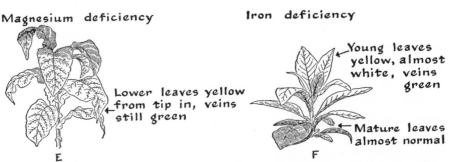

Magnesium deficiency

Lower leaves yellow from tip in, veins still green

E

Iron deficiency

Young leaves yellow, almost white, veins green

Mature leaves almost normal

F

Figure 3-8. *Symptoms of mineral deficiency in the tobacco plant. (Redrawn after J. E. McMurtrey from the book* Hunger Signs in Crops, *published jointly by the American Society of Agronomy and the National Fertilizer Association, 1941, pp. 43-53.)*

$H_2PO_4^-$ and $HPO_4^=$. The symptoms of phosphorus deficiency are less characteristic than those of nitrogen deficiency and are not always readily recognized by visual observation. In general, the phosphorus-deficient plant is stunted in its growth; the leaves are dark green in color (Fig. 3-8B), and there is often a tendency to develop purple or reddish anthocyanin pigments. These symptoms may be accompanied by the development of areas of dead tissue on leaves, petioles, or fruits, often resulting in leaf fall.

Potassium deficiency results in yellowing of the leaves, often in the form of a mottling which ultimately develops into an area of dead tissue at the tip and around the margin of the leaf (Fig. 3-8C). As in all deficiencies, growth is restricted, and the stems are often so weak that the plants are readily blown down by wind.

Lack of calcium causes rapid and quite spectacular disintegration of the terminal growing regions of shoot and root in many species, a symptom which develops first as malformation of the youngest leaves (Fig. 3-8D). The symptoms of calcium deficiency are, however, often complicated by the fact that calcium plays a role not only within the plant but also in regulating the uptake of other ions from the soil or nutrient solution by the root. Calcium deficiency may, for example, result in the uptake of abnormally high and even toxic amounts of magnesium. The symptoms of magnesium toxicity, rather than calcium deficiency, may therefore appear in plants grown in soils or nutrient solutions which are low in calcium and high in magnesium.

Magnesium is required by the plant, as we have seen in Chapter 2, for the formation of chlorophyll, and the symptoms of magnesium deficiency commonly include yellowing or chlorosis of the leaves, which develops upward from the base of the plant (Fig. 3-8E). This characteristic symptom is frequently accompanied by death of portions of the leaf or the entire leaf.

Deficiency of sulfur is infrequent under the usual conditions of plant growth, since in soil the $SO_4^=$ ion commonly taken up by the plant is normally abundant. The deficiency is known principally from those instances in which it has been brought about in nutrient culture. The symptoms are characterized by yellowing of the younger leaves in the early stages, while in severe deficiency even the older leaves may become pale green in color. Roots are less severely affected and may actually be larger in slightly sulfur-deficient plants than in normal ones.

The characteristic symptom of deficiency of iron is the striking yellowing of the young leaves referred to earlier. This yellowing, iron chlorosis, sets in quite suddenly because iron, unlike other elements such as nitrogen, cannot be withdrawn from the older leaves and used by the plant to alleviate the deficiency. Iron chlorosis affects most strikingly the interveinal areas of the leaf, which may be almost a pure white, while the veins remain a darker color and are often relatively green (Fig. 3-8F). The chlorotic leaves do not die at once, as they do in other deficiency induced chloroses, and may remain on the plant over rather long periods as a terminal cluster of white or yellow leaves on twigs whose mature leaves are entirely green.

Although the chemical role of boron in the plant is quite unknown, the physiological symptoms of boron deficiency are striking and relatively constant from plant to plant. The outstanding symptom is the death of the growing regions of stem and root. Growth of the plant and production of new leaves therefore cease, and for this reason boron deficiency in tobacco was once referred to as "top sickness." Boron deficiency in fleshy organs results in disintegration and browning of the internal tissues, a symptom which results in heart rot of sugar beets, internal browning and cork formation in apples, and water-soaked brown areas in cauliflower.

In the development of manganese deficiency the successive leaves of the growing plant become paler and exhibit dead brown or gray spots. This chlorosis, like that due to iron deficiency, is particularly marked in the interveinal areas of the leaf, but, unlike iron deficiency, the spotting and death of the leaves soon leads to their loss.

Deficiency of copper is manifested in many species by a withering of the tips of the young leaves, leading ultimately to loss of the leaves. Plants may also wilt, even under conditions of good water supply.

Zinc deficiency in annual plants is often first manifested by yellowing of the lower leaves at the tips and margins. Dead areas develop in the leaves, and the leaves may be malformed. In citrus, as well as in deciduous fruits, the young leaves are stunted in their growth and remain clustered in short branches or rosettes, so that zinc deficiency of these crops has been known as "little leaf" disease.

The element molybdenum is required by the plant in its metabolism of nitrogen. Thus the amount of molybdenum required for normal plant growth is larger when molecular nitrogen or nitrate is used as a source of nitrogen than when ammonium ions are utilized.

A Comparison of Mineral Deficiency Symptoms

One of the ways in which knowledge concerning mineral deficiency symptoms is most valuable is in the diagnosis of plant nutritional deficiencies under field or horticultural conditions. A deficiency in any of the elements required by the plant results in reduction of growth, and it is therefore impossible to determine which element a plant lacks by observation of this one symptom alone. In certain instances, growth of a particular part of the plant is affected more severely than the growth of other parts, and this may be used as one basis for diagnosis. In many deficiencies the leaves are chlorotic, and since the age of leaves affected and the pattern of the chlorosis vary greatly, these symptoms are useful in diagnosis. The visually detectable deficiency symptoms are summarized in a systematic way in Table 3-4. With the aid of the information in this table, it is possible to trace a set of symptoms to their origin in deficiency of a particular element. It should be borne in mind, however, that individual species of plants differ somewhat in their manifestations of individual deficiencies, and that different levels of deficiency result in more or less severe manifestations of these symptoms. Plants which are simultaneously deficient in several elements may, in addition, show a complex of overlapping deficiency symptoms.

Table 3-4. *A Key to Plant-Nutrient Deficiency Symptoms.* (*From McMurtrey, in* Diagnostic Techniques for Soils and Crops. *American Potash Inst., 1950, p. 243.*)

SYMPTOMS	ELEMENT DEFICIENT
A. Older or lower leaves of plant mostly affected; effects localized or generalized.	
B. Effects mostly generalized over whole plant; more or less drying or firing of lower leaves; plant light or dark green.	
C. Plant light green; lower leaves yellow, drying to light-brown color; stalks short and slender if element is deficient in later stages of growth........	Nitrogen
CC. Plant dark green, often developing red and purple colors; lower leaves sometimes yellow, drying to greenish brown or black color; stalks short and slender if element is deficient in later stages of growth................	Phosphorus
BB. Effects mostly localized; mottling or chlorosis with or without spots of dead tissue on lower leaves; little or no drying up of lower leaves.	
C. Mottled or chlorotic leaves, typically may redden, as with cotton; sometimes with dead spots; tips and margins turned or cupped upward; stalks slender...	Magnesium
CC. Mottled or chlorotic leaves with large or small spots of dead tissue.	
D. Spots of dead tissue small, usually at tips and between veins, more marked at margins of leaves; stalks slender....................	Potassium

Table 3-4. (*Concluded*)

SYMPTOMS	ELEMENT DEFICIENT
DD. Spots generalized, rapidly enlarging, generally involving areas between veins and eventually involving secondary and even primary veins; leaves thick; stalks with shortened internodes...............	Zinc
AA. Newer or bud leaves affected; symptoms localized.	
B. Terminal bud dies, following appearance of distortions at tips or bases of young leaves.	
C. Young leaves of terminal bud at first typically hooked, finally dying back at tips and margins, so that later growth is characterized by a cut-out appearance at these points; stalk finally dies at terminal bud.............	Calcium
CC. Young leaves of terminal bud becoming light green at bases, with final breakdown here; in later growth, leaves become twisted; stalk finally dies back at terminal bud...	Boron
BB. Terminal bud commonly remains alive; wilting or chlorosis of younger or bud leaves with or without spots of dead tissue; veins light or dark green.	
C. Young leaves permanently wilted (wither-tip effect) without spotting or marked chlorosis; twig or stalk just below tip and seedhead often unable to stand erect in later stages when shortage is acute..................	Copper
CC. Young leaves not wilted; chlorosis present with or without spots of dead tissue scattered over the leaf.	
D. Spots of dead tissue scattered over the leaf; smallest veins tend to remain green, producing a checkered or reticulating effect.........	Manganese
DD. Dead spots not commonly present; chlorosis may or may not involve veins, making them light or dark green in color.	
E. Young leaves with veins and tissue between veins light green in color...	Sulfur
EE. Young leaves chlorotic, principal veins typically green; stalks short and slender...	Iron

Quantitative Relationships Between Mineral Supply and Plant Growth

We have discussed earlier the varied systems which may be used to determine what constitutes an optimal nutrient solution for a particular plant. Let us now consider the way in which plant growth and plant yield respond to variations in the level of one essential mineral in a nutrient solution containing all other minerals in optimal concentration. Figure 3-9A gives data from an experiment in which one nutrient, potassium, is varied in an otherwise complete soil medium. At low

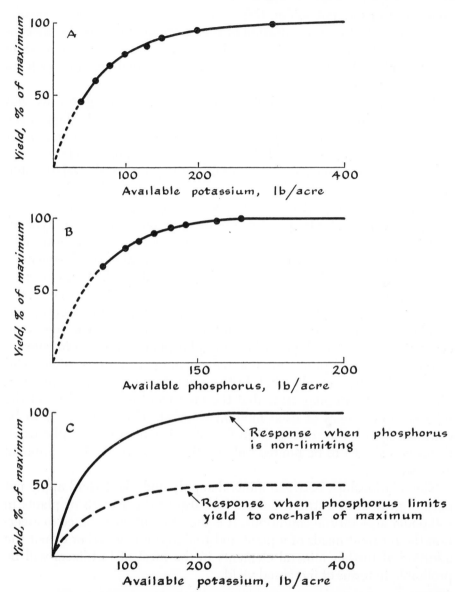

Figure 3-9. *Yield of corn as related to concentration of available soil minerals. A. Yield in relation to soil potassium. B. Yield in relation to soil phosphorus. C. Yield in relation to potassium concentration at two different levels of soil phosphorus.* (*A and B after data of Bray, in* Diagnostic Techniques for Soils and Crops. American Potash Inst., 1948, pp. 57, 58.)

concentrations of potassium, the final yield of plant is approximately proportional to the concentration of this nutrient supplied. As the concentration of potassium is increased further, however, the increase in yield of plant becomes progressively less and tends to approach an upper maximum limit.

The formulation of this relation, the law of diminishing returns, was first worked out by the German plant physiologist Mitscherlich in the years after 1909. Although the example given concerns a particular element, potassium, it should be appreciated that similar relations can be obtained for other elements. Figure 3-9B portrays the relationship between yield of plant and concentration of available phosphorus. Let us now ask ourselves what will happen if we combine two deficiencies, say potassium and phosphorus. Figure 3-9C illustrates the type of growth response to be expected with varying potassium concentrations but in a medium containing only a low concentration of phosphate— enough to permit only half of the maximum plant yield. It may be seen that the response of the plant to potassium will be similar to that shown in Figure 3-9A, except that the growth at all potassium concentrations will be but half that obtained when phosphate is present in high concentration. Thus if both potassium and phosphate are given in concentrations capable of producing one half of the maximum possible yield of plant, then the actual yield is but one quarter of the maximum possible. In general, we may state that the final yield is the product of the relative sufficiencies of each mineral element. This situation is to be contrasted with that discussed in Chapter 2, where rate of photosynthesis was shown to be limited only by the factor available in minimal amount.

The relationships between mineral supply and plant yield apply not only to growth in nutrient culture but also to the growth of plants in soil under agricultural conditions. It is therefore of importance to ascertain the nutrient needs of a plant and to determine whether or not the addition of further mineral elements in the form of fertilizers will be profitable in terms of increased yield.

Methods for the Diagnosis of Plant Mineral Status

While it is possible to detect severe mineral deficiency symptoms visually, it is not so possible to detect slighter deficiencies in this way. In order that crop plants may be grown economically, minerals must be supplied in such quantities as to assure high yields, but they must not be supplied in such excess as to be wasteful or even injurious to the plant. The determination of the quantity of each mineral element which must be added to a particular soil to assure optimal production of a particular crop is a matter of considerable interest.

Perhaps the most straightforward method for the assessment of a plant's nutrient needs lies in the determination of whether the final yield is increased by addition of particular minerals or combinations of minerals. This method, commonly carried out in small field plots, is the ultimate basis for fertilizer practices. Since the time needed for the conduct of fertilizer field trials is considerable, other quicker methods, methods based on chemical analysis of plant or soil, have been developed.

In the first of these chemical methods, the soil itself is analyzed chemically for its content of each element. On the basis of this information, and on the basis of additional information concerning the correlation between the soil content of each element and the crop yield, conclusions can be drawn as to the need for further addition of minerals to the soil in question. For the application of this method, the crop plant is grown in the soil, either in pots or test plots, and the yield determined with and without the addition of various minerals at various concentrations and in various combinations. With this knowledge, and with knowledge of the chemically determined level of each element in the soil, suggestions can be made as to the needs of the crop for additional minerals.

The diagnosis of the mineral status of a plant by chemical analysis of the soil is complicated by the fact that the concentration of a particular element in the soil does not bear any direct relation to the amount of that element available to the plant. This will be taken up again in Chapter 6. Many minerals are found in soils in forms which are unavailable to plants. Analytical methods, which determine only that portion of each element which is actually available, must therefore be used. We do not possess the necessary information to do this satisfactorily for such critical elements as phosphorus and nitrogen.

Still another method for the diagnosis of the plant's nutrient status is based on the fact that the concentration of each essential element in the plant depends on the concentration and amount of this element available to the plant from the soil or nutrient solution. By analyzing plant tissues for their content of a particular element, and with knowledge of the correlation between tissue content of each element and final yield, it is possible to draw conclusions concerning the need of the plant for further supplies of minerals. The concentration of each nutrient element in plant tissue varies not only with nutrient supply but also with the species, with the climatic conditions, and with the portion of the plant chosen for analysis. With many species the leaves are particularly responsive to changes in the mineral supply present in the soil or nutrient solution, and the leaves are therefore often used for diagnostic mineral analyses. The data of Figure 3-10 show how leaf analysis may be used for the diagnosis of the nutritional status of a particular species, Ladino clover, with respect to a particular element, phosphorus. For

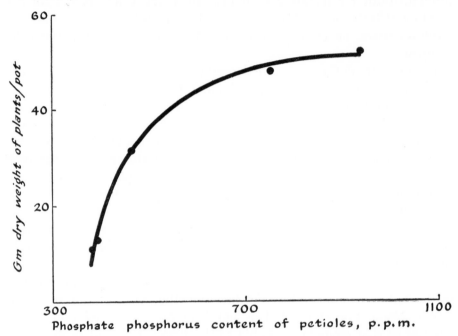

Figure 3-10. *Plant yield as related to tissue phosphorus content in Ladino clover. Plants were grown in soil supplied with varying amounts of phosphate fertilizer and the petioles analyzed at the time of harvest.* (After Ulrich, in Diagnostic Techniques for Soils and Crops. *American Potash Inst., 1948, p. 183.*)

this experiment, clover plants were grown in a soil containing all of the nutrient elements in excess, except for phosphorus. To a series of large pots, increasing amounts of phosphate were added. After a period of growth, leaf samples were removed from the plants of each pot and analyzed for phosphorus. The data of Figure 3-10 show that the yield, the amount of plant material produced per pot increased with increasing phosphorus content of the leaf tissue up to a critical level. Above this level the plants absorbed phosphorus, but this did not result in a further proportional increase in yield. Low concentrations of leaf phosphorus, on the contrary, are associated with decreased yield. If we were now to analyze the leaves of Ladino clover growing under conditions of unknown nutritional status, we could, by reference to the curve of Figure 3-10, decide whether the phosphorus content found indicated a need on the part of the crop for further phosphorus in order to achieve maximum yield.

The methods outlined above for phosphorus may, of course, be extended to other essential elements. In particular, nitrogen and potassium have been the subject of extensive investigation by leaf analysis. Leaf and other tissue analyses have been used for the determination of nutritional needs in pineapple, sugar cane, sugar beet, grapes, deciduous fruits, and other crops. The determination of nutritional status by plant analysis is perhaps the most generally satisfactory method available for the purpose, and it is finding an increasingly wide application.

Acidity and Plant Growth

A factor of general importance for the growth of plants in nutrient culture or in soil is the concentration of hydrogen ions present in the substrate. Hydrogen ions are of course always present in aqueous media. In pure water, their concentration is 10^{-7} M (molar), and a solution containing hydrogen ions at this concentration is known as a neutral solution. Hydrogen-ion concentrations greater than 10^{-7} M result from the addition of acids such as HCl. Such solutions are known as acid solutions. The addition of alkalis, such as KOH, results in solutions which contain hydrogen ions at concentrations less than 10^{-7} M, due to the fact that in aqueous media the product of (H^+) and (OH^-) concentrations must always equal 10^{-14}. The hydrogen-ion concentrations found in biological materials generally cover the range from approximately 10^{-4} M to 10^{-9} M, from slightly acid to slightly alkaline. Because these concentrations are low, and because expression of these concentrations in terms of molarity is unwieldy, a more convenient manner of expression has been defined in the pH scale. The pH of a solution is merely the negative logarithm of its hydrogen-ion concentration. Thus a pH of 4 represents a hydrogen-ion concentration of 10^{-4} M.

$$\text{Hydrogen-ion concentration} = 10^{-4} \text{ M}$$
$$\text{Log (base 10) of } 10^{-4} = -4$$
$$p\text{H} = -\log_{10}(\text{hydrogen-ion conc.}) = 4$$

Similarly, a pH of 7 represents a neutral solution, whereas a pH of 9 represents an alkaline solution with a hydrogen-ion concentration of 10^{-9} M.

The pH or hydrogen-ion concentration of the soil or nutrient solution determines the suitability of the medium as a substrate for plant growth in at least three different ways. In the first place, very high or very low hydrogen-ion concentrations are injurious to plant roots and inhibit their growth and functioning. This nonspecific toxic action occurs in general at pH's of roughly 4 or below and 9 or above, so that the pH range of 4–9 covers the range suitable for the growth of most plants. In the second place, the hydrogen-ion concentration determines the behavior of certain essential minerals in the soil or nutrient solution. At a pH of about 6 or above, inorganic iron precipitates from solution as $Fe(OH)_3$ and is deposited as insoluble Fe_2O_3. Plants grown in media at pH's exceeding 6 tend, therefore, to become chlorotic due to iron de-

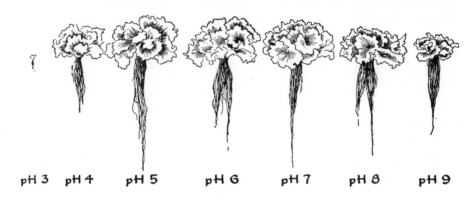

pH 3 pH 4 pH 5 pH 6 pH 7 pH 8 pH 9

Figure 3-11. *The growth of lettuce in nutrient solutions maintained at varying pH levels.* (*After Arnon and Johnson, from Hoagland,* Inorganic Plant Nutrition, *Chronica Botanica, 1948, plate 23.*)

ficiency, unless special precautions are taken to keep iron in solution. Other essential elements, such as manganese, may similarly be precipitated and made unavailable to the plant at high pH values of the nutrient solution. Moreover, the hydrogen-ion concentration of the nutrient also influences plant growth through specific effects on the entrance of other elements into the plant. Very high or very low hydrogen-ion concentrations tend, for example, to impede the uptake of calcium ions by the root.

Figure 3-11 shows how the growth of a particular plant, lettuce, varies with the pH of the nutrient media. In this experiment, iron was supplied in the form of a complex organic salt, which, while available to the plant, was not precipitated at pH values above 6. It can be seen that good growth took place over the range of pH 5 to pH 8, somewhat less growth at pH values of 4 and 9, and essentially no growth at higher or lower values. It is characteristic of the response of plants to pH that a rather broad range of pH values of the nutrient is suitable for supporting maximum growth, and that pH values outside of this range are markedly injurious. When plants are grown in nutrient culture, it is therefore essential to determine and adjust the pH of the nutrient to keep it within the favorable range.

Elements Other Than the Essential Ones Contained in Plants

Although plants require only the twelve essential minerals ordinarily taken up through their roots, they may, and often do, take up other minerals which happen to be present in the soil or nutrient solution. Some sixty different elements have, in fact, been found in one or another species of higher plant. Such nonessential elements as gold, lead, mercury, and arsenic are taken up in small amounts by roots if these elements are present in a soluble form in the nutrient, and even elements not ordinarily present in significant quantities in nature, such as plutonium, can be absorbed if proffered to the plant. We shall see in Chapter 4 that although plants possess, to a marked degree, the property of selectively admitting the essential elements, this selectivity is not an absolute one, and any element can apparently be taken up to some slight extent. The presence of an element in a plant does not necessarily indicate its essentiality but may merely signalize the fact that this element is present in the medium surrounding the roots.

Two of the most abundant elements of the earth's crust are silicon and aluminum, and both of these are taken up by many species. Silicon, in the form of silicic acid, H_2SiO_3, or of silicates such as K_2SiO_3, is absorbed particularly abundantly by the roots of many grasses and deposited in the cell walls in the form of silica, SiO_2. Aluminum is similarly absorbed and may cause visible responses in the plant. In Hydrangea, for example, the normal red or white flowers may change to blue or violet if the plant contains abundant aluminum.

The element selenium is of some importance in the western United States, since several species of plants, especially certain species of Astragalus, are able to accumulate large quantities of this element. Selenium is nontoxic or only slightly toxic to the plant, but when the selenium-containing plant is grazed, it causes in the animal the serious disease known as alkali poisoning, or "blind staggers." Selenium resembles sulfur in its chemical properties, and it is believed that the seleniferous plants accumulate selenium by manufacturing selenium-containing analogs of plant compounds which should properly contain sulfur. In any case, the selenium-containing plant material is much more toxic to the animal than a corresponding amount of inorganic selenium.

It is a curious fact that higher animals require in their economy at least two elements which are not essential to the plant. The amount of these two elements, iodine and cobalt, available to the animal depends largely on the amount taken up more or less accidentally by plants. Many areas of the world are deficient in either iodine or cobalt. Plants will thrive in these areas, but the animals feeding on these plants contract deficiency diseases unless their diets are supplemented with the appropriate element.

Salinity

A special instance of the relation of plants to nonessential elements is that involving high concentrations of salts, particularly common table salt, NaCl. Many soils of arid regions are saline and contain concentrations of salts well above the levels found in fertile soils or nutrient solutions. This is important, since high concentrations of any salt, even of a salt of an essential element, are injurious to the growth of crop plants. Plant species vary greatly in their tolerance of high salt concentrations. Oats, peas, and peaches, for example, are damaged by rather low salt concentrations, whereas sugar beets and cotton are somewhat more resistant. At the other end of the scale are the *halophytes,* species particularly adapted to growth under saline conditions such as occur along the sea coasts or in the undrained interior basins of the West, including Death Valley and the valley of the Great Salt Lake. Among the halophytes characteristic of the native vegetations of these highly saline regions are the genera Salicornia, Atriplex, and Allenrolphea.

Much of the 20 million acres of land under irrigation in the western United States is sufficiently saline to depress crop yields, and some land has necessarily been abandoned for agriculture because of the accumulation of excessive salt. These accumulations result from the transport of salts to the soil surface by ground or surface water followed by the subsequent evaporation of the water. With repeated irrigation or flooding, followed by evaporation, the salt content of the soil builds up to very high levels. The amount of salt carried in our river and irrigation waters is spectacular. The Colorado River alone, containing about 800 parts per million of total dissolved salts, carries some 6 to 10 million tons of salts annually, and since much of this water is used for irrigation of plants, most of the salt is ultimately deposited in the soil.

The damage to crop plants by excessive amounts of salt increases progressively as the salt concentration of the soil is increased. At low levels, such as 0.2 per cent of total salts, growth is depressed, the exact amount of decrease depending somewhat on what particular salts are concerned. At higher levels, such as 2 per cent of total salts, most plants other than the salt-tolerant halophytes are killed. The injurious effects of high salt concentrations are due primarily to interference with the uptake of water by the plant, a matter which will be considered further in Chapter 5. At high salt concentrations, plant damage depends primarily on total salt concentration in the soil or nutrient, and is much the same without regard to the chemical nature of the salts involved.

How are the halophytes able to tolerate the high salt concentrations so noxious to nonhalophytic species? One answer to this question appears to lie in the ability of halophytes to take up freely the sodium salts which constitute the bulk of the salt of saline soils. Nonhalophytes in general tend to exclude the nonessential sodium ion, which acts then as an osmotically active material (Chap. 4), hindering the uptake of water from the external solution. In the halophytes, high external salt concentrations are balanced by high internal salt concentrations due to the ready ingress of sodium, and salinity therefore presents no barrier to water uptake.

Summary

Twelve mineral elements essential to plant growth are, in general, taken up from the soil through the roots. These essential nutrients may be divided, on the basis of the amounts required, into the major elements—nitrogen, phosphorus, sulfur, calcium, potassium, and magnesium—and the minor elements—iron, manganese, copper, zinc, boron, and molybdenum. Whereas maximal growth of the plant requires the presence of from a few parts to a few hundred parts per million of each major element in the nutrient medium, the minor elements are required in smaller concentrations—on the order of a few hundredths to one part per million.

Soil normally contains a great variety of organic and inorganic constituents in addition to the essential plant nutrients. The determination of the exact nutrient requirements of the plant must therefore be done not in soil, but in artificial culture media. Both sand and liquid nutrient culture have been and are used for the study of plant nutrition.

Through the techniques of nutrient culture, it has been possible to devise relatively simple nutrient solutions which supply the correct amounts of each element and the correct proportion or balance between these elements. Since higher plants possess in general similar requirements both as to major and minor nutrient elements, essentially the same nutrient solution may be used to support the satisfactory growth of a wide variety of plant species.

When a particular nutrient element is present in the soil or nutrient medium in insufficient quantity, the plant develops symptoms of malnutrition which are more or less specific for the particular element involved. The visually observable symptoms can be used to diagnose the particular deficiency. Analytical determination of the amount of a particular element present in the plant or in available form in the soil can be further used to diagnose the quantitative well-being of a plant with regard to this element, and may be made the basis for fertilizing of plants or crops.

Plants take up small amounts of many of the mineral elements present in the soil in addition to the twelve essential ones. In many instances these materials are innocuous both to the plant and to the animals which feed on the plant. In other cases, elements are taken up which, while they bear no relation to the plant economy, are nonetheless essential to the welfare of animals (iodine and cobalt); others may be toxic to the animal (selenium). Finally, the presence of certain materials in the soil, such as high concentrations of soluble salts may be generally deleterious to plant and animal welfare alike. With the exception of a few specialized forms, the halophytes, plants are unable to grow and thrive in soils made saline by the accumulation of large amounts of soluble mineral matter.

QUESTIONS

1. The "little-leaf" disease of peaches, now known to be due to a zinc deficiency, was originally cured in the field by the application of large quantities of commercial iron sulfate. Explain.

2. How would you account for the 164-pound increase in weight of the willow tree used in van Helmont's experiment?

3. Describe in detail how you would establish the essentiality or nonessentiality of the element sodium for a higher green plant.

4. Wheat plants grown in a medium low in silicon become highly susceptible to fungus attack, and may die as the result of infection. Would you therefore consider silicon an essential element for wheat? Explain.

5. What is meant by the law of diminishing returns? How does it affect agricultural practice?

6. Why do plants often grow better in drip culture than in solution culture? How might one improve the growth of a plant whose roots are immersed in an optimal nutrient solution?

7. Mention several ways for assessing the degree to which a soil is supplying a particular plant with its essential mineral elements.

8. The fact that plants can be grown to maturity in a synthetic nutrient solution has prompted some people to propose that vegetables be grown in "tank-farm" factories in the city, rather than on the soil of farms. What is your opinion of such a proposal?

9. Explain why selenium is of great agricultural importance, despite its nonessentiality for plants.

GENERAL READING

Hambidge, G., ed., *Hunger Signs in Crops.* Washington, D. C.: The American Society of Agronomy and the National Fertilizer Association, 1941. A symposium by leading agronomists, with particular attention to important crop plants.

Hoagland, D. R., *Lectures on the Inorganic Nutrition of Plants.* Waltham: Chronica Botanica, 1948. Lucid, semipopular lectures by a leader in the field.

Kitchen, H. B., ed., *Diagnostic Techniques for Soils and Crops.* Washington, D. C.: American Potash Inst., 1948. Up-to-date information on analytical methods and their applications.

Stout, P. R., and Overstreet, R., "Soil Chemistry in Relation to Inorganic Nutrition of Plants." *Ann. Rev. Plant Physiol.,* 1: 305, 1950. A detailed discussion of the way in which soil furnishes minerals to plants.

CHAPTER 4

Permeability and the Absorption of Nutrients

The Problem

The growing plant must take up some twelve nutrient elements from the soil or nutrient solution. These nutrients ordinarily enter the plant through the root, an organ particularly adapted for such activity in that it is highly branched and bears a myriad of root hairs which contribute to the surface it presents to the soil. The root system is responsible for the uptake not only of mineral elements but also of water, which, as we shall see in Chapter 5, must be supplied to the leaves in tremendous quantities. Thus, through the root must pass a continuous supply of water and nutrient elements en route to the other portions of the plant. These requirements demand that cell surfaces of the root be suitable for the ready passage of water and dissolved materials. At the same time, however, these same cell surfaces must restrain the outward passage of the materials which go to make up the substance of the plant. We shall now consider the facts concerning this one-way traffic through the plant cell, the mechanisms by which the penetration of water and nutrient elements into the cell is achieved and the egress of cellular constituents is denied.

The principles governing the penetration of dissolved materials through cellular surfaces are not unique to roots but are common to plant cells in general. In fact, much of the original work on which our present concepts are founded has been done not with roots, but with a variety of other plant cells and tissues. We will therefore first discuss the general principles governing the entrance and exit of materials to and from plant cells and return later in the chapter to the specific problem of the entrance of mineral nutrients into the root.

74

The Plant Cell and Its Membranes

A typical mature parenchymatous cell consists of a thin layer of protoplasm surrounding the large central vacuole, which is in turn surrounded by the cell wall. A dissolved material, or solute, as it approaches the plant cell from the external environment, first comes in contact with the cell wall. The cell wall contains, however, a great many pores, which, while too small to be visible under the microscope, are nevertheless of substantial proportions in comparison with the usual molecular dimensions. Hence this structure does not constitute any significant barrier to the passage of most solutes. The principal barriers to the passage of solutes into and out of the plant cell are two membranes, an outer plasma membrane which separates the cell wall from the protoplasm, and an inner vacuolar membrane which separates the protoplasm from the vacuolar contents. These membranes are thin and delicate, too thin to be seen and microscopically differentiated from the protoplasm. They are known primarily by their property of selective permeability, that is, they permit the ready passage of certain materials but greatly impede and slow the passage of others. From the chemical characteristics of the substances which readily pass the protoplasmic membranes, and from other evidence, it is thought probable that these membranes are different in chemical constitution from the bulk of the protoplasm, and that they may be constituted primarily of phospholipids (Chap. 12). This supposition is supported also by the fact that model phospholipid membranes, artificially prepared, possess many of the properties of selective permeability displayed by the natural protoplasmic membranes themselves. Be that as it may, the protoplasmic membranes behave as though they were of a generally lipid or fatty character, and their properties of selective permeability are destroyed by chemical agents such as ether or chloroform, which possess the ability to dissolve, and hence disorganize, fatty structures.

Chemical substances can be divided into two broad groups with respect to the laws they follow in their penetration into or out of plant cells. The first group, composed of those substances which ionize little or not at all, is typified by such materials as water and sugars. In their entry into the cell, these compounds follow the simple laws of diffusion, moving always from solutions of higher concentration into regions of lower concentration with respect to the particular compound. So far as the movement of these nonionic materials is concerned, the protoplasmic membranes merely interpose a barrier which slows down the rate at which the final diffusion equilibrium or equality of inside and outside concentrations is attained. Materials capable of extensive ionization, for example such mineral salts as KCl or $Ca(NO_3)_2$, do not follow simple laws of diffusion in their entrance into the plant cell. The component ions of such salts appear to be taken up individually and may be actively accumulated within the living cell, so that the concentration of an individual ion within the cell may be many times the concentration of this same ion in the external solution.

Entrance of Nonionized Substances into the Cell

The rate of penetration of any substance into a cell may be estimated by analyzing samples of cell contents after the cell has been placed in a solution containing the substance of interest. This direct approach

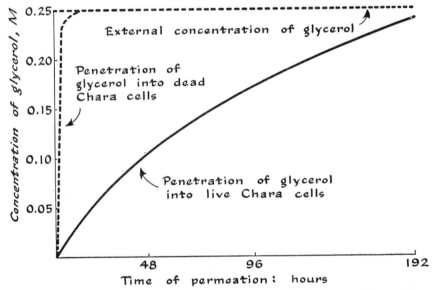

Figure 4-1. *Rate of penetration of a nonionized solute, glycerol, into living and dead cells of the alga Chara. (Data from Collander and Bärlund,* Acta Bot. Fenn., 11, 1933, pp. 29, 36.)

has been elegantly applied by the Finnish plant physiologist Collander, who used for his work the large cells (10 to 20 mm³ per cell) of the alga *Chara ceratophylla.* Cells of Chara were placed in solutions of a wide variety of chemical substances, and the cellular contents were analyzed periodically for their contents of the various materials. Let us consider as an example the experiment for which data are given in Figure 4-1.

In this experiment, living Chara cells were placed in a dilute (0.25 molar) solution of the substance glycerol. Small samples of cell contents were removed at intervals for 192 hours and analyzed for their content of glycerol. The data of Figure 4-1 show that the concentration of glycerol within the cell rises steadily with time and approaches the concentration of the external solution as a limit. Figure 4-1 also shows that the membranes of the living cell interpose a considerable barrier to the entrance of glycerol. Thus glycerol penetrates into the interior of dead cells almost 1000 times more rapidly than it does into living cells. Since in the dead cells the membranes are disorganized or ineffective, the rate of penetration into them is a measure of the rate of diffusion of glycerol molecules in aqueous solution, and we can therefore con-

Table 4-1. *Rates of Penetration of Various Substances into Living Cells of Chara. (After Collander and Bärlund, Acta Bot. Fenn., 11, 1933, pp. 62, 86.)*

SUBSTANCE IN EXTERNAL SOLUTION	TIME REQUIRED FOR INTERNAL CONCENTRATION TO ATTAIN HALF EXTERNAL CONCEN- TRATION, MIN.	PARTITION OF SUBSTANCE BETWEEN OLIVE OIL AND WATER (AMOUNT IN OIL/AMOUNT IN WATER)
Methyl alcohol	1.3	78.0×10^{-4}
Methyl urea	190	4.4×10^{-4}
Urea	320	1.5×10^{-4}
Glycerol	1,700	0.7×10^{-4}
Erythritol	28,000	0.3×10^{-4}
Sucrose	42,000	(very small)

clude that the penetration of glycerol into Chara is about 1000 times slower than the diffusion of this substance in pure water.

By comparing the rates of penetration of a variety of substances into Chara cells it has been possible to formulate simple rules relating cell permeability to the chemical nature of the permeating molecule. To compare the rates of penetration of different substances, it is necessary to express these rates in some common manner. Such a measure can be, for example, the time which is required for the concentration of the substance inside the cell to attain one half the concentration of the same substance in the external solution. A comparison of the rate of penetration of a series of substances expressed in this way is given in Table 4-1. Certain materials such as methyl alcohol penetrate rapidly; others such as sucrose penetrate with extreme slowness. The property of these varied substances most closely correlated with their rate of

penetration is their solubility in oily materials. This property is ex
pressed in Table 4-1 in terms of the partition of each material between
water and an oil, in this case, olive oil. Those substances showing the
greatest affinity for oil are the same substances which penetrate most
rapidly into Chara cells. Oil or lipid solubility is, then, an important
general principle governing the penetration of materials into or out of
plant cells. This principle is in turn one of the chief foundations for the
view that the protoplasmic membranes may be composed of lipids, and

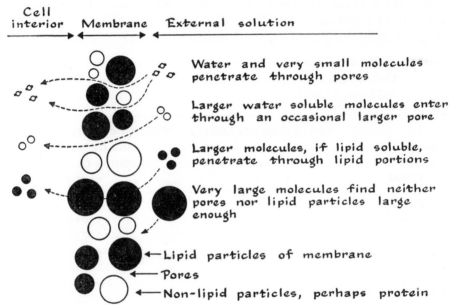

Figure 4-2. *A highly schematized view of the possible structure of
a cell membrane.* (*Adapted from Gerard,* Unresting Cells, *Harper
and Bros., 1949, p. 117.*)

that those substances which are most soluble in this lipid layer penetrate the cell most rapidly.

A second general principle concerned in the passage of substances in
and out of plant cells has to do with the size of the molecules involved.
This is particularly true of water, which penetrates Chara at least 100
times more rapidly than do larger molecules of the same low affinity for
lipids. Conversely, too, very large molecules penetrate more slowly
than smaller molecules of equal lipid solubility. The protoplasmic membrane, then, would appear to be not a simple lipid sheath, but rather a
sievelike sheath containing areas particularly suited to the penetration

of small molecules. These areas must be sufficiently close together so as to limit the size of the continuous lipid areas and hence to hinder the penetration of excessively large molecules. These concepts are portrayed in a highly schematic way in Figure 4-2.

What, now, can we say concerning differences in permeability between different cells, different tissues, and different species of plants? There are great differences in the details of the permeability characteristics of different plants, but the same general principles appear to apply. One striking fact is that the relative contributions of lipid areas and sieve areas to the over-all permeability differ widely between plants. In Chara, as we have seen, permeability is governed mainly by lipid solubility of the permeating solute. In the sulfur bacterium Beggiatoa, on the other hand, molecular size is the primary determinant of the entrance rate of solutes. Most cells of higher plants, insofar as they have been examined, follow the rules laid down above for Chara, with lipid solubility the dominant factor in permeation. Even among the higher plants, however, quantitative differences in rate of permeation of substances are considerable. Urea, a substance extensively investigated in this regard, penetrates leaf cells of Taraxacum some 200 times faster than it does the leaves of Hippuris. Despite this wide range in absolute rates of penetration in different species, the comparative rates at which individual substances are taken up relative to one another are generally similar over a wide range of plant materials.

It can be seen that molecules move into and out of cells at rates much slower than would be the case if the protoplasmic membranes did not present a barrier to diffusion. This barrier is a very great one for substances such as sugars, which must always be present within the cell if proper cell functioning is to be maintained. The characteristics of the barrier are such, however, as to permit a much more rapid exchange of very small molecules, in particular those of water.

Permeability to Water

The process of diffusion involves the movement of molecules of a solute from a solution of its own high concentration to a solution of lower concentration, the diffusion process continuing until the concentrations of solute in all portions of the solution are equal. We have seen that the movement of nonionic solute molecules from an external solution into the interior of a plant cell is such a diffusion process, and one in which the attainment of the final equilibrium is slowed by the presence of a barrier, the protoplasmic membranes. We may discuss the movement of water into and out of plant cells in exactly the same terms used in the discussion of solute movement.

Pure water contains H_2O molecules at their highest possible concentration. An aqueous solution containing some dissolved material other than water contains water at a lower concentration than pure water because a portion of the molecules in any unit volume of solution are foreign, nonwater molecules. If a solution containing a dissolved material is brought in contact with a pure water, the water will diffuse from the region of its higher concentration (the pure water) into the region of its lower concentration (the solution). This is what happens when we place a living plant cell in pure water. The water tends to diffuse from the external region of high concentration into the cell interior, which contains many dissolved materials—sugars, mineral salts, and so on. Measurements of the rate of water entry, made by methods to be described in the following section, have shown that water penetrates into and out of plant cells by a factor of 10,000 to 1,000,000 times more rapidly than does sucrose. This demonstrates then, in a semiquantitative way, how the properties of the protoplasmic membranes are adjusted to permit entrance and egress of water and at the same time almost completely retain such materials as the sugars. For many practical purposes, we may regard the plant cell as surrounded by a membrane which permits the passage of water but restrains the passage of such molecules as the sugars.

The Osmotic Relationships of Plant Cells

The tendency of water to enter or leave a plant cell can be conveniently described in osmotic terms. Here we will be concerned not with the rate of water movement, but rather with the final equilibrium conditions attained. Suppose we place a plant cell containing a certain concentration of internal solutes in a solution of pure water. Let us suppose, also, that the cell membranes are wholly impermeable to the solutes contained in the cell, so that they cannot leak out, and that only water is able to move through the membrane. Water now moves into the cell, diluting the cell contents and increasing the cell volume. If the cell wall exerts a resistance to the volume increase caused by the water uptake, a pressure will be developed on the cell contents. The maximum pressure which can be developed in this way is known as *osmotic pressure* of the cell contents, and the process through which it is developed, the diffusion of water through a selectively permeable membrane, is known as *osmosis*.

A situation strictly analogous to that of the living cell obtains in a simple osmometer (Fig. 4-3), in which an artificial semipermeable membrane is used to cover the open end of a small chamber, which is in turn attached to a long, vertical glass tube. The chamber contains a solution of a solute which cannot pass the semipermeable membrane. As water moves through the membrane and into the osmometer, it dilutes the solute and at the same time increases the volume of the solution, thus causing it to rise in the vertical arm of the osmometer. The process of water uptake will continue until the increase of pressure on the solution in the osmometer, due to the weight of the column above it, increases the rate of outward movement of water molecules from

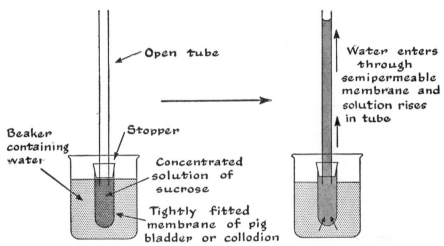

Figure 4-3. *Water uptake in a simple artificial osmotic system.*

the osmometer to a point where it just balances the rate of inward movement. This introduces a new concept, namely, that the rate of diffusion of water through a membrane depends not only on gradients in water concentration but also on gradients in the pressure to which the water is subjected.

Water movement into an osmometer such as that described above will continue until the tendency of water to diffuse into the osmometer, due to the diffusion gradient of water, is just balanced by the tendency of water to escape from the osmometer, due to the pressure exerted on the osmometer contents by the liquid column. If the final concentration of the solute inside the osmometer is 1 M, then the height of the column will be approximately 212 meters, and the pressure exerted on the contents of the osmometer will be approximately 22.4 atm. Since the osmotic pressure developed in an osmometer depends on the concentration of the osmotically active solute it contains, we may refer to this concentration of the osmometer contents as the *osmotic concentration* of the solution. The terms osmotic concentration and osmotic pressure, although they are expressed in different units, can both be used to refer to and describe the osmotic properties of a solution.

The laws governing the osmotic pressure of solutions are analogous to the laws which govern the pressure-volume relationships of gases. Just as the pressure of a gas varies in proportion to the concentration of the gas (Boyle's law), so also the osmotic pressure developed by a solution varies in proportion to the concentration of the osmotically active (nonpermeable) solute. Just as the pressure of a given concentration of gas increases directly with the absolute temperature, so also the osmotic pressure developed by a solution increases directly with

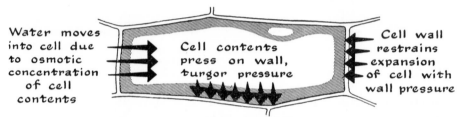

Water moves into cell due to osmotic concentration of cell contents

Cell contents press on wall, turgor pressure

Cell wall restrains expansion of cell with wall pressure

Figure 4-4. *A diagrammatic representation of osmotic concentration, turgor pressure, and wall pressure.*

the absolute temperature. Thus osmotic pressure can, strictly speaking, be related to osmotic concentration only if the temperature is known. However, since the increase in osmotic pressure of a solution is only 1/273 for each degree rise in temperature at 0° C, this factor is not quantitatively an important one over the relatively narrow range of temperature at which plants operate.

Unlike the osmometer, a plant cell has no tube in which solution may rise as water is taken into the cell in response to a diffusion gradient. Also unlike the ideal osmometer, the membranes and wall of the cell are not rigid, but expand as water is taken in. When a plant cell is placed in water, and as water moves into the cell interior, the cell contents press upon the cell wall. Such a cell is said to be *turgid*, and the pressure with which the cell contents press upon the wall is known as the *turgor pressure* (Fig. 4-4). The cell wall, under tension as it restrains and confines the expansion of the cell contents, presses back with a pressure equal in magnitude, but opposite in direction, to the turgor pressure. This back pressure exerted by the cell wall is known as the *wall pressure*. As more and more water is taken in by the cell contents, the wall is further and further extended, and the turgor pressure increases. At final equilibrium the tendency of water to enter the cell, which is due to the osmotic concentration (*OC*) of the cell contents, will be balanced by the tendency of water to leave the cell, which is due to the turgor pressure (*TP*). At this point, then, the turgor pressure just balances the osmotic pressure. To put it another way, at water equilibrium, osmotic pressure minus turgor pressure equals 0.

$$OP \qquad = \qquad TP \qquad\qquad \text{or}\quad OP - TP = 0 \qquad (1)$$

Osmotic pressure due   Turgor pressure with
to cell contents   which cell contents
                   press on cell wall

In general, both osmotic pressure and turgor pressure are measured in terms of their equivalent concentrations rather than as actual pressures. Equation 1 above is therefore ordinarily written as:

$$OC \qquad = \qquad TP \qquad\qquad \text{or}\quad OC - TP = 0 \qquad (2)$$

Osmotic concentration   Turgor pressure ex-
of cell contents   pressed as concentra-
                  tion of solute needed
                  to give this pressure

The initial entrance of water into a plant or artificial osmotic cell is, as we have seen, due to the greater tendency of water to diffuse into, rather than out of, the cell. This difference in diffusion tendencies is known as the *diffusion pressure*, and the net tendency of water to move into the cell as the *diffusion pressure deficit* (*DPD*). When a cell is placed in pure water, and when the cell is not under turgor (*TP* = 0), then the diffusion pressure deficit of the cell is equal to the osmotic concentration of the cell contents.

$$DPD \qquad\qquad = \qquad\qquad OC \qquad\qquad (3)$$

Diffusion pressure deficit   Osmotic concentration
(when *TP* = O)

At the final equilibrium given by Equation 2, when the tendency of water to enter the cell due to osmotic concentration is just balanced by the tendency of water to leave the cell due to the turgor pressure, the diffusion pressure deficit of the cell is of course 0; that is, there is no net tendency of water to enter the cell.

$$DPD \quad = \quad 0 \quad = \quad OC - TP \qquad (4)$$

Diffusion pressure
deficit (at water
saturation)

The diffusion pressure deficit of the cell interior is, then, a quantity which, like osmotic concentration and turgor pressure, can be expressed either in the dimensions of pressure or of concentration equivalent to this pressure.

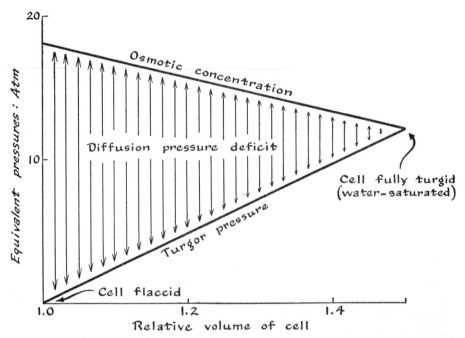

Figure 4-5. *Changes in osmotic concentration of cell contents and of turgor pressure which accompany changes in volume of the plant cell caused by gain or loss of water. The diffusion pressure deficit is equal to the difference between the osmotic concentration and the turgor pressure.*

During the course of water uptake by a cell, the turgor pressure gradually increases from 0 (cell not turgid) to a value equal to the osmotic concentration. At all times the diffusion pressure deficit of the cell is equal to the difference between the osmotic concentration and the turgor pressure, a relation expressed in Equation 5.

$$DPD \quad = \quad OC \quad - \quad TP \qquad (5)$$

Diffusion pressure defi-   Osmotic concentration   Turgor pressure of cell
cit of cell contents   of cell contents   contents

This equation is a general and basic one which may be used in the description and analysis of many aspects of water movement in the plant. Let us see how these quantities change as a plant cell takes up water. The data of Figure 4-5 describe the changes in each of the three components of Equation 5 which occur when a cell without turgor (at incipient plasmolysis, see below) is placed in a solution of pure water. As water is taken in, the volume of the cell increases, with a resultant expansion of the cell wall. At the same time, the elastic cell walls restrict and confine the cell contents, and the turgor pressure rises sharply. The increase in cell volume results, in turn, in dilution of the osmotically active constituents of the cell interior, so that *OC* decreases steadily. Finally, as the turgor pressure nears the *OC*, the *DPD* decreases to 0 at water saturation.

Plasmolysis and Deplasmolysis

Before we can discuss the quantitative measurement of the osmotic quantities of plant cells, we must first consider the behavior of such cells when they are placed in solutions containing dissolved solutes, rather than in pure water. Suppose we place a plant cell in a solution containing enough sucrose so that the osmotic concentration of the sucrose solution is greater than the osmotic concentration of the cell contents. Such a solution is said to be *hypertonic* to the cell. We have already seen that sucrose penetrates the cell membranes only very slowly, and in short experiments, at least, sucrose cannot enter the cell to equalize the inner and outer osmotic concentrations. Water, which can move readily through the membrane, will leave the cell, passing from a region of higher water concentration to one of lower concentration. As water leaves the cell, the cell decreases in volume until the cell wall is no longer under tension. Further loss of water from the cell contents results in the contraction of the protoplasm away from the cell wall. The cell is now said to be *plasmolyzed,* and the stage of plasmolysis at which the first sign of shrinkage of cell contents from cell wall becomes detectable is referred to as the stage of *incipient plasmolysis*. These several stages of water loss from cell to hypertonic solution, which are summarized in Figure 4-6, may be readily seen and followed in thin layers of plant tissue mounted under the microscope. Many of the basic observations concerning the osmotic relations of plant cells have been made microscopically with strips of epidermal tissues from leaves of Zebrina or Rhoeo, or from the inner surface of the scales of onion bulbs.

Plasmolyzed cells often recover their turgor if they are returned to pure water or to solutions less concentrated than the cell contents

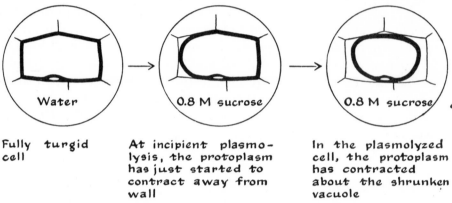

| Fully turgid cell | At incipient plasmolysis, the protoplasm has just started to contract away from wall | In the plasmolyzed cell, the protoplasm has contracted about the shrunken vacuole |

Figure 4-6. *Successive stages of water loss which occur when a turgid cell is transferred to a solution of osmotic concentration greater than that of cell contents.*

(hypotonic solutions). Successive cycles of plasmolysis and *deplasmolysis* can, in fact, often be repeated many times on the same tissue. Since the osmotic concentrations of plant cells fall generally in the range of 0.2 to 0.8 molar, the hypertonic solutions needed to achieve plasmolysis are also of this range of concentrations, roughly from 0.3 to 1.0 molar, depending on the particular tissue concerned.

The phenomena of plasmolysis and deplasmolysis have an application in the study of the permeability of cell membranes to water and to dissolved solutes. A simple method for measuring the rate of water entry into a cell consists in first plasmolyzing the cell until the protoplasmic contents have contracted from the cell wall. If the plasmolyzed cell is now placed in water, the rate at which water is taken up can be determined by measuring the rate at which the cell contents in-

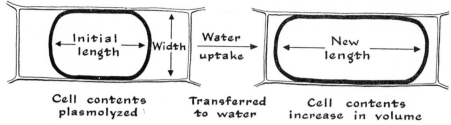

Cell contents   Transferred   Cell contents
plasmolyzed   to water   increase in volume

Figure 4-7. *Measurement of water entry into a plant cell by the deplasmolysis method. The volume increases can be measured very readily with cylindrical cells.*

crease in volume (Fig. 4-7). Similarly, the permeability of the plant membrane to dissolved solutes can be measured by placing the cell in a hypertonic solution of the substance in question. Water moves out of the cell rapidly, and plasmolysis occurs. As the cell remains in the solution, the plasmolyzing solute will gradually enter the cell, and as the osmotic concentration of the cell increases due to this permeation, water will again return to the cell (Fig. 4-8). Thus the rate

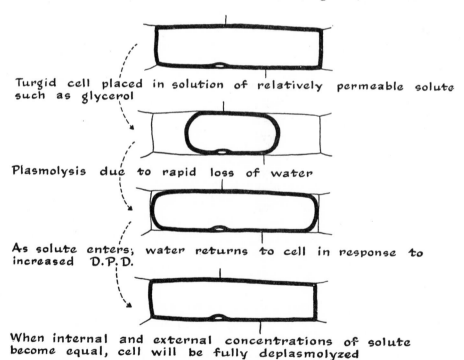

Turgid cell placed in solution of relatively permeable solute such as glycerol

Plasmolysis due to rapid loss of water

As solute enters, water returns to cell in response to increased D.P.D.

When internal and external concentrations of solute become equal, cell will be fully deplasmolyzed

Figure 4-8. *Plasmolysis and deplasmolysis due to rapid loss of water followed by slower entry of solute and water.*

of spontaneous deplasmolysis due to entry of the plasmolyzing agent into the cell can be used as a measure of permeability of the cell to the solute in question. Many of the measurements of cell permeability discussed earlier in this chapter have actually been done by this method rather than by the more direct but more difficult analytical procedure.

Measurement of the Osmotic Quantities

The osmotic concentration of the contents of plant cells can be measured either by physical measurements on the expressed plant juice or by plasmolytic measurements on the intact cell. Physical measurements are usually carried out on juice or sap, primarily the vacuolar contents which have been expressed from the plant tissue under high pressure. The osmotic concentration of the juice is conveniently determined from the freezing point depression, a standard chemical procedure based on the fact that the freezing point of a molar aqueous solution is depressed 1.86° C below the freezing point of pure water, and that the freezing point depression of a solution is proportional to the concentration of the solution. This method is cumbersome, however, in comparison to the following plasmolytic one.

The plasmolytic determination of osmotic concentration is carried out by placing similar cells or pieces of plant tissues in a series of solutions of graded concentration. Sucrose or a similarly effective plasmolyzing agent might be used as the solute. After a period of time, the tissues from each solution are inspected under the microscope, and the minimum concentration of solute needed to bring about incipient plasmolysis is determined. The OC of this external solution is then just equal to the OC of the plant tissue when the TP of the tissue is zero. The OC in the orginal tissue will be less than that of the tissue at incipient plasmolysis, since the tissue decreases in volume during plasmolysis, a factor which can be corrected for by measurements of cell volume before treatment and at incipient plasmolysis. The procedures involved in the plasmolytic determination of the OC are shown in Figure 4-9.

Since the diffusion pressure deficit represents the net water-accumulating tendency of the cell, we may determine it by placing cells in solutions of varying concentration until we find a solution from which water movement into or out of the cell does not take place. This method may be applied to excised strips or discs of tissue which are immersed in a series of graded concentrations of sucrose. The strips or discs are weighed or measured, and then reweighed or remeasured after a period in the graded series of solutions. The solution in which the tissue neither gains nor loses weight, or, alternatively, neither in-

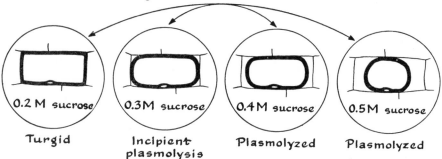

Similar cells or tissue fragments placed in solutions of graded concentrations

0.2 M sucrose   0.3M sucrose   0.4M sucrose   0.5M sucrose

Turgid   Incipient plasmolysis   Plasmolyzed   Plasmolyzed

Figure 4-9. *Determination of the osmotic concentration of plant cells by the plasmolytic method. In this example the osmotic concentration of the cell contents at incipient plasmolysis is equivalent to that of 0.3 M sucrose.*

creases nor decreases in size, is the solution whose *OC* equals the *DPD* of the tissue.

There is no direct method for the measurement of turgor or wall pressure, but these quantities may be calculated from the measured *OC* and *DPD* of the tissues by the relationship given in Equation 5 above.

The Accumulation of Ionic Materials

The uptake of ionic substances by plant cells is characterized by one feature which is entirely absent in the case of the permeation of nonionic materials we have discussed. This new feature is due to the fact that living cells can accumulate ionic materials, that is, they can continue to take up an ion even if the concentration level of this ion inside the cell is far above the concentration of the same ionic species in the external medium. From the point of view of diffusion, the accumulation of salts by a cell is not only unorthodox but impossible. When substances penetrate into cells in response to a diffusion gradient, they may, at most, attain an internal concentration equal to the external concentration. We may conclude, therefore, that the entrance into, and accumulation of, ionic materials by cells is not a simple diffusion process. On the contrary, ion or salt accumulation is a process which requires the expenditure of energy by the plant, energy to do the osmotic work involved in moving ions against a concentration gradient.

Since the penetration of salts into plant cells is complicated by the phenomenon of accumulation, it is hardly possible to make exact comparisons of the relative permeabilities of plant membranes to ionic and nonionic materials. Generally speaking, however, the rates of penetration of salts are much smaller than the rates of penetration of such small molecules as urea or glycerol. Solutions of mineral salts can even be used as plasmolyzing agents. As is the case with nonionic molecules, plant membranes greatly restrict the rate at which ions

Table 4-2. *Accumulation of Certain Ions by Algal Cells as Evidenced by Comparisons of Cell Composition with External Milieu.* (*Adapted from Höber,* Physical Chemistry of Cells and Tissues, *Blakiston Co., 1945, p. 244.*)

ION	NITELLA CLAVATA		RATIO OF INTERNAL/	VALONIA MACROPHYSA		RATIO OF INTERNAL/
	CELL CONTENTS, MOL $\times 10^3$	POND WATER, MOL $\times 10^3$	EXTERNAL CONCEN- TRATION	CELL CONTENTS, MOL	SEA WATER, MOL	EXTERNAL CONCEN- TRATION
K^+	54.3	0.051	1065	0.50	0.012	42
Na^+	10.0	0.217	46	0.09	0.498	0.18
Ca^{++}	10.2	0.775	13	0.0017	0.012	0.14
Cl^-	90.8	0.903	100	0.597	0.580	1.0

move into the cell. Thus the initial rate of uptake of mineral salts by Chara is on the general order of 1,000,000 times slower than would be the case for pure diffusion through a liquid medium. The protoplasmic membranes not only slow down the entry of ions into plant cells, they also possess the ability to select or discriminate between different ions, to permit the entrance of certain species of ions in abundance but to restrict greatly the entrance of other ions. These are some of the important aspects of the permeation of ionic materials into plant cells.

That plant cells possess the ability to accumulate ions to concentrations far higher than those in the surrounding medium was first clearly recognized through comparisons of the ionic composition of algal cell contents with that of the waters in which these algae grow. The data of Table 4-2 show that the fresh-water alga Nitella accumulates K$^+$ ions to a concentration more than 1000 times greater than the concentration of K$^+$ in the surrounding medium. The marine alga Valonia similarly accumulates K$^+$ ions, although not so strikingly as does Nitella. In Valonia, however, it is apparent that certain ions such as Na$^+$ and Ca^{++} are partially excluded from the cell, since they are present inside

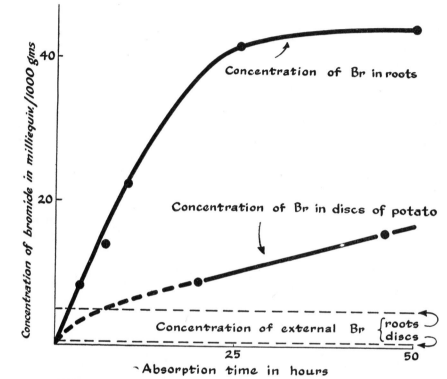

Figure 4-10. *Ions of mineral salts such as KBr are accumulated by plant tissues to concentrations far above that in the external medium. (After Prevot and Steward, Plant Physiol., 11, 1936, p. 525.)*

the cell at concentrations considerably lower than those in the external sea water.

The study of ion uptake and accumulation has been carried out largely with excised root systems of higher plants or with fragments of tissue excised from fleshy organs such as the potato tuber or the carrot root. Figure 4-10 illustrates how these tissues absorb and accumulate the ions of KBr if they are placed in a dilute solution of this salt. With both these tissues, active salt accumulation is wholly dependent on the presence in the tissue of a vigorous respiratory metabolism. Thus roots, if they are to accumulate salts, must receive a continuous supply of oxygen, which is provided by bubbling air or oxygen through the nutrient medium. This oxygen is required for the respiratory processes of the root. Accumulation is slowed or prevented entirely by decreases in respiratory rate brought about either by decreasing the oxygen content of the nutrient medium or by the application to the tissue of chemical substances which specifically inhibit respiration. Accumulation of salts by a tissue depends also on the food supply of the tissue. If roots which contain only a small amount of respirable

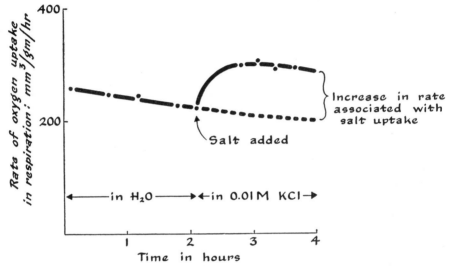

Figure 4-11. *The rate of respiratory oxygen uptake by barley roots as influenced by the presence of salt. (Adapted from Milthorpe and Robertson, Australian J. Exp. Biol. Med. Sci., 26, 1948, p. 191.)*

reserve material (such as sugars) are excised from the plant and placed in a well-aerated nutrient solution, they accumulate salts for only a short period of time as compared with roots which contain abundant reserve respiratory material. All of these facts point to an intimate relationship between the energy-using process of salt accumulation and the energy-yielding process of respiration. So closely is salt accumulation coupled to respiration that the rate at which plant tissues take up oxygen actually increases during periods of active ion uptake. The increase in respiratory rate which accompanies salt uptake can amount to from 20 to 150 per cent of the basal respiration, as is shown in Figure 4-11. The specific manner in which respiratory energy is geared to osmotic work, as well as the mechanism which links respiratory rate to salt uptake, remains, however, to be discovered.

Selective Uptake of Ions

It has already been indicated that algal cells discriminate between various ions and are capable of accumulating large amounts of K^+ ion while simultaneously rejecting other ions such as Na^+. This is true also of the uptake of ions by roots and other higher plant tissues. Generally speaking, salts of monovalent cations such as K^+ are taken up and accumulated at a more rapid rate than salts of di- or polyvalent

Table 4-3. *The Ability of Plants to Select and Discriminate Between Four Different Cations Present in the Nutrient Solution at Equivalent Concentrations. Analyses of Entire Plants. (After Collander, Plant Physiol., 16, 1941, p. 696.)*

| SPECIES | PERCENTAGE OF TOTAL PLANT CATIONS MADE UP BY | | | | TOTAL CONCENTRATION OF CATION |
	Na	K	Mg	Ca	MEQUIV/KG DRY WT.
Fagopyrum (buckwheat)	0.9	39	27	33	3230
Helianthus (sunflower)	2.3	54	17	27	3020
Zea (corn)	2.9	70	16	11	2420
Solanum (potato)	4.1	44	25	27	4290
Atriplex hortense (halophyte)	19.7	39	31	10	4790
Plantago maritima (halophyte)	28.5	39	11	21	4370
Nutrient solution	25	25	25	25	. . . .

cations such as Ca^{++} or Mg^{++}. Similar relations hold among the anions, salts of Cl^-, Br^-, or NO_3^- tending to be accumulated more rapidly than salts of $SO_4^=$. The power of plants to accumulate cations selectively is shown clearly by the data of Table 4-3, data taken from an experiment of Collander in which plants of different species were all grown in the same nutrient solution. This nutrient supplied all of the essential anions and minor elements as well as the four cations Na^+, K^+, Ca^{++}, and Mg^{++} at equal concentrations. It can be seen that most plants, including such cultivated species as corn and potato, accumulated K^+ to a greater degree than any of the other three ions, and that they also tended to exclude Na^+. Among the plants tested, only those which normally grow in salty places, and which therefore belong to the group of halophytes (Chap. 3), accumulated Na^+

approximately in proportion to the amount present in the nutrient medium. The ability of halophytes to take up the Na^+ ion is, as noted earlier, undoubtedly related to the ability of these species to survive under conditions unsuitable for the usual nonhalophytic plants.

Unequal Uptake of Anions and Cations

Plants not only possess the ability to discriminate between various ions of similar charge, but they are also capable of taking up unequal amounts of cation and anion of a given salt. This is particularly marked in cases where K^+ or some other readily absorbed cation is present in the outside solution as the salt of a divalent or other slowly absorbed anion. Conversely, if anions such as NO_3^- or Cl^- are present in the nutrient solution as salts of such slowly absorbed cations as Ca^{++} or

Table 4-4. *Disparity in Anion and Cation Uptake by Wheat Roots.* (*After Lundegårdh,* Annals Agr. Coll. Sweden, 8, 1940, p. 257.)

SALT PRESENT IN EXTERNAL SOLUTION	CATION	ANION	RATIO OF CATION/ANION ACCUMULATION
NaCl	Na^+ (slowly taken up)	Cl^- (rapidly taken up)	0.25 (excess anion uptake)
KCl	K^+ (rapidly taken up)	Cl^- (rapidly taken up)	1.37 (approximate equality)
CsCl	Cs^+ (very rapidly taken up)	Cl^- (rapidly taken up)	7.75 (excess cation uptake)

Mg^{++}, anion accumulation may predominate over cation uptake. Examples of unequal uptake in the case of wheat roots are given in Table 4-4. It is impossible, of course, for a plant simply to take up ions of one charge and leave ions of the opposite charge in the outside solution, since large electrical fields would be set up. Electrical balance of anions and cations must be preserved both inside and outside the cell. An excess of cation uptake over anion uptake must be accompanied by such changes in ionic composition of cell and nutrient as to maintain electrical neutrality in both places. One way in which this is achieved is by the production of new organic anions within the cell. The new anions, those of the organic acids (Chap. 10), are produced by roots or other tissues in amounts just sufficient to accommodate any excess cation taken in. The anions of the organic acids remain in the cell, serving to balance the absorbed cations, while hydrogen ions pass to the external medium where they compensate for the cations which have been removed. In the case of excess anion absorption, on the other hand, these same organic acids disappear in amounts just sufficient to compensate for the excess anion uptake. Ionic balance in the external medium is maintained by the appearance there of bicarbonate and hydroxyl ions. Thus, the plant has at its disposal a flexible metabolic system by means of which it is able to adjust itself to variations in the ionic nature of the surrounding medium and inequalities in the rate of uptake of individual ions which are caused by such variations.

Ion Antagonism

The ionic composition of the nutrient medium not only influences the uptake and accumulation of the individual ions but affects also the permeability of the protoplasmic membranes toward water and nonionized solutes. If a plant or plant tissue is placed in a solution of a single mineral salt, it is frequently found that the permeability of the tissue toward other materials is greatly increased or decreased, and the solution is said to be an unbalanced one. In a solution containing two salts, each of which would greatly influence permeability if present singly, permeability may be maintained at a normal level. These effects, due to mutual interactions of salts and their ions on permeability, are known as *ion antagonisms.*

The best-studied case of ion antagonism is that involving the monovalent ions K^+ and Na^+ and the divalent Ca^{++} ion. The way in which these ions influence permeability can be demonstrated strikingly by experiments involving the loss of pigment from fragments of red beet root. The red pigment is contained in the vacuoles of the individual cell of the beet root. When fragments of the root are placed in distilled water, the pigment permeates outward at such a slow rate as to be hardly detectable. If, however, the tissue fragments are placed in a dilute solution of NaCl, a rapid outward diffusion of pigment occurs. This is due to a great increase in permeability of the membranes. If, now, the tissue is transferred to a solution containing $CaCl_2$ in addition to NaCl, the permeability is again decreased, and the loss of pigment slows down and ceases. The Ca^{++} ions have "antagonized" the permeability-increasing effect of the Na^+ ions.

The phenomenon of ion antagonism has many manifestations. Cells or tissues may survive much longer in balanced salt solutions containing both monovalent and divalent cations than they do in solutions containing either type of cation alone. The suboptimal growth of plants in nutrients which are qualitatively complete, but in which there is an undue preponderance of one species of cation, may be due in part to ion antagonism effects. In all of these manifestations, however, it is probable that the final visual symptoms are but end effects of disturbances of membrane permeability. The fact that cations do influence the character of the plant membrane suggests in turn that this membrane may be in whole or in part composed of materials that possess anionic character. This would be true of a membrane composed of phospholipid molecules, since these substances ionize to form organic anions. One proposal as to the mechanism by which ions act as they do in influencing membrane permeability is that the monovalent ions may act in the direction of dispersing or decreasing the binding forces between adjacent molecular components of the membrane, whereas polyvalent cations function in the reverse way, binding adjacent components more closely together. This proposal, which is hardly more than a restatement of the experimental facts, is at least a useful aid in remembering the effects of ions on membrane permeability

Summary

The absorbing cells of the root possess the ability to take up water and mineral nutrients from the external solution while simultaneously preventing the egress of materials contained within the roots themselves. This one-way traffic between root and environment is due to the characteristics of selective permeability of the two membranes which invest the protoplasm of each cell. The outer of these membranes invests the protoplasm and separates it from the cell wall, while the inner membrane separates protoplasm from vacuolar contents.

Nonionizable solutes enter and leave the cell by diffusion, travelling always from regions of higher to regions of lower concentration. Although the movement of such nonionized solutes continues until concentrations within and without the cell are equalized, the time required to attain diffusion equilibrium depends on the rate at which the solute in question is able to traverse the protoplasmic membranes. Rate of permeation of a solute into or out of a living plant cell depends in turn on two principal properties: its molecular size and solubility in fatty solvents. Generally speaking, substances move through the protoplasmic membranes at rates proportional to their solubility in fatty or lipoid materials, a fact which has suggested that the protoplasmic membranes may be largely composed of such fatty materials. Thus sugars, which have a low affinity for lipids, move into and out of cells sluggishly, whereas the more fat-soluble glycerol enters cells relatively rapidly. Superimposed on the factor of lipoid solubility is that of molecular size. Small molecules such as those of water enter plant cells much more rapidly than would be expected on the basis of lipoid solubility, whereas very large molecules are slowed in their movement below the expected rate. The protoplasmic membranes therefore combine lipid and sievelike properties.

The movement of water into and out of cells is governed to a large measure by the principles of osmosis. These principles concern the passage of water through membranes readily permeable to water itself but less permeable to dissolved solute molecules. Water tends to move from regions of high water concentration to regions of lower water concentration or, to put it conversely, water tends to move from regions of low solute concentration to regions of high solute concentration. This tendency is counteracted by the pressure with which the cell contents press on the elastic cell wall. The net tendency of water to enter the cell, the diffusion pressure deficit, is, in fact, equal to the difference between the osmotic pressure of the cell contents and the turgor pressure exerted by the cell contents on the cell wall. The direction of water movement in the plant is determined in large measure by gradients in the diffusion pressure deficit.

Ions, unlike nonionized materials, do not penetrate the cell simply in response to diffusion gradients but are taken up actively and may be accumulated within the cell to concentrations far higher than the external concentration. This process of ion accumulation, which makes possible the uptake and retention by the plant of high concentrations of the mineral nutrients essential to plant growth, is an energy-requiring process driven by, and wholly dependent on, the energy liberated in respiratory metabolism.

QUESTIONS

1. If a starfish egg is placed in an NH_4Cl solution, its cytoplasm becomes more alkaline. If, however, NH_4Cl is injected into the cell, the cytoplasm becomes more acid. Explain.

2. Arrange the following substances in order based on their probable relative rates of entry into plant cells: ethyl alcohol, sucrose, water, potassium nitrate, glycerol.

3. Explain in detail how you would study the rate of penetration of sucrose into a plant cell.

4. The narcotic action of such substances as chloroform and diethyl ether seems to be correlated with their lipoid solubility. What does this suggest about their mode of action?

5. Define the following and mention at least one method for measuring each: (a) osmotic pressure, (b) turgor pressure, (c) diffusion pressure deficit. Which is most important in determining the water status of a cell?

6. The rate of penetration of various substances into plant cells is markedly affected by the hydrogen-ion concentration of the external medium. Suggest a mechanism for this effect.

7. What evidence indicates that aerobic respiratory activity is associated with the uptake and accumulation of salts by plant cells?

8. Certain cells secrete very large molecules, such as protein enzymes. Can you suggest a possible mechanism?

GENERAL READING

Brooks, S. C., and Brooks, M. M., *The Permeability of Living Cells*. Berlin: Gebrüder Borntraeger, 1941. A comprehensive survey of permeability literature, dealing with animal as well as plant cells.

Crafts, A. S., Currier, H. B., and Stocking, C. R., *Water in the Physiology of Plants*. Waltham: Chronica Botanica, 1949. A well-organized, comprehensive advanced survey.

Höber, R., ed., *Physical Chemistry of Cells and Tissues*. Philadelphia: Blakiston Co., 1945. Excellent material on plant cells is included. The chapters emphasize general principles and supply a wealth of details.

Kramer, P. J., and Currier, H. B., "Water Relations of Plant Cells and Tissues." *Ann. Rev. Plant Physiol.*, 1: 265, 1950. A review of modern concepts.

Meyer, B. S., "The Water Relations of Plant Cells." *Botan. Rev.*, 4: 531, 1938. A brief, clear summary of the basic facts.

Meyer, B. S., and Anderson, D. B., *Plant Physiology*. New York: D. Van Nostrand, 1939. Chapters X and XI give an excellent account of osmotic and permeability phenomena.

CHAPTER 5

Water Economy

Transpiration

Of all the materials used by the plant for its growth and maintenance, that taken up in the largest amount is water. The bulk of the
water absorbed by the plant through the roots is not retained, however,
but evaporates into the air from the leaves and other aerial parts of
the plant. This water loss by evaporation is known as *transpiration*.

The occurrence of transpiration seems to be a natural consequence of
the basic facts of plant anatomy. The leaves consist of water-filled mesophyll cells whose wet surfaces are in intimate contact with the intercellular spaces. These spaces, in turn, lead through the stomata to the outside atmosphere. Water therefore evaporates from the mesophyll cells
and is conducted through the intercellular spaces to the external air.
The water lost from the leaf mesophyll is replaced by water brought up
from the roots through the vascular system of the plant. A plant may
thus be thought of as a sort of wick, through which water is brought up
from the soil through the root, conducted through the stem, and evaporated from the leaf into the air.

The Magnitude of Transpiration

The total quantity of water removed from the soil by a growing
plant is large in comparison to the amount present in the plant at any
one time. A single mature corn plant, for example, contains approximately 2 liters of water, but during the course of its growth it may
have removed 100 times this amount from the soil. An acre of corn
plants has been calculated to use up some 1300 tons of water during
the growing season, an amount equivalent to that which would fall
on this acre during an 11-inch rainfall.

Although the proportion of the water retained to the water lost varies with the species and with environmental factors, we can conclude that the great bulk of the plant's water requirement is concerned with transpiration. If the rate of water loss from the leaves exceeds substantially the rate of water replacement by absorption from the soil and transport through the stem, then the cells of the leaf gradually lose their turgor and become flaccid; the plant wilts. Wilting, if sufficiently prolonged and severe, can result in permanent injury and even death of the plant.

We usually think of organisms as well adjusted to their environment, and we have abundant evidence that processes which are harmful to plant welfare tend to be eliminated in the course of evolution. How can it be, then, that transpiration, a process which may, and often does, lead to so dangerous a process as wilting, has persisted as a feature of the economy of plants? The principal answer to this question probably is to be found in the fact that the leaf is above all an organ adapted to the efficient conduct of photosynthesis. The effectiveness of the leaf in photosynthesis depends upon the large thin layers of cells which are so suitable for the absorption of light. These cells must be in intimate contact with the surrounding atmosphere, so that CO_2 and O_2 may be readily exchanged. From the point of view of the plant, it is merely an unfortunate coincidence that the structural features of the leaf which are required for photosynthesis happen to be conducive also to constant and extensive water loss.

Measurement of Transpiration

The quantitative study of water loss may be approached in either of two general ways. On the one hand, the water taken up by the plant may be followed by various methods. On the other hand, the water evaporated from the plant may be collected and measured in a suitable manner.

Perhaps the simplest of methods for the study of water loss consists merely of weighing a plant, pot and all, allowing it to transpire for a short period, and then ascertaining how much water must be added to the pot to bring the total weight back to the original. Alternatively, the loss of weight experienced by the pot may be taken directly as a measure of the water loss. The weight changes of the plant are due, of course, not only to water loss but also to gain or loss of solid material through photosynthesis and respiration. The changes in weight due to vigorous transpiration are, however, much larger, often several hundred times larger, than the changes in weight due to exchange of CO_2 and O_2. Only small errors are introduced, then, by regarding weight loss of a plant during the experiment as due solely to transpiration.

Transpiration measurements based on weighing of intact plants are

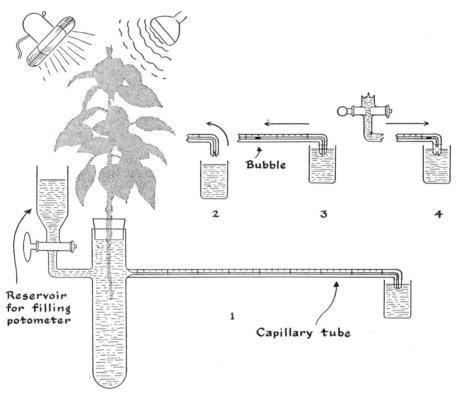

Figure 5-1. *The potometer consists of a water-filled vessel into which the cut end of a transpiring twig is sealed. To this vessel a water reservoir and a long graduated capillary tube are attached. The capillary tube dips into a beaker of water (1); an air bubble is admitted into the tube (2). The rate of movement of this bubble is an indirect measurement of the rate of water uptake by the twig (3). The bubble may be pushed back to the starting point by allowing water from the reservoir to flow into the system (4).*

restricted to plants grown in containers. Modifications of the method have been devised for the study of the transpiration of branches, twigs, or leaves excised from the intact plant. These modifications are of course applicable to plants growing in nature or in the field. One simple approach lies in the excision of a leaf or twig which is then transferred immediately to a sensitive balance on which the initial weight can be rapidly read. As water is lost from the leaf and its weight decreases, the rate of this decrease can be noted. From this we can estimate the original rate of transpiration of the leaf on the plant, if we assume that during the first short interval after excision the transpiration of the leaf continues at its original level.

Figure 5-2. *The device used by Guettard in 1748 for the collection and identification of the material lost by plants in transpiration. (After Guettard, from Maximov,* The Plant in Relation to Water, *ed. by Yapp, G. Allen & Unwin, Ltd., 1929, p. 108.)*

A more elegant method for the study of the transpiration of excised leafy shoots makes use of the potometer, a device shown in Figure 5-1. The leafy shoot is sealed into the mouth of a glass jar filled with water. Into this glass jar is also sealed a horizontal glass capillary, which is filled with water except for a small bubble of air entrapped near its far end. As the shoot loses water through the leaves, water is taken up from the jar in which it is sealed. The jar, in turn, draws upon the water in the capillary. Knowing the diameter of the capillary, we can judge the rate of withdrawal of water by measuring the speed of movement of the air bubble. This method, while well suited to determination of the influence of environmental factors on transpiration, cannot be used for the determination of transpiration rate of the original intact plant. Among the complications which might arise would be, for example, the possibility that cells of the shoot with high diffusion pressure deficits would take up and retain water, which would then appear as water uptake in the potometer but would not represent actual water loss from the plant.

The collection and estimation of the water lost as vapor from the leaves of transpiring plants is a straightforward way of measuring

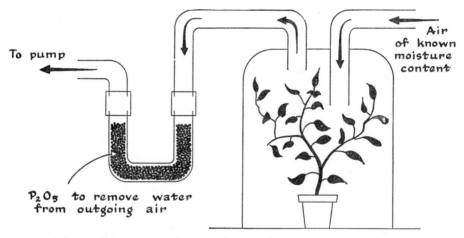

Figure 5-3. *Rate of water loss is determined by collection of the transpired water from a moving air stream.*

transpiration, but it necessitates sealing the plant in some sort of enclosure, so that the vapor may be confined. This general method was used as early as 1748 by the French physiologist Guettard, who enclosed a shoot inside a large glass vessel. The water vapor lost by the plant condensed on the walls of the container, flowed down the walls, and was collected in a suitable vessel (Fig. 5-2). In this simple experimental arrangement, the atmosphere surrounding the leaf is obviously more moist than it would ordinarily be in the open air. Since atmospheric humidity is an important factor in the regulation of transpiration rate, it is clear that this and similar methods will not tell us about transpiration rates of plants under natural conditions. It is therefore essential to use an arrangement such as that shown in Figure 5-3, in which a continuous stream of air is drawn over the plant. If the rate of air flow is sufficiently great, the composition of the atmosphere surrounding the plant will remain essentially similar to that of the external environment. The difference in moisture content of samples of the inlet and effluent air, together with knowledge as to the rate of air flow over the plant, will then tell us the rate of water loss from the plant. Moisture content determinations may be made by passing measured samples of the gas streams through tubes containing a water-absorbing agent, such as phosphorus pentoxide, and determining the gain in weight of the tubes. Still other more complex devices may be used for the continuous determination and recording of water content in the two gas streams. In principle, this method is not only direct but also adaptable to a great variety of conditions. It is, however, used infrequently because of the elaborate instrumentation involved.

Environmental Factors and Transpiration

The transpiration of the plant exhibits a daily rhythm, increasing during the daylight hours and decreasing again each night. An example of the daily transpiration cycle is given in Figure 5-4, which is based on data obtained (1907) for alfalfa by Briggs and Shantz at Tucson, Arizona. The differences between maximum and minimum rates of transpiration are so great that water loss during a single daylight hour may equal or exceed the transpiration during the entire night.

By comparison of the daily march of transpiration with daily fluctuations in environmental factors, such as light, temperature, and relative humidity, we may try to discover which of these factors is most closely associated with water loss. During the day, as the intensity of the sun's radiation increases, other factors also increase. Thus, in general, air temperature increases rapidly during the morning hours, while the relative humidity of the air decreases. It is clear from Figure 5-4, however, that transpiration follows solar radiation more intimately than it does air temperature. The work of Briggs and Shantz, as well as that of other more recent workers, has led to the conclusion that rate of transpiration is controlled predominantly by solar radiation, although many other factors enter in to a greater or lesser extent. Let us consider the way in which these factors interact to control the rate of water loss by plants.

Transpiration results physically from the difference between the concentration of water vapor in or at the leaf surface and that in the surrounding atmosphere. Saturated air is in equilibrium with liquid

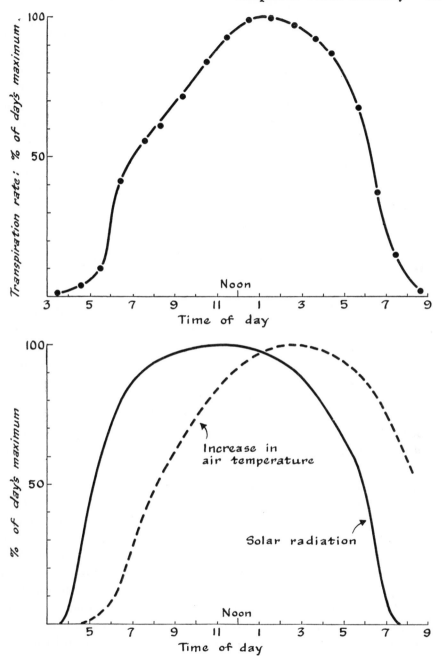

Figure 5-4. *The daily march of transpiration in a field of alfalfa. Transpiration follows solar radiation, although with an appreciable lag. (Adapted from Briggs and Shantz, J. Agr. Research, 5, 1916, p. 583.)*

water and contains a definite concentration of water vapor, a concentration which depends upon the temperature. This concentration may be expressed as a pressure, since water vapor is a gas and may be measured in terms of the height of the column of mercury which its pressure can support. Thus water at 100° C is in equilibrium with a water vapor pressure of 1 atm or 760 mm of Hg. At 0° C, on the other hand, water is in equilibrium with a water vapor pressure of only 4.58 mm of Hg. The vapor pressures of water vapor in equilibrium

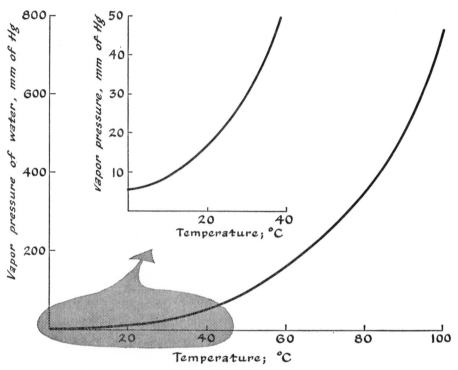

Figure 5-5.   *The vapor pressure of water in relation to temperature.*

with pure water at intermediate temperatures are given in Figure 5-5.

The air of the environment external to the plant ordinarily contains water vapor at some concentration lower than saturation. Suppose that a sample of air contains only one half the concentration it would need for saturation at the particular temperature. This air has, then, a relative humidity of one half, or as generally expressed, of 50 per cent. Relative humidity is thus the ratio of the actual water content of the air to the maximum amount the air is capable of containing at the same temperature. If air at a relative humidity of 50 per cent is brought in contact with liquid water at the same temperature, it will of course take up water vapor until it reaches saturation. We may say that air which is not already saturated with water possesses a *saturation deficit*.

The concepts of relative humidity and saturation deficit are ones which depend upon the prevailing temperature. Thus air with a relative humidity of 50 per cent and a saturation deficit of 50 per cent at one temperature will possess a relative humidity of 100 per cent and a saturation deficit of 0 at some lower temperature. This is not true of the vapor pressure of water contained in the atmosphere. If air with a given concentration of water vapor is warmed under conditions where it may expand, its water vapor pressure remains constant, even though the relative humidity decreases. The *vapor pressure deficit*, or difference between the actual water vapor pressure and that needed to saturate the air at the same temperature, is, like the saturation deficit, a function of temperature.

The transpiration of the leaf depends, then, on the difference between the vapor pressure of water in or at the leaf and the vapor pressure of water in the atmosphere. Since leaves generally have a temperature equal to, or slightly higher than, that of the surrounding atmosphere, this difference in vapor pressures is, in general, equal to, or greater than, the vapor pressure deficit of the atmosphere itself.

We have considered the leaf as consisting essentially of an evaporating surface saturated with pure water, but have neglected the facts brought out in Chapter 4 concerning the osmotic pressure of the cell contents. The leaf cells do not, of course, contain pure water, but rather a solution whose vapor pressure is less than that of free water because of the presence of solutes. We have seen, too, how the tendency of a cell to take up water depends not on its osmotic concentration but on the diffusion pressure deficit, which is, in general, less than the osmotic concentration. It is interesting to compare the vapor pressure deficits which obtain in the atmosphere with the diffusion pressure deficits usual for plant cells. To make this comparison, the two quantities must be expressed in similar terms, for example in atmospheres, as is done in Table 5-1. It is clear from the data in this table that the diffusion pressure deficits of living plant cells, usually less than 20 atm, are very much smaller than those of the atmosphere. Thus even a *DPD* of 22.4 atm, a high *DPD* for normal plant tissue, is in equilibrium at 20° C with air at a relative humidity of 98.2 per cent, and cells with this *DPD* will lose water to air with relative humidities lower than 98.2 per cent. Relative humidities in the range of 90 per cent would be in equilibrium only with tissues with the enormous *DPD* of 140 atm, far greater than those usual for plant materials. The osmotic concentration and the *DPD* of the cell, therefore, play only a minor role in restricting water losses by transpiration.

The daily march of transpiration, as we have seen earlier, follows closely the daily course of the light energy incident upon the plant. The role of light in the regulation of transpiration rate is twofold, and depends both upon influences on leaf temperature and on control of stomatal opening. When leaves are exposed to and absorb light energy, a portion of the energy is used for the conduct of photosynthesis, but a far greater proportion is converted into heat and results

Table 5-1. *Diffusion Pressure Deficit in Relation to Atmospheric Humidity at 20° C.*

RELATIVE HUMIDITY OF AIR, %	ABSOLUTE VAPOR PRESSURE OF WATER IN AIR, MM OF HG	DIFFUSION PRESSURE DEFICIT WITH WHICH AIR IS IN EQUILIBRIUM, ATM
100	17.54	0
99	17.36	13.4
98	17.19	26.9
97	17.01	40.6
95	16.66	68.4
90	15.79	140
80	14.03	298

merely in the warming of the leaves above the temperature of the surrounding air. This results in an increase of the vapor pressure of water at the cell wall surfaces in the leaves and in turn an increase in the differential between leaf vapor pressure and vapor pressure in the external atmosphere. Since transpiration rate depends primarily on the gradient in water vapor pressure from leaf to external atmosphere, heating of the leaves increases this rate. In actual fact, heating of leaves a few degrees above air temperature can result in very great increases in transpiration rate.

Let us take for example a leaf at 20° C which is transpiring into an atmosphere also at 20° C and with a relative humidity of 80 per cent. The vapor pressure at the cell wall surfaces of the leaf will be approximately that of pure water, or 17.5 mm of Hg. That in the air will be 80 per cent of 17.5, or 14.0 mm of Hg. The gradient or difference in water vapor pressure of 3.5 mm of Hg will, other things being equal, determine the rate of transpiration. Suppose, now, that light falls on the leaf and increases its temperature to 30° C. This temperature rise would not be an uncommon one, as has been found by direct measurements of leaf temperatures. The vapor pressure of water at the cell wall surfaces of the leaf will now be raised to 31.8 mm of Hg, and the differential between the leaf and atmospheric pressures of water vapor will hence be increased to 31.8–14.0, or 17.8 mm of Hg. The transpiration-determining differential in vapor pressure has thus been increased from 3.5 to 17.8, an increase of fivefold.

One might ask what prevents the temperature of leaves from rising, with continued illumination, to temperatures so high as to be injurious. That this does not regularly occur is due to the fact that, as the leaves are warmed, they in turn lose heat by radiation to the surrounding air at an increasing rate and, in addition, are cooled by the increasing evaporation of water from their surfaces. A balance, or steady state, is ultimately achieved in which the rate of heat gain is just balanced by these losses. The leaf temperature at which the balance is attained depends, of course, on the intensity of illumination, availability of water, and other factors, but it is frequently found to be between 2° and 10° C above the prevailing air temperature.

In addition to its physical effects on vapor pressure gradients, light also plays a dominant role in the regulation of transpiration through its influence on the stomatal mechanism, the stomata closing in darkness and opening in light. The physiology of this response and its role in transpiration are considered later in this chapter.

The movement of air over a transpiring leaf increases water loss by removing water vapor as it escapes, thus preventing accumulations of water vapor near the leaf surface. Such accumulations of water vapor near the leaf surface decrease the magnitude of the vapor pressure gradient from leaf to external atmosphere and increase the pathway water vapor molecules must traverse by purely diffusional motions.

Continued transpiration by the aerial parts of the plant depends on a continued supply of water to the shoot from the roots. If the roots are unable to obtain water due to drying out of the soil, transpiration continues for a time as the leaves and other organs are depleted of their water, and then gradually decreases as the leaves wilt.

Among the other factors influencing the availability of water in the soil, the most important are soil salinity, soil temperature, and soil aeration. The uptake of water by roots is depressed by low soil water content, by high soil solute concentrations, by low soil temperatures, and by poor soil aeration. Any of these factors can lead to wilting and decreased transpiration.

The Stomata

The stomata constitute the main avenue for the escape of water vapor from the leaves of land plants. This can be shown most directly by a study of leaves which possess stomata on their lower surface only.

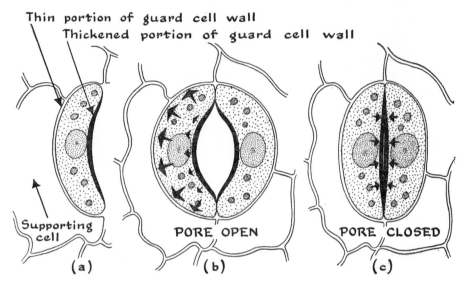

Figure 5-6. *Stomatal movements. (a) That part of the guard cell wall which abuts on the stomatal pore is thicker than the remainder of the wall. (b) Thus, when the cell becomes turgid, the thin peripheral wall is caused to bulge outward, distorting and pulling the thick elastic inner wall along with it. This opens the stomatal pore. (c) When the cell becomes flaccid, the thick, inner elastic wall contracts, thus closing the stomatal pore.*

In such leaves, approximately 97 per cent of the total gas exchange occurs through the epidermal surface which bears the stomatal pores, and only 3 per cent occurs directly through the cuticularized upper epidermis. Stomata usually occur with a frequency of 50 to 300 per mm^2 of leaf surface, although up to 1300 per mm^2 have been reported. An individual stoma of corn, a representative species, is approximately 4μ wide by 26μ long, and has an elliptical pore area of about 90μ^2. The entire corn plant possesses on the order of 200 million stomata, whose aggregate area, when fully open, approximates 1.5 per cent of the total leaf surface.

The pore or aperture of the stoma is bounded by two sausage-shaped guard cells. In most cases the aperture is formed by the division of an ellipsoidal epidermal cell, followed by separation of the walls between the two daughter cells. The two cells resulting from the division are the guard cells, and the pore between them is the stomatal pore. The guard cells differ from ordinary epidermal cells not only in shape but also in their possession, generally, of green plastids and localized thickenings of their cell walls. The guard cell walls abutting on the stomatal pore are thicker than the opposite walls, which are in contact with the ordinary epidermal cells. This makes it possible for the guard cell to control the degree of opening of the pore. When the guard cell becomes turgid, the pressure exerted on its walls causes the thinner and weaker side to bulge outward first. The outward bulging distorts the inner thicker wall, thus pulling it outward and opening the pore. When, on the contrary, the guard cells are flaccid, their inner thick walls rest snugly against one another, closing the pore. These movements are summarized in Figure 5-6.

Diffusion Through the Stomata

The diffusion of water vapor molecules through stomata is much more rapid per unit of evaporating area than is diffusion from a large free water surface. This is due to the fact that as water molecules escape from an evaporating surface, the air immediately above becomes increasingly concentrated with respect to water vapor. Since the over-all rate of evaporation depends on the magnitude of the vapor pressure gradient between the water and the air above, the presence of this water vapor is a deterrent to further evaporation. If a large evaporating surface is divided into a number of small surfaces or pores, separated from each other by distances of several times their own diameter, then the escaping water vapor covers not only the pores themselves, but also the intervening surface from which no evaporation is occurring. The subdivision of a large evaporating surface into many smaller pores essentially increases the volume of air directly above the surface into which water vapor can escape. The dead spaces between pores which do not contribute directly to evaporation serve as reservoirs for the escaping water molecules. The over-all effect is to steepen the gradient in water vapor pressure between evaporating surface and air (Fig.

5-7). The participation of the interpore area as a reservoir for water vapor causes the rate of evaporation from a pore to be proportional not to pore area, but rather to pore perimeter. Thus it is possible for a multiperforate membrane to permit the passage of as much water vapor as a completely open surface of equal area.

In general, the stomata of leaves are so distributed as to permit quite

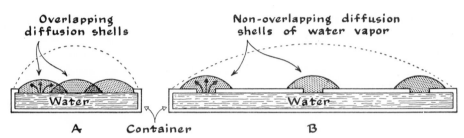

Figure 5-7. *Diffusion of water vapor from a water surface into the atmosphere through an equal total area but divided into (A) one large pore, (B) smaller pores well separated from one another.*

efficient gas exchange. The stomata on the underside of a sunflower leaf, for example, are approximately eight diameters apart, and at 20° C are capable of carrying from three to six times more water vapor than the maximum observed rate of transpiration and twenty times more CO_2 than that required for the maximum observed rate of photosynthesis. Thus, despite their small area, the stomata are apparently not, in their open condition, any serious barrier to gaseous diffusion through the leaf surface.

Stomatal Physiology and the Regulation of Transpiration

The preceding discussion has shown that the stomata, when open, constitute no great barrier to the free diffusion of gases through the leaf epidermis. We know, however, that under certain conditions the guard cells may be altered in such a way as to cause partial or complete closure of the stomatal aperture, and that such closure results in appreciable interference with free diffusion. The reduction of transpiration incident to closing of the stomatal apertures is illustrated in the curves of Figure 5-9. Water loss is greatly decreased by stomatal closure, particularly as the stomata narrow to less than one-fifth of their fully open diameter. We will therefore turn our attention to the physiology of the stomata and to the mechanisms responsible for their movement.

The study of the factors which regulate the opening and closing of the stomata necessitates methods for determination of stomatal aperture. Microscopic observation of the stomata is the direct approach, but because of the opacity of many leaves, this is not always feasible with the ordinary microscope utilizing transmitted light. Microscopes that use reflected light, however, permit direct observation of the stomata, but since such examination requires that the leaf be illumi-

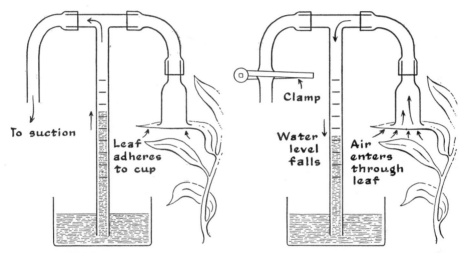

Figure 5-8. *The porometer, a device for following opening and closing of the stomata in terms of resistance of the leaf surface to gas flow.*

nated, the effect of light on stomatal aperture cannot be investigated by this means. Thus, still other methods have been devised. It is possible to determine the condition of the stomata in preserved epidermal specimens which have been stripped from leaves during the period of experimentation, fixed, and then examined at leisure. Still another method involves the use of the porometer shown in Figure 5-8, the principle being that the rate at which air can be sucked through the leaf is a function of stomatal aperture. A small cup is sealed to the surface of the leaf, a suction of a few centimeters of water is applied, and the rate of air passage through the leaf is measured as the rate of pressure drop on the water manometer of Figure 5-8. Still another method, which is at best only semiquantitative, has been widely used because of its simplicity and convenience. This is the so-called injection method, which is based on the penetration or nonpenetration of a series of solvents of differing surface tension and solubility characteristics. If the stomata are fully open, ethyl alcohol will penetrate them and infiltrate the leaf, giving it a water-soaked appearance. If the pores are only partly opened, benzene will enter, but butyl alcohol will not. If the pores are almost entirely closed, xylene is able to enter the leaf, but benzene cannot. If the pores are completely closed, none of these liquids will enter the leaf. All of these methods have been used extensively in the study of stomatal physiology.

The movements of the stomata are controlled by the turgor pressure of the guard cells. When the guard cells are turgid, the stomata are open, and when the guard cells become flaccid, the stomata close. The opening and closing of the stomata are controlled by environmental factors, of which light and water content of the leaf tissue are most important. It has been known for many years that stomata are usually closed at night, but that they open rapidly after sunrise. This behavior may be modified if the leaf is seriously water deficient, in which case the stomata may remain closed during the entire day.

The exact cause of stomatal movement in response to light has long been a matter of dispute, but it now seems to be clear that the CO_2 content of the substomatal cavity is the critical factor. When the atmosphere of the substomatal cavity contains CO_2 at the concentration present in normal air (0.03 per cent), the guard cells are flaccid, and the stomata are closed. Reduction of the CO_2 concentration below this value results, however, in prompt opening of the stomata. The degree of opening increases linearly with lowering of CO_2 until a CO_2 concentration of 0.01 per cent is attained, after which further reduction in the CO_2 concentration fails to produce any further opening. Since light causes stomatal opening, it would be logical to assume that stomatal opening is brought about by the photosynthetic utilization of CO_2 and consequent reduction of CO_2 concentration in the substomatal cavity below the 0.03 per cent level. Since light influences stomatal opening in leaves whose guard cells are devoid of chloroplasts, photosynthesis of the guard cells themselves cannot be the primary factor involved. Photosynthesis of the other tissues of the leaf must therefore contribute to the stomatal movements.

High temperatures, generally above 25° C, cause stomatal closure in many plants. Again, this may possibly occur through effects on the CO_2 content of the substomatal cavity involving changes of the balance between respiration and photosynthesis. The response of the stomata to light is thus dependent on the temperature.

In summary, stomatal movements are influenced primarily by

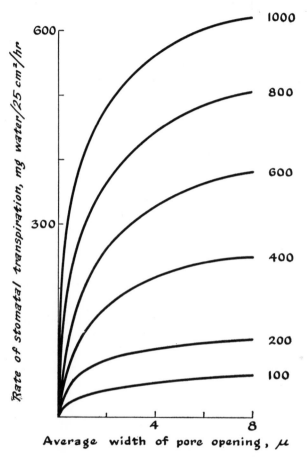

Figure 5-9. *The relation of stomatal opening to water loss in leaves of the birch. The successive curves refer to environmental conditions successively more conducive to transpiration. The figures at the right refer to the maximum evaporation water loss (mg/25 cm²/hr) from wet blotting paper kept at each of the environmental conditions. (After Stålfelt, Planta, 17, 1932, p. 60.)*

light and secondarily by water content of the leaf and temperature. Closing of the stomata under conditions of water deficit or excessively high temperature operates in the direction of slowing transpiration, particularly when water loss is rapid (Fig. 5-9). Thus the stomata may, under certain conditions, serve as protective mechanisms against excessive transpiration.

The Movement of Water in the Stem

It is generally agreed that the xylem is the pathway of the upward translocation of water both in the roots and stem and in the vascular elements of the leaf. Among the reasons for this conclusion are the following: (1) The anatomy of the xylem obviously fits it for transport purposes, and the xylem is the only vascular tissue with sufficient cross-sectional area to permit of the upward translocation of the amounts of water required by the leaves. (2) Removal of a ring of phloem from the stem does not interfere appreciably with the upward movement of water, whereas the removal of a cylinder of xylem seriously disturbs or even destroys water transport. (3) Upward water movement continues for some time in shoots cut from the plant and placed with their bases in water. If the water contains a dye or other type of marker molecule, the marker, which presumably moves together with the water, can be observed to rise in the xylem. (4) The contents of the xylem are very dilute and watery as compared to the contents of the conducting elements of the phloem. The phloem, as we shall see in Chapter 7, is concerned with the mass movement of solutes rather than of water *per se*.

The study of the way in which water is moved upward in plants against the force of gravity has been a classical problem of plant physiology. There is today general agreement that the phenomenon of water movement has its explanation in a set of principles known as the *transpiration-cohesion-tension theory* of water transport, which is based on suggestions first put forward by the Irish plant physiologist H. H. Dixon.

The transpiration-cohesion-tension theory, summarized in Figure 5-10, suggests that as the transpiring leaves lose water vapor to the air, the diffusion pressure deficit of these cells tends to rise. This augmented diffusion pressure deficit of the cells of the leaf mesophyll causes water to enter them from the vascular elements of the leaf. The water in these elements is hence placed under tension. The water in the xylem extends, however, in a continuous column from root to leaf. The tension on the water in the upper portions of the xylem is therefore transmitted downward through the entire water column. If the cohesive tendency of the water in the elements of the xylem is sufficiently great, the removal of water from the top of the column by evap-

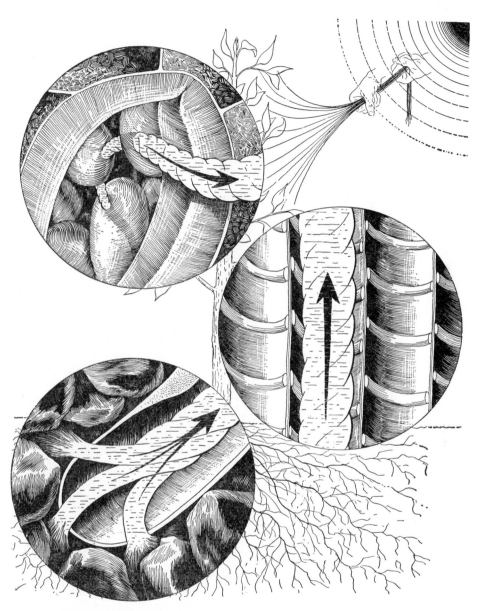

Figure 5-10. *The transpiration-cohesion-tension theory of water movement. The evaporation of water through the stomata from the surfaces of leaf parenchyma cells results in tension on the water column in the xylem. This tension is transmitted to the absorbing cells of the roots.*

oration will then result in the remainder of the column being bodily pulled upward toward the leaf. At the lower end of the column of water in the xylem, water is removed from the living cells of the root. This results in an increased diffusion pressure deficit of the root cells and therefore in an increased water absorption by the root.

Many kinds of evidence support the transpiration-cohesion-tension theory of water transport. It can be demonstrated that the xylem elements of trees are actually under tension when the plant is under conditions of rapid water evaporation. This tension is manifested as a contraction in the diameter of the trunk or the cells of the xylem, and is of such a magnitude as to indicate that the xylem cells are under tensions of considerably more than one atmosphere. Water, when it is free of gas bubbles and other small particulate impurities, also has been found experimentally to have a cohesive force more than sufficient to withstand the tensions developed in the xylem. Again, although atmospheric pressure can raise water to a maximum of approximately 32 feet, an actively transpiring twig can be made to lift a water column to much greater heights. Finally, the entire process of transpiration can be simulated in an artificial model, consisting of a porous porcelain ball or atmometer connected to a water-filled glass tube dipping into a reservoir of mercury (Fig. 5-11). If dry air is blown over the atmometer, water is evaporated from the surface of the porcelain, thus creating a negative pressure, or tension. This tension is transmitted through the water column to the mercury, which is then drawn up the tube. The rate of movement of mercury up the tube is increased by environmental influences which hasten the evaporation of water from the atmometer. For example, a black bulb is more effective than a white bulb if the system is illuminated, due to the increased heating of the transpiring surface. A swift stream of air from a fan played onto the atmometer increases evaporation from the bulb and the rate of water rise.

Thus, according to the transpiration-cohesion-tension theory of water movement, the energy for the lifting of water in a tree is furnished ultimately by the sun *via* the evaporation of water from leaves. The stem is passive, the xylem elements constituting a pipeline through which columns of water are pulled under tension. The theory not only accounts satisfactorily for the rise of water in plants but also appears at present to be the only explanation for the transport of the amounts of water moving through a plant under conditions of rapid transpiration.

There are certain restricted circumstances under which water rises in plants even under conditions where the transpiration rate is negligible, or even zero. Under these conditions, it appears that the water, rather than being pulled up from above, is pushed up from below through a positive action of the root system. That roots can in fact eject water under pressure may be easily demonstrated. If a stem of a healthy,

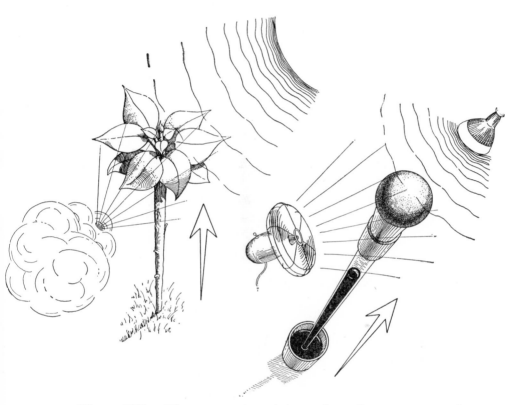

Figure 5-11. *The evaporation of water through a porous porcelain atmometer can result in tension in the water within the system. Water or mercury can be lifted through considerable distances in this model system. As in the plant, factors which increase evaporation increase water tension and water movement in the atmometer.*

well-watered plant is cut off slightly above the ground level, the stump will often exude or bleed. Since the exudate comes from the xylem, exudation is particularly marked and prompt if the plant has not been actively transpiring before excision of the shoot, so that the water in the xylem is not under tension. The expression of xylem fluid under these conditions, although slow, can be carried out against a considerable pressure. This pressure may be measured by attaching a manometer to the stump, as depicted in Figure 5-12. Thus, actively bleeding tomato roots may develop root pressures in excess of 9 atm. Such a pressure would be capable of pumping water to a height of approximately 90 meters, or high enough to reach the tops of most trees. Although pressures of this magnitude can be developed, most observed root pressures fall in the range of 2 to 3 atm. Moreover, the quantities of water moving through the xylem by this mechanism are very small

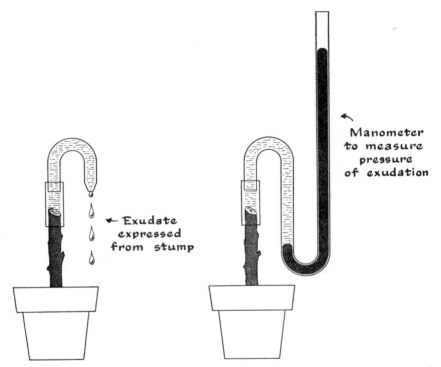

Manometer to measure pressure of exudation

← Exudate expressed from stump

Figure 5-12. *The bleeding, or exudation, from cut stumps takes place under pressure.*

as compared to the amounts moved upwards during active transpiration.

The rise of water in plant stems is therefore the direct result of a gradient in *DPD* which increases from base to apex. Whether the water column of the xylem is under tension or under pressure depends on the relative rates of water supply to, and loss from, the stem. When the rate of supply lags, stem tension results; when water supply is adequate, positive pressures may be observed. Thus, the transpiration-cohesion-tension mechanism and root pressure cooperate in raising water to the tops of plants, and both are, in fact, manifestations of the basic *DPD* gradient.

Summary

The large surface area, the extensive and ramified intercellular spaces, and the numerous stomatal openings of the leaf make possible efficient photosynthesis. These same features result in transpiration, the evaporative loss of water to the atmosphere by the leaves of plants.

The rate of water loss from leaves depends on the gradient in water vapor pressure between the external atmosphere and the intercellular spaces or cell surfaces abutting on these spaces. The internal spaces of the leaf, since they are essentially saturated with water vapor, tend to lose their water by diffusion outward whenever the atmosphere is not itself saturated. Sunlight, by falling on leaves and warming them, increases the vapor pressure of water at these surfaces, increases the outward gradient in water vapor pressure, and increases the rate of transpiration. Light, then, is a major factor in determining the rate of evaporative water loss by plants.

The bulk of the water lost by leaves passes outward from the intercellular spaces through the stomatal openings, pores some $100\mu^2$ in area and of which some 50–1000 may be present per square millimeter of leaf. The stomata are ordinarily closed at night, but open in the morning in response to light, a response which is due to changes in the turgor of the guard cells which abut on the stomatal pore. Changes in turgor of the guard cells, in turn, appear to be mediated through photosynthetic removal of CO_2 from the substomatal cavity. Although the outward passage of water vapor from the leaf is greatly lessened when the stomatal pores are completely closed, the partly open stomata do not in general appear to constitute an important barrier to water loss.

The principal upward movement of water through the plant is a direct result of evaporative water loss from the leaves. As water evaporates from the leaf surfaces, the leaf cells, in response to their increasing diffusion pressure deficits, draw in water from the vascular tissues. The resultant tension on the contents of the xylem is transmitted downward through the stem, and water is pulled bodily upward in a continuous column from root to leaf surface. Under conditions of zero transpiration, water may be forced up the stem by pressures developed within the root system.

QUESTIONS

1. The addition of large quantities of fertilizer to the soil may reduce transpiration. What is a possible reason for this effect?

2. What methods are available for the determination of the degree of stomatal opening? Which gives the most accurate data? Why?

3. Transpiration rate has sometimes been measured by placing anhydrous blue cobalt chloride paper in contact with a leaf and noting the time required for it to turn pink. What errors are inherent in this method?

4. Which environmental factors are most important in the control of transpiration rate? Suggest an explanation for the action of each.

5. In certain plants the stomata are located only in depressions of the epidermis. How would transpiration in such plants compare with that in species not bearing sunken stomata?

6. Can a plant transpire into an atmosphere of 100 per cent relative humidity? Explain.

7. Certain bacteria cause wilting of infected plants under conditions where normal plants remain turgid. Suggest several ways in which such wilting could be brought about.

8. How could one measure the velocity of water movement in an intact tree trunk?

GENERAL READING

Crafts, A. S., Currier, H. B., and Stocking, C. R., *Water in the Physiology of Plants*. Waltham: Chronica Botanica, 1949. A well-organized, comprehensive advanced survey.

Curtis, O. F., and Clark, D. G., *An Introduction to Plant Physiology*. New York: McGraw-Hill Book Co., 1950. Chapters 6–9 are of great value to students desiring further information on this subject.

Dixon, H. H., *Transpiration and the Ascent of Sap in Plants*. London: Macmillan & Co., Ltd., 1914. Convincing arguments by the author of the transpiration-cohesion-tension theory.

Kramer, P. J., *Plant and Soil Water Relationships*. New York: McGraw-Hill Book Co., 1949. An up-to-date picture, with selected references, by a current leader in the field.

Maximov, N. A., *The Plant in Relation to Water*, ed. and trans. by R. H. Yapp. London: G. Allen & Unwin, Ltd., 1929. An older, but very readable account, with many ecological considerations.

CHAPTER 6

The Soil as a Medium for Plant Growth

The soil is a storehouse of the water and minerals required for the growth of plants, and as such is of significance not only to plants which grow directly in it but also to the animals which utilize plant materials as food. The relations of the plant to the nutrient elements and to the water contained in soil are, of course, based on the same principles which govern the growth of plants in nutrient culture. Soil, however, is a complex medium, made up of many components which differ in their physical and chemical properties. Certain of the nutrient elements essential to plant growth are combined in soil in varied forms which may be more or less available to the plant. The water of the soil exists in various states which are not equally available to the plant. The factors which govern the growth of plants in soil are, therefore, somewhat more complex, and the interrelations between these factors somewhat more delicate, than is the case in a simple nutrient culture. From the standpoint of agriculture, however, it is soil that is used as a medium for plant growth, and we must therefore consider the varied aspects of the soil in its relations to the plant.

Root and Soil

The mineral and water resources of the soil are tapped by the plant through a prodigiously ramified system of roots and root hairs which bring the plant into intimate contact with many of the soil particles beneath it. This thorough exploitation of the soil is achieved not only by the repeated branching of the root as it penetrates downward, but also by the production of the hairs which develop in enormous numbers on the roots of many species. As the individual root grows through the soil, often at a rate of several centimeters per day, it follows an intricate and winding path between the surrounding soil particles. At some distance back of the growing tip, root hairs develop as outgrowths of the epidermal cells. These hairs, some 10μ in diameter and from a few microns to one millimeter in length, enormously increase the area over which the root is in actual contact with the soil, and provide a major

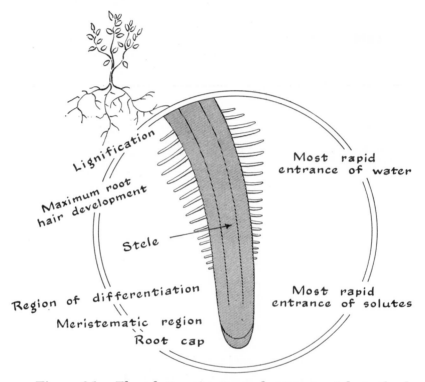

Figure 6-1. *The relation of water and nutrient uptake to the devel-opment of a young root.* (*Adapted from Kramer,* Plant and Soil Water Relationships, *McGraw-Hill Book Co., 1949, p. 113.*)

portion of the actual absorbing area of the root system. Studies on the uptake of materials by young roots have indicated, as shown in Figure 6-1, that the root hairs provide the main point of entrance for water into the plant, although mineral nutrients are taken up more actively by the growing regions of the roots themselves. Finally, in the older portions of the root, the deposition of suberin and other water-impervious materials in the cell walls not only decreases absorption by the root but also prevents leakage from the conducting elements. This

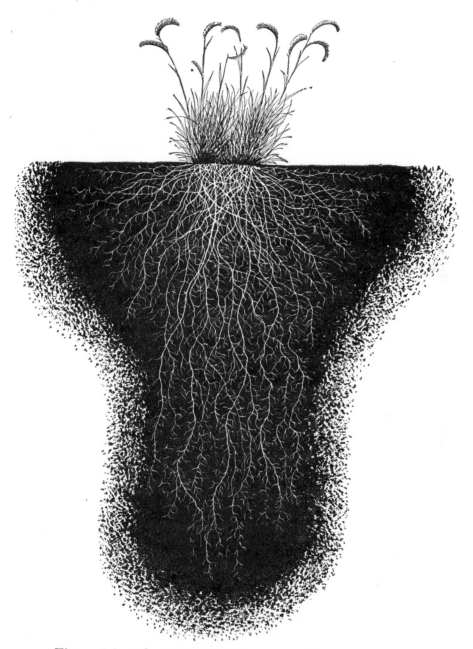

Figure 6-2. *The root system of a mature plant of blue grama grass.* (*Adapted from Weaver and Clements,* Plant Ecology, *2nd ed.,* McGraw-Hill Book Co., 1938, p. 316.)

insures an efficient transport of materials through the vascular system upward to the aerial portions of the plant.

A feeling for the extent to which roots penetrate and explore the soil (Fig. 6-2) can be gained from the fact that total root length of individual plants must be measured in miles, and the number of root hairs counted in millions or billions. Thus a single wheat plant has been found to possess as much as 44 miles of roots, while a single rye plant, growing in a container 12 inches square and 22 inches deep, produced 387 miles of roots in four months. During each day of the four-month period, therefore, an average of 3.1 miles of new roots must have been laid down by the plant. This total root length was divided among some 13 million roots, all actively engaged in the uptake of water and nutrients. In addition, some 14 billion root hairs provided further absorbing area.

In general, the roots of shrubs and trees grow less rapidly and less profusely than those of herbaceous species, but even so, a mature tree may possess several miles of roots spread over an area of soil as large as, or greater than, the area covered by the branches. With trees, as with other forms, the depth to which the roots penetrate the soil depends greatly on the porosity of the soil and depth of both soil and the water table. In porous, well-drained soils, roots of alfalfa may penetrate to a depth of more than 30 feet. In dense or poorly drained soils, on the contrary, lack of aeration confines root growth to a shallower layer, occasionally to as little as a few inches of surface soil. With cultivated plants, and in our usual agricultural lands, the roots are mainly concentrated in the upper 5 feet of soil.

The Formation of the Soil

Soil, that portion of the earth's crust in which the roots of plants grow, is formed by the weathering of the parent rocks. Climate, gravity, the action of microorganisms, and the activities of plant roots themselves combine to disintegrate the parent materials to smaller and smaller particles. Rain, falling on the earth's surface, leaches the more soluble components from the upper layers and carries them to deeper layers where they are often redeposited. In their final form, the particles of the soil contain not only fragments of the original parent rock but also entirely new minerals formed through the combined action of leaching and the interaction of the leached components of the varied parent minerals. Soil, then, is a complicated mosaic of rock particles, characteristic soil minerals, dead and living roots and microorganisms, and spaces which may be filled with either air or water. Of these numerous components, only two, the soil solution and the oxygen-containing air, are essential for the growth of plants. Nevertheless, the other soil components greatly affect plant development and the stability of the soil over long periods of cropping. Thus the mineral particles of the soil

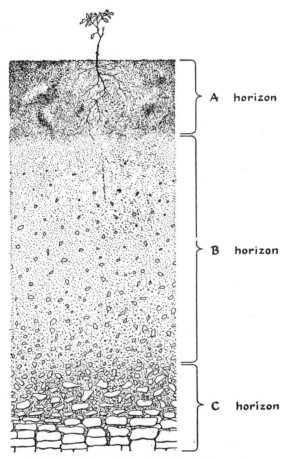

Figure 6-3. *A soil profile.* (*Adapted from Lyon and Buckman,* Nature and Properties of Soils, *4th ed., Macmillan Co., 1943, p. 3.*)

not only provide mechanical support for the plant but also serve as a reservoir of nutrient elements from which the soil solution and the plant may draw. Soil may therefore be regarded as a unit, made up of many separate but nonetheless interrelated and interacting ingredients.

The weathering agencies which transform rocks to soil—the rain, changes in temperature, the activities of soil bacteria and fungi, and the roots of plants—all concentrate their influence on the upper layers of the soil, and diminish in effectiveness in the lower strata. Any given soil, therefore, changes in appearance and in constitution as one goes from the surface downward; soils possess a profile. A soil profile, such as might be exposed in a deep trench, as depicted in Figure 6-3, is characteristically composed of successive more or less distinct layers or horizons. The uppermost layer, the A-horizon to a soil scientist, contains the bulk of the plant roots as well as much of the soil's nonliving organic matter. In most soils the mineral matter of the A-horizon is also more completely weathered and disintegrated than that of the lower layers. The B-horizon, lying immediately below the A-horizon, is generally less weathered than the upper layer, but may have an accumulation of clay particles which have been carried down from above by the action of rain. Still lower lies the C-horizon, which is composed of the parent materials from which soil has been derived by the physical and biological processes of weathering.

The nature of the soil profile thus depends in part on the composition of the parent rock, but it is determined also by the conditions under which weathering has taken place. Of the several environmental factors controlling soil genesis, the two outstanding ones are rainfall and temperature. The former controls the rate of leaching from higher to lower horizons, while the latter controls the rate and kinds of biological activity which contribute to soil formation.

The Constituent Soil Particles

A soil is in general composed of particles of a wide range of sizes, the largest of which may be seen with the unaided eye, whereas the smallest are too minute to be resolved even under the microscope. A soil or soil horizon may be characterized in part by the proportion of particles in each size category which it contains, and for convenience individual names have been applied to particles of particular size ranges. The larger particles are referred to as coarse sand or gravel, somewhat finer particles as sand, still smaller particles as silt, and the finest particles as clay. The size ranges of particles in these several rather arbitrary categories are summarized in Table 6-1. The distribution of particles among these various size ranges is the basis for the naming of many soil types. Thus a soil in which sandy particles predominate is referred to as a sand, whereas one in which silt particles predominate is known as loam. Clay particles predominate in a clay soil. Many of our agricultural soils are loams, which may be further characterized (Table 6-1) as sandy, silt, or clay loams, depending on the proportion of sand and clay particles present. All fertile soils contain a considerable amount of clay, and this fraction contributes properties which are of great significance for plant growth.

Table 6-1. *The Size of Soil Particles and Their Distribution in Various Kinds of Soils.*

| | | PERCENTAGE FOUND IN A TYPICAL: | | |
KIND OF PARTICLE	DIAMETER, MM	SANDY LOAM	CLAY LOAM	CLAY
Coarse sand	2.00–0.20	65	30	1
Fine sand	0.20–0.02	20	30	9
Silt	0.02–0.002	5	20	25
Clay	Below 0.002	10	20	65

The Clay Minerals and Cation Exchange

The larger rock particles of soil, the sands and gravels, are chemically similar to the rocks and minerals from which the soil is derived. They represent, in an ideal case at least, merely fragmented parent rock. The smaller particles of the soil, the clay particles, do not, however, correspond in chemical constitution to the parent rock. The original rock minerals are relatively inert and resistant to chemical change, so long as they are present as large particles. As these larger particles are further weathered, and as the surface they present to leaching is increased by this fragmentation, they disappear as such, and new minerals, the clay minerals, appear. The clay minerals are a quite characteristic group of substances, formed as a result of weathering from many different parent rocks. Of these minerals, two, montmorillonite and kaolinite, are perhaps the most typical. Both are made up primarily of aluminum, silicon, and oxygen, but they differ in crystallographic properties, that is to say, in the manner in which the constituent atoms are fitted together in the crystal lattice of the mineral. Both are composed of repeating layers of identically positioned atoms, and, in montmorillonite in particular, water as well as other materials may penetrate between the layers, hydrating the crystal and pushing apart the constituent sheets. Clay has thus an enormous surface, and it is primarily because of its surface properties that it is so important to plant growth.

Clay minerals, particularly montmorillonite and its close relatives, are so constituted that the sheets or layers of atoms possess occasional spots in which there is an excess of negative charge. These charges are satisfied by the binding of cations, which are taken up from the soil solution in contact with the clay. For example, a clay in contact with an acid solution takes up hydrogen ions. If such a clay is washed with a solution containing a different cation, such as calcium, then calcium ions are taken up, and hydrogen ions liberated. It is said that calcium ions have been exchanged for hydrogen. Similarly, clays may take up and bind potassium, ammonium, sodium, and other cations. This reversible binding of cations, a property which is possessed to an outstanding degree by clay particles, is known as *cation exchange*. In a fertile agricultural soil, the clay particles are charged with a variety of cations, particularly calcium, hydrogen, potassium, and magnesium. These bound cations, which are not readily removable from the soil by leaching, constitute a reserve of soil minerals available for plant growth.

The Soil as a Source of Plant Nutrients

To be capable of supporting a good growth of plants, a soil must, of course, contain a readily available supply of all of the major and minor elements essential to plant growth. The predominant minerals of soil are, however, oxides and related complex derivatives of silicon and aluminum, materials which do not contribute directly to the nutrition of the plant. The plant nutrients themselves constitute a relatively small proportion of the total weight or bulk of even a very fertile soil, as can be seen from the representative figures of Table 6-2 and Figure

Table 6-2. *Concentrations and Amounts of the Essential Elements of Plant Nutrition Found in Representative Agricultural Soils. (After Leeper,* Introduction to Soil Science, *Melbourne University Press: New York, Cambridge University Press, 1948, p. 125.)*

ESSENTIAL ELEMENT	PERCENTAGE IN SOIL	AMOUNT, LB/ACRE
Fe	3.5	70,000
K	1.5	30,000
Ca	0.5	10,000
Mg	0.4	8,000
N	0.1	2,000
P	0.06	1,200
S	0.05	1,000
Mn	0.05	1,000
B	0.002	40
Zn	0.001	20
Cu	0.0005	5
Mo	0.0001	2

6-4. Even the values for the total amount of a specific essential element in a soil do not necessarily reflect the fertility of the soil with regard to this element, since the material in question may be present in the soil in a variety of chemical forms and combinations, some of which may be completely unavailable to the plant. Consideration of the soil as a source of plant nutrients involves, therefore, questions relating to the forms in which each essential element may be present and the availability to the plant of each of these forms.

Although the elements calcium, magnesium, and potassium are present in soil as components of the parent rock materials, they are not in this combined form available as plant nutrients. The amount of these

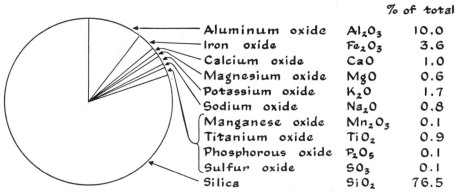

		% of total
Aluminum oxide	Al_2O_3	10.0
Iron oxide	Fe_2O_3	3.6
Calcium oxide	CaO	1.0
Magnesium oxide	MgO	0.6
Potassium oxide	K_2O	1.7
Sodium oxide	Na_2O	0.8
Manganese oxide	Mn_2O_3	0.1
Titanium oxide	TiO_2	0.9
Phosphorous oxide	P_2O_5	0.1
Sulfur oxide	SO_3	0.1
Silica	SiO_2	76.5

Figure 6-4. *The principal inorganic components present in the A-horizon of representative agricultural soils. Although all of the individual elements are calculated as their oxides, they are not necessarily present in soil in this form. (Adapted from Byers et al., Soils and Men, U. S. Department of Agriculture Yearbook, 1938, p. 917.)*

three elements available to the plant depends on the amount of each which is adsorbed on the clay fraction as exchangeable cations. Cations bound in this way may pass into the soil solution and hence into the plant root, or they may be taken up directly from the clay particle by the process of contact exchange. In this process the root appears to give off and exchange hydrogen ions for clay-bound nutrient ions.

Since only the exchangeable nutrient cations are of major importance for the nutrition of plants in soil, the assessment of the nutrient status of a soil demands determination of exchangeable, rather than total, calcium, magnesium, and potassium. This is ordinarily achieved by leaching a measured soil sample with a solution of ammonium acetate.

Table 6-3. *The Calcium and Potassium Balance of Representative Soils. (Modified after Leeper, Introduction to Soil Science, Melbourne University Press: New York, Cambridge University Press, 1948, pp. 168, 170.)*

	CALCIUM	POTASSIUM
	LB/ACRE	
Average total amount of mineral in A-horizon	10,000	30,000
Amount of exchangeable mineral in plowed layer	600	150–1,000
Removed annually by:		
Wheat crop	3	6
Potato crop	1	22
Average crop	4.5	15
Average annual loss by leaching	8	2

The ammonium ions, then, replace the exchangeable cations bound to the surfaces of the clay particles, and the amounts of the individual ions freed can be estimated in the soil extract. A comparison of the total and the exchangeable calcium and potassium of representative soils is presented in Table 6-3. Table 6-4 shows how the sum of the exchangeable cations is divided among the three principal nutrient elements. Sodium, which is of course not required as an essential element by crop plants, is usually present to an appreciable extent in soils and often constitutes a significant proportion of the exchangeable cations.

The amount of exchangeable, and hence available, calcium, magnesium, and potassium in fertile soils is usually large in comparison with the amount removed in a single crop. The data of Table 6-3 show, however, that in regard to potassium in particular, a succession of crops may deplete the nutrient level to a very considerable extent. Replenishment of the exchangeable potassium by the addition of potassium-

Table 6-4. *Exchangeable Cations of the Plowed Layer of Two Representative Soils. (After Leeper, Introduction to Soil Science, Melbourne University Press: New York, Cambridge University Press, 1948, p. 168.)*

	TOTAL EXCHANGEABLE CATIONS, MEQUIV/100 GM	PERCENTAGE OF TOTAL			
		Ca	Mg	K	Na
Humid forest soil	9.2	58	37	2	3
Arid soil	8.9	49	28	10	13

containing fertilizers is, therefore, frequently essential under agricultural conditions, a matter which will be considered below.

The element phosphorus is present in soils in a variety of chemical forms, the majority of which are quite insoluble and hence unable to provide the plant with the phosphate ions required in its nutrition. In addition, phosphates added to the soil are often precipitated or fixed in insoluble and unavailable forms, a process which may extend over months or years in some soils but which may in others be completed in periods as short as a few days. It is clear, then, that the total phosphorus content of a soil will bear little relation to the phosphorus available to the plant.

Although plants take up their phosphorus as water-soluble phosphates, the total amount of phosphorus in a soil in this form at any one time is in general much less than that consumed during the growing season by a crop. The water-soluble phosphates must therefore be continuously renewed from less available forms associated with the soil particles themselves. Although these less available forms do slowly go into solution, it is of importance that they are not readily soluble and hence not easily leached from soil by rain. The phosphorus economy of the soil, so far as plant growth is concerned, is based on a delicate balance between ability to supply the plant on the one hand, and ability to resist leaching on the other.

A measure, semiquantitative at best, of the relatively available phosphorus in the soil is the amount extractable by dilute citric acid or dilute acid ammonium bisulfate. The relation between the amount of phosphorus thus extracted and the total amount in the soil is given for two representative soils in Table 6-5. This table also shows that the amount of phosphorus consumed by a growing crop can readily exceed the soil supply over a period of a few years. Phosphorus deficiency is therefore widespread under agricultural conditions, and phosphorus fertilization of soil is an important agricultural practice. It has been estimated that over 1.5 million tons of phosphorus-containing fertilizers are applied in the United States alone each year, but that this amount constitutes only about half of the phosphorus which would be required for maximal crop production.

The sulfur of soil occurs, generally, as sulfates and as organic sulfur compounds. Although the latter are, of course, the result of the biological incorporation of sulfur into living organisms, all of the sulfur of the soil is ultimately derived from sulfur-containing minerals of the parent rock. In the soil, as in nutrient solution, sulfate is apparently the chief form in which sulfur is taken into the plant, the organic sulfur serving perhaps as a reservoir through which sulfate is made available through continued oxidation. Although soils in general contain only from 0.01 to 0.1 per cent of total sulfur, this amount is sufficient for long-continued plant growth, since the amount removed by the plant from the soil is relatively small. Sulfur deficiency is therefore not widespread over the world, although it has been noted in the western United States. The incidence of sulfur deficiency in soils is lessened also by the fact that sulfate ions are frequently added when nitrogen is supplied as ammonium sulfate or when phosphorus is supplied as the fertilizer super-phosphate, a mixture of calcium phosphates and sulfates.

Nitrogen, unlike the nutrient elements considered above, is not con-

Table 6-5. *The Phosphorus Balance of Representative Soils.* (*After Pierre, in* Soils and Men, *U.S. Dept. of Agr. Yearbook, 1938; and Leeper,* Introduction to Soil Science, *Melbourne University Press, 1948.*)

	LB/ACRE
Total P in plowed layer	
Northern forest soils	620
Middle western prairie soils	1140
Water-soluble P in plowed layer	less than 1
Other readily available P	50–200
Removed per year by continuous cultivation	
To corn	14
To wheat	3.6
Average of all crops	3.8
Loss per year by leaching and erosion	10.6
Total average yearly loss	14.4

tained in the parent rocks from which soils are derived, and the soil's content of nitrogen depends almost wholly on the biological processes considered in Chapter 11, by which molecular nitrogen of the atmosphere is fixed in forms generally available to higher plants.

The red and yellow colors of soils are due to insoluble iron salts, such as ferric oxide, Fe_2O_3, and to the more complex iron silicates. These substances may make up as much as 10 per cent of the soil weight, and even though they are themselves unavailable to plant roots, they are usually accompanied by soluble or exchangeable iron in amounts sufficient to support the growth of plants. In soils which are highly alkaline, certain of the minor elements, such as manganese, copper, and zinc, are precipitated in unavailable forms. The plant may therefore suffer deficiencies of these elements, even though there are present in the soil large amounts of the individual nutrients in insoluble form. In such alkaline soils, any added iron, manganese, copper, or zinc is promptly precipitated and rendered unavailable to the plant. For this reason, deficiencies of any of these four elements are sometimes corrected by spraying the foliage of the plant directly with a soluble salt of the nutrient rather than by soil application.

Boron, although it is widespread in soils in insoluble forms, is principally available to the plant in the form of water-soluble borates. The total amount of such borates in the soil is often small in comparison with the amounts removed by growing crops, and this deficiency must therefore be made good by the application of borates to the soil.

Large areas of the earth's surface are deficient in one or another of the elements needed for the growth of plants. This is particularly true of phosphorus and nitrogen and of the minor elements other than iron. It is not surprising, therefore, that the native floras of the world have developed quite varied quantitative requirements for the essential elements, and that a particular species may be able to grow and thrive in a soil whose content of essential nutrients is so low as to be unsuitable for the growth of our usual crop plants. Specifically, some native species grow and flourish in soils which are so low in available phosphorus that they will not serve to support the growth of most crop plants. There are areas of Australia which contain so little available copper that they will not support the growth of crop plants, although they support the vigorous growth of a native vegetation adapted to such soils. Thus, the concept of what constitutes a sufficiency of a particular nutrient element in the soil is a relative one, and one which depends wholly on the plant or crop concerned. Generally speaking, a soil is considered to be deficient in a nutrient element if it will not support the maximal growth of a desired crop plant, regardless of whether or not some other species of plant, perhaps a species native to that soil, might be able to grow and thrive under the existing conditions.

Fertilizers

The facts discussed above have shown that there are two circumstances which necessitate the addition of essential nutrient elements to the soil as fertilizers: (1) Many soils contain amounts of available nutrients which, while adequate for the growth of their own native vegetations, are inadequate for optimal growth of introduced crop plants. (2) The constant removal of nutrient-containing plant material from the soil in the form of plant products constitutes a continued drain on the mineral reserve of the soil. The fact that mineral elements are removed from the soil by cropping was first clearly formulated by the German chemist Justus von Liebig in 1840, who also suggested that soil fertility might be established and maintained by the artificial addition of mineral elements. The general theory behind our practices of soil fertilization have, therefore, been known to us for only a little over 100 years.

In a balanced native vegetation, in which no crop is removed, the several essential elements are continuously cycled—continuously taken up by plants, utilized, and returned to the soil as dead vegetation, ready for further passage through other plants. To a large extent, the same situation prevails in a balanced agricultural system. In such a system, a portion or even the bulk of each crop is returned to the soil either directly as unutilized plant material or indirectly as manure of domestic animals. The drain of cropping on the essential nutrient elements of the soil becomes particularly severe in our modern agriculture, in which the crop, once removed, is not generally returned to the soil as animal excreta. Under these conditions, the nutrient elements of which the soil has the smallest reserve in relation to crop requirement are the first to require replenishment. The nutrients with which fertilization is most frequently concerned are nitrogen, phosphorus, and potassium. It is common practice to describe the composition of a fertilizer by a formula which gives the percentage of each of these elements present. A 5–10–5 fertilizer, for example, is one which contains 5 per cent nitrogen, 10 per cent phosphoric acid, and 5 per cent potassium, whereas a 0–6–0 fertilizer salt contains only 6 per cent phosphoric acid and no nitrogen or potassium. Such fertilizers may be applied to the soil at rates of a few hundred pounds to several tons per acre, so that of the order of a hundred to a few hundred pounds per acre of each essential element is supplied by the treatment.

Soil Acidity and Alkalinity

Just as acidity or alkalinity is an important feature of a nutrient solution, so, also, the acidity or alkalinity of the soil is of significance for the growth of plants. Although some species, oats for example, can grow in soils of a wide range of acidities, other species are confined to soils of a particular and narrower range of acidity or alkalinity. Thus Azalea and to a lesser extent potato thrive best in relatively acid soils, whereas sugar beet and alfalfa are intolerant of acidity, and do best on neutral or alkaline soils.

The acidity or alkalinity of an agricultural soil is determined chiefly by the extent to which the clay fraction is charged with hydrogen ions. In humid climates, leaching of water through the soil tends to remove calcium, potassium, and other mineral cations from the clay and to replace them by the hydrogen ions of the water. The hydrogen-charged clay behaves as a weak acid and in aqueous suspension imparts an acid pH to the surrounding water. Conversely, a clay fully charged with mineral cations imparts an alkaline pH to the surrounding medium due

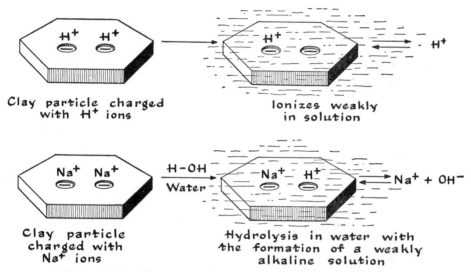

Figure 6-5. *Clay particles impart an acid or alkaline reaction to the surrounding medium depending on whether they are charged with H^+ ions or mineral cations.*

to hydrolysis of the weakly ionized salt, just as weakly ionized salts, such as sodium acetate, are alkaline in solution (Fig. 6-5). Clays highly charged with sodium ions are particularly alkaline in suspension, because sodium ionizes from the clay to a greater extent than calcium, potassium, or magnesium. Soils with pH values below 5.5 are commonly treated with lime (CaO) or limestone ($CaCO_3$) for correction of the acid condition, a treatment known as liming. This treatment not only neutralizes the acidity of the soil solution, but tends also to correct its cause by exchanging calcium ions for the hydrogen of the clay fraction. Conversely, excessive alkalinity may be corrected by addition of an acidic material to the soil. This is often accomplished through the use of elemental sulfur, which is slowly oxidized to sulfuric acid by microorganisms of the soil. The hydrogen ions of the sulfuric acid are then exchanged for a portion of the mineral cations of the soil's clay fraction.

The pH of the soil is, then, regulated by the composition of the exchangeable cations combined with the clay fraction. Soil conditions favorable to plant growth are achieved by an appropriate balance between the hydrogen ions bound by the clay and the varied mineral cations, including particularly the bound calcium, potassium, magnesium, and sodium.

Soil Organic Matter

As the plant completes its life span and dies, its tissues are normally returned to the soil either directly as plant residues or indirectly in the form of animal remains. Through these agencies, the soil is kept supplied with organic material, and it is indeed characteristic of soils that they contain organic matter, in contrast to the purely inorganic parent rock. Plant and animal remains, once contributed to the soil, do not long retain their original state, but are rapidly attacked by the many forms of bacteria and fungi which make up the soil microflora. A portion of the organic matter is used as substrate for the respiration of soil microorganisms; in fact, the great bulk of the carbon returned to the soil as organic debris is liberated as CO_2 in this way, and again becomes available for photosynthesis of the green plant. Another fraction of the organic matter added to the soil is used in the growth of the soil microorganisms, and at any given moment a considerable proportion of the soil organic matter is thus made up of living microbial cells.

As plant and animal residues are decomposed by the soil microorganisms, the more readily utilizable plant constituents, such as the sugars and the amino acids, are first attacked, whereas the more resistant plant constituents, such as the lignin of the cell walls, are destroyed much more slowly. Thus, as the decomposition of organic material in soil progresses, the inert lignin and related woody materials become relatively more abundant. The soil organic matter, or humus, which imparts to soils their brownish or black colors, consists, then, mainly of lignin and other relatively inert materials.

The organic matter of the soil is of course not required directly for the growth of the higher plant, and, as we have seen in Chapter 3, plants may be grown satisfactorily in nutrient solutions devoid of organic matter. The continued supply of organic matter, which makes possible the continued growth of the soil microorganisms, is, as discussed below, essential to the welfare of the soil itself.

Soil Structure

The aggregation of the small elementary particles of soil into larger compound particles or granules gives to soil some of the unique properties which so well adapt it to the growth of plants. Through this aggregation, soil combines the properties contributed by the small clay particles—the properties of cation exchange and high water-holding

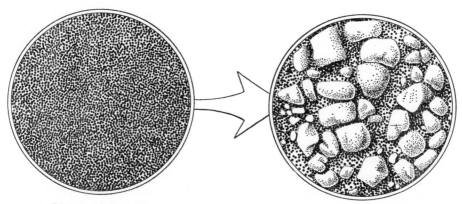

Figure 6-6. *Clay particles are joined into larger aggregates through the activities of microorganisms and plant roots.* (*Adapted from Swaby, J. Gen. Microbiol., 3, 1949, p. 254.*)

capacity—with the properties characteristic of large particles—properties of free drainage of excess water and adequate aeration of plant roots. Probably no single feature of soil is more important in terms of agricultural productivity than this property of aggregation. Without aggregation, an otherwise fertile soil becomes highly compacted and thus unsuitable for optimal root growth because of its hardness and poor aeration.

The development of granular structure by the aggregation of small particles to larger particles is chiefly a biological process and depends primarily on the growth in soil of microorganisms and of roots. The granulation of soil depends in part on the aggregation of clay particles by a meshwork of fungal hyphae, which mechanically binds the particles into cohesive lumps (Fig. 6-6). Sterile and ungranulated clay has been shown to develop granular structure after inoculation with any one of a number of fungi, provided only that a source of organic nutrient for the fungus is also present in the clay. Certain bacteria also show soil-granulating activity, a property which appears to reside in the sticky gums which these forms produce. The purified bacterial gums granulate clay just as do the living bacteria themselves.

Earthworms have been shown, especially by Charles Darwin, to contribute measurably to the formation of a desirable type of granular soil structure. They accomplish this by ingesting soil, passing it through their alimentary tract, and then excreting a vermiform casting, consisting of soil particles cemented together. Darwin estimated that approximately 15 tons of such castings may be ejected from the alimentary tracts of earthworms per acre of agricultural land. This is enough to produce a uniform layer of castings roughly 0.1–0.2 inch thick over the entire acre. Since this total is contributed by an estimated 25,000–50,-000 worms per acre, it follows that each earthworm contributes of the order of one pound of castings per year. Despite this prodigious figure, the over-all importance of the earthworm to soil structure is probably less than that of bacteria and fungi, because of the great variability in the number of earthworms found in different soils.

Finally, roots, particularly the roots of grasses, exert a powerful granulating effect on soil. It has long been known that land such as the virgin prairie, which has supported a grass vegetation for many years, possesses particularly well-developed granular structure. Soils whose structures have deteriorated under cultivation may have their structures improved by a few years under sod. We do not know whether the beneficial effect of grasses on soil structure is due to mechanical binding effects exerted by their numerous fine roots or whether grass roots liberate materials which are particularly beneficial to the growth of soil-granulating microorganisms. From an empirical standpoint, however, the long-term pasture is one of our best means of restoring soil fertility, through its beneficial effect on the numerous processes which lead to the development of a desirable granular structure.

Soil structure, both in its development and in its maintenance, depends, then, on organic matter as a source of nutrient for the structure-forming microorganisms which are so important in soil aggregation. This is of particular importance today, since our modern agricultural procedures, in which soil is subjected to a great deal of mechanical agitation and compaction, tend to destroy soil structure, to promote soil erosion, and to remove from the soil the upper layers in which the structure is best developed.

Soil Water

The plant absorbs from the soil greater quantities of water than of any other single substance. As with the other essential nutrients, the mere total water content of a particular soil gives us but little information about the amount available for plant growth. Although the proportion of the water in a sandy soil which cannot be removed by plant roots constitutes only a relatively small fraction of the total, as much as half of the total water in clay soils may be unavailable to plants. It is therefore of interest to consider the types of moisture measurements which yield a meaningful picture of the water relationships between plant and soil.

It has been brought out in recent years that the soil may be regarded as a sort of water reservoir. The reservoir is full when the soil contains that amount of moisture which is retained after gravitational drainage of excess water. Under these circumstances, rapidly attained after a heavy rain or irrigation, the soil is said to be at *field capacity*. The soil water reservoir is empty, from the point of view of the plant, when there is no longer present sufficient available water to keep the plant from wilting. The water content of the soil at this point is referred to as the *permanent wilting point*. Soils differ widely in the amount of water held at these two critical values, and therefore differ widely in the amount of water which they retain in forms available to the plant. The determinations of moisture content at field capacity and at the wilting point are perhaps the most significant measurements which can be made to relate plant growth to soil water.

Field capacity is attained by adding excess water to a soil and then allowing gravitational drainage to come to completion. The water content at field capacity is also approximately equal to the water content at the *moisture equivalent*, which may be rapidly attained in the laboratory by centrifuging excess moisture from a thoroughly wet soil sample with a force of 1000 × gravity.

The permanent wilting point is determined empirically as the amount of water remaining in a soil after a test plant growing in it has removed all the available water (Fig. 6-7). Thus a soil is said to be at the permanent wilting point when the selected test plant will not recover from wilting without the addition of more water to the soil. Although the amount of water present in the soil at the permanent wilting point varies with the soil concerned, it does not vary greatly with the kind of test plant used.

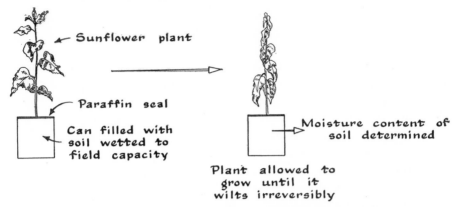

Figure 6-7. *Irreversible wilting is achieved when the plant will not recover when placed in a moist chamber. The moisture content of the soil at this time is called the permanent wilting point.*

The soil water reservoir may be looked upon as constructed of a vast number of interconnecting spaces, the spaces between the soil particles. Some of these spaces, those between the larger particles and granules, are quite large. Others, those between individual clay particles for example, are minute. After the soil has been saturated, water drains out of the larger spaces, drawing in air from the atmosphere above the soil as it does so. At field capacity, then, water is retained as films around each individual particle and in the smaller pores or capillaries in which the capillary forces are sufficiently large to prevent water drainage (Fig. 6-8). It is primarily this capillary water which is available to, and

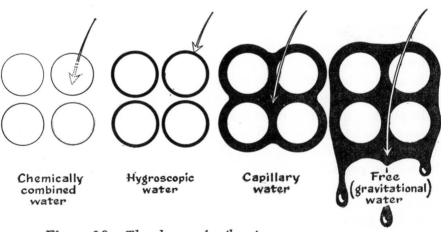

Figure 6-8. *The classes of soil water.*

utilized by, the plant. If the available capillary water is removed, for example by transpiration or by drying of the soil in air, water is retained in the soil in the finest capillaries as well as in the form of hygroscopic water, thin films a few molecules thick surrounding the soil particles (Fig. 6-8). The hygroscopic water, together with the water chemically combined in the structure of the soil minerals, is, however, unavailable to plants.

The distinctions between gravitational, capillary, and hygroscopic water are only qualitative distinctions which enable us to visualize three different conditions between which there are actually all possible

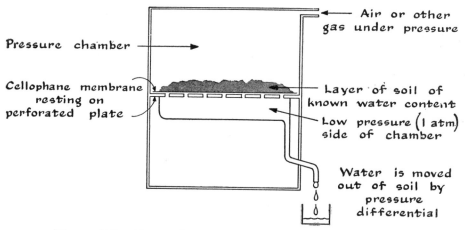

Figure 6-9. *Removal of water from soil under applied pressure. The pressure needed to remove water from the soil is a measure of the tension under which the water is held. (Adapted from Richards, Soil Sci.,* **51**, *1941, p. 380.)*

intermediate states. Generally speaking, the more water contained in a soil, the more readily it can be removed; the less water a soil contains, the more difficult it is to remove. One quantitative method for determination of the tenacity with which water is held by soil is shown in Figure 6-9. This method depends on the fact that, after soil has been allowed to drain to field capacity, more water can be removed from the smaller spaces by use of forces greater than that of gravity. This is done by placing a thin layer of soil upon a porous membrane so arranged in a chamber that one side of the soil layer can be submitted to a high pressure of air. Under the influence of this pressure differential, water is driven out of the soil, and as the pressure differential is increased, more and more water is expressed. In the curves of Figure 6-10, the pressure needed to remove water is plotted against water content for two different kinds of soil. Characteristic of both is the fact that the lower the water content of the soil, the greater is the pressure needed to remove more water. To phrase it differently, the more a soil has been

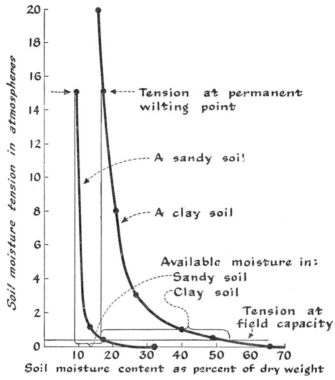

Figure 6-10. *Moisture tension as a function of moisture content of the soil. The sandy soil holds little water; the clay soil holds more water. In both cases the available water is that held between tensions of 0.3 and 15 atm. (By permission, from* Plant and Soil Water Relationships *by Kramer. Copyright, 1949, McGraw-Hill Book Co., Inc., p. 31.)*

depleted of its water, the greater is the force with which the remaining water is held.

The wilting point, at which plants can no longer remove water from the soil, corresponds to a tension on the scale of Figure 6-10 of about 15 atm. Only that water held at tensions between field capacity (approximately 0.3 atm) and 15 atm is, therefore, available to plant roots. Figure 6-10 shows how this amount, the available water, is relatively large in a fine-textured clay soil, and relatively small in a coarser sandy soil. The tension with which water is held in the soil increases very rapidly with decreasing water content in the region of the permanent wilting point. For this reason, the water content of the soil at the permanent wilting point is relatively independent of the plant used in its determination, even though individual species may vary somewhat in their ability to extract water from the soil.

Water moves with extreme slowness through soil which is drier than field capacity. Thus, as the soil is dried to the permanent wilting point by the removal of water through roots, this dry soil is not appreciably supplied with water from other wetter regions. The plant roots, rather, continue their growth into adjoining wetter regions of soil. As the upper layers of a soil are depleted of their water by the action of roots, the roots may penetrate downward to quite amazing depths, as we have seen earlier in this chapter. A corollary of the slow movement of water through dry soils is the fact that soils cannot readily be wetted to a moisture content less than field capacity. When water is placed on a dry soil, the water passes downward as a moving front at approximately the field capacity. Behind this front is completely moist soil; ahead of this front lies dry soil.

After the soil has been wetted to field capacity, water is gradually lost through transpiration and approaches the wilting point in the absence of an additional supply of water. Thus the water tension in the soil after irrigation increases steadily as water is lost to plant roots. As the soil moisture tension increases, the residual water appears to become progressively less available to the plant, as reflected in lowered rates of water uptake and water loss. Whether the wilting point is ultimately attained or whether the soil is returned to field capacity from some intermediate tension depends on the intervals between waterings. The water status of the plant in soil is necessarily one of alternate feast and famine. The most that is done by rain or by irrigation is to lessen the intensity and the duration of the famine.

Summary

Soil is a mosaic of rock particles, plant roots, microorganisms, decaying organic matter, aqueous soil solution, and interconnecting air passages. Although all of these components affect plant welfare, only two, the soil solution and the oxygen-containing air, are entirely essential to plant growth.

Soil is formed through weathering of the parent rock by the action of water, wind, and other climatic factors, together with the effects brought about by living organisms. The nature of a soil depends less on the characteristics of the parent rock than it does on the climatic and other conditions under which soil genesis has taken place.

The constituent mineral particles of a soil vary in size over a wide range, the smallest and most characteristic particles being those of the clay fraction. Not only do the minute spaces between clay particles retain water in a form available to plant roots, but the clay minerals also possess the property of cation exchange, by which such minerals as calcium, potassium, and magnesium are bound in nonleachable form until they are required by the plant.

The development and maintenance of a granular structure is a principal factor in soil productivity. Through such granulation, soil is able to combine the properties of the small constituent clay particles with properties such as free water drainage and adequate root aeration made possible by the presence of larger capillary spaces between the composite granules. Granulation is mainly accomplished by various soil microorganisms which utilize organic matter in the soil to produce the cementing materials.

The soil is a water reservoir for the plant. It is full at field capacity, when water has drained out under the influence of gravity, and empty at the wilting point, when the roots can no longer take up water rapidly enough to supply their transpirational needs. Water is held under tension by soil, and the lower the water content of a soil, the greater the tension with which this water is held. Since roots can take up water only against tensions less than some 10–15 atm, this value corresponds to the permanent wilting point of the soil. Water held more firmly by the soil is unavailable to the plant.

QUESTIONS

1. Lichens are often observed growing on bare rock. What is their source of mineral nutrients? What does this indicate about the role of lichens in soil formation?

2. Why is it better to irrigate intensively on few occasions rather than lightly on more frequent occasions?

3. Discuss the various biological agents involved in the granulation of soil. What is the relative importance of each?

4. A soil rich in calcium phosphate may actually supply too little phosphorus for optimal plant growth. Explain.

5. What is meant by cation exchange? Explain what happens when a clay soil becomes depleted of exchangeable cations and then recharged by the addition of fertilizer salts.

6. Explain why the permanent wilting point is relatively independent of the kind of plant used in its determination. Why do different soils have different permanent wilting points?

7. In what ways does soil organic matter contribute to enhanced agricultural productivity?

8. Why may cultivation of land previously in grass lead to erosion, floods, and dust storms?

GENERAL READING

Baver, L. D., *Soil Physics,* 2nd ed. New York: John Wiley & Sons, 1948. An advanced treatise for students with a detailed knowledge of the field.

Jenny, H., *Factors of Soil Formation.* New York: McGraw-Hill Book Co., 1941. The story of how soils are formed.

Lutz, H. J., and Chandler, R. F., Jr., *Forest Soils.* New York: John Wiley & Sons, 1946. Fundamental soil concepts applied to forests. Clear, readable, and accurate.

Lyon, T. L., and Buckman, H. O., *The Nature and Properties of Soils,* 4th ed. New York: Macmillan Co., 1943. A general introduction to soil science.

Russell, Sir E. J., *Soil Conditions and Plant Growth,* 7th ed. London: Longmans, Green, 1942. A masterful discussion of the basis for many of our present beliefs.

Soils and Men. U. S. Dept. of Agriculture Yearbook, 1938. A popularly written volume for the lay reader.

Veihmeyer, F. J., and Hendrickson, A. H., "Soil Moisture in Relation to Plant Growth." *Ann. Rev. Plant Physiol.,* 1: 285, 1950. A detailed account of recent advances, together with simplifying generalizations.

CHAPTER 7

Translocation: The Redistribution of Nutrients

Introduction

That substances should be transported within the plant is a logical consequence of the fact that the separate organs are dedicated to specific physiological functions. The sugars synthesized photosynthetically in the green leaves are required by all the tissues of the plant. Similarly, the nutrient elements absorbed by roots are required by, and conducted to, the leafy shoot. To the movement of solutes within the plant the term *translocation* is applied. The primary pathways for the movement of materials within the plant are, of course, the vascular elements of the xylem and phloem. The principal questions to be considered in relation to translocation are, then: (1) In which of the vascular tissues does any particular solute move? (2) By what mechanism is the movement accomplished?

It has long been clear that the elements of the xylem bear the chief responsibility for the upward conduction of water. The pathway of sugar movement was not known, however, until the anatomical and physiological description of the phloem by the German botanist Hartig, in the years 1837-1862. In the course of his anatomical study of the bark, Hartig observed that the elongated sieve tubes appeared to be suited to the conduction of materials, and tested this by means of girdling experiments. In this technique, first applied by the Italian Malpighi in 1675, a ring of the sieve-tube-containing bark is completely removed from a stem, leaving the vessel-containing xylem intact In a stem girdled in this way (Fig. 7-1), growth and swelling, accompanied by an accumulation of sugars, may take place above the ring. Since this occurs only when active leaves are present on the shoot above the girdle, Hartig concluded that materials produced in the leaves are translocated downward in the bark and accumulate if the bark is interrupted by a girdle. These qualitative observations have been confirmed repeatedly over the years, and the simple technique of girdling has provided a fair share of our present knowledge of translocation. Conversely, the girdling experiments have served to support the view that the upward movement of water takes place in the xylem, since the

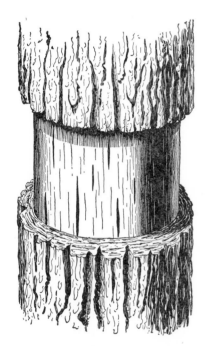 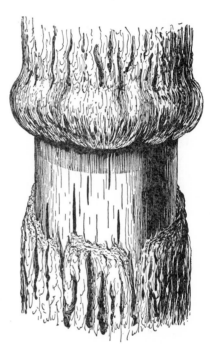

Figure 7-1. *Girdling of a woody shoot by removal of a ring of bark, leaving the xylem intact. Left, immediately after removal of the bark; right, a few weeks later. (Adapted from Stephen Hales, Vegetable Staticks, 1727.)*

transpiration stream is influenced little or not at all by the removal of a ring of bark.

Although the fact that materials may be moved downward from the leaf through the bark has been established for some time, and although Hartig, over 100 years ago, suspected that the sieve tubes might be responsible for this movement, it is only relatively recently that conclusive evidence concerning the role of sieve tubes in translocation has been obtained. Perhaps the best evidence is that provided by the German plant physiologist Schumacher, who demonstrated in 1930 that when the dye eosin is taken up by the vascular tissues, it specifically causes blockage of the sieve tubes without affecting the other cells. Since vascular tissues treated with eosin are no longer capable of translocating solutes, it may be concluded that the sieve tubes themselves are the effective agents.

The Experimental Study of Translocation

Translocation of materials through the phloem from the leaf occurs not only toward the growing root but also toward other actively grow-

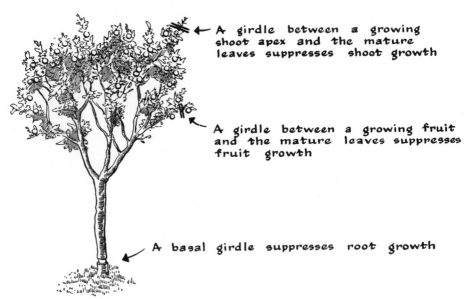

Figure 7-2. *Removal of the phloem by girdling between a growing organ and the photosynthetic leaves suppresses growth and prevents an increase in dry weight of the organ.*

ing centers, such as the shoot apex or the developing fruit. Thus the increase in size and dry weight of any growing region is suppressed by a girdle between the growing organ and its source of photosynthate, as shown in Figure 7-2. Translocation from the leaves, therefore, may occur toward either the tip or the base of the plant.

The quantity of materials translocated from leaves may be determined by a method first introduced by Julius Sachs. Sachs found that leaves lose more weight overnight when they remain attached to a plant than they do when they are excised. As the data of Table 7-1 show, a sunflower leaf may lose 12 per cent of its dry weight during a single 10-hour night, if it is attached to the plant. This loss represents that due to both translocation and respiration of the leaf. The latter loss can be measured, however, with similar leaves which are cut off and allowed to remain for the same period of time in a moist atmosphere. The respiratory weight loss in the example of Table 7-1 is only about one-fifth of that resulting from translocation.

In what form are materials translocated from the leaf? An early approach to this problem is also credited to Sachs. He showed that a considerable proportion of the decrease in leaf dry weight during the night can be attributed to the loss of various carbohydrates. In a specific instance, a series of bean leaves were found to have lost by transloca-

Table 7-1. *Loss of Weight from Sunflower Leaves by Translocation During the Night.* (*Modified from Sachs,* Gesammelte Abhandlungen über Pflanzen-Physiologie, *Vol. 1. W. Engelmann [Leipzig],* 1892, p. 376.)

	DRY WEIGHT, GM
Attached to Plant	
Weight of 500 cm^2 of leaf:	
At beginning of night period	4.02
At end of night period (10 hours)	3.54
Loss of weight overnight	0.48
(Loss due to both translocation and respiration)	
Detached from Plant (petiole in water)	
Loss of weight overnight (respiration)	0.08
Loss Due to Translocation Alone	0.40

tion 99.3 mgm of dry weight per gram of leaf during the course of a single night. Analyses of similar leaves at the beginning and at the end of the night period showed that 97.7 mgm of sugars had been lost by translocation during the same period. Sugars, therefore, accounted for 98 per cent of the translocated material in this instance. That sugars, and particularly sucrose, represent an important transport material is evident also from the fact that the sucrose content of the phloem of the stem fluctuates rhythmically, increasing as photosynthesis produces sucrose in the leaves, decreasing toward the end of the night as the sugar reserves of the leaf are depleted (Fig. 7-3). Many nitrogen-containing materials—amino acids, vitamins (Chap. 11), and other substances contained in the protoplasm of the leaf cells—are also transported in the phloem, moving out in great quantities during the night.

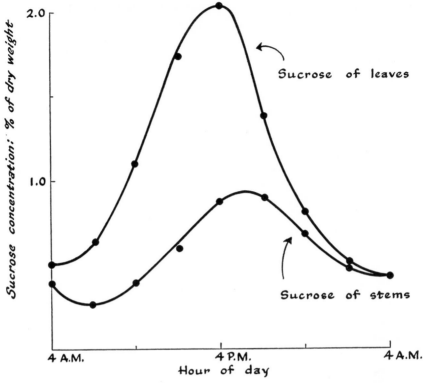

Figure 7-3. *Diurnal rhythm in sucrose content of leaves and stems of the corn plant. (After Loomis, Iowa State Coll. J. Sci., 9, 1935, p. 514.)*

We still lack a detailed balance sheet showing the relationship of each material lost by the leaf in translocation to the amount of material which appears in the stem and other receiving organs as a result of the movement.

The Path and Course of Translocation

What is the over-all path of translocation in the plant? Which organs of the plant export and which receive the materials formed during the course of photosynthesis? Experiments of the English plant physiologist Goodall, patterned after those of Sachs outlined above, have supplied us with a fairly complete picture of the sources and destinations of the materials translocated in the tomato plant.

The changes in weight of each plant organ due to the combined effects of photosynthesis and respiration can be discovered by dismembering the plant and determining the changes in dry weight of each component organ during the day or during the night. The additional effect of translocation can be obtained by determining the changes in dry weight of each organ as they occur in an intact plant. The scheme of such an experiment is outlined in Figure 7-4 for the tomato plant. In a typical experiment the bulk of the material translocated was ex-

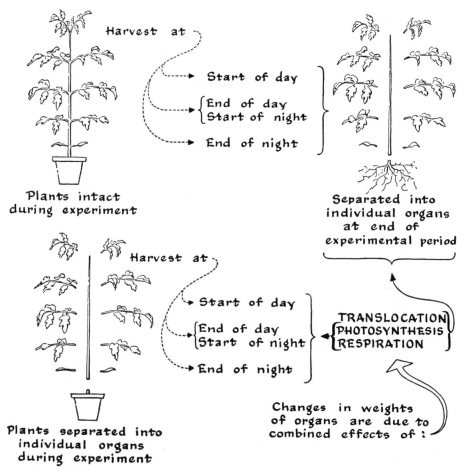

Figure 7-4. *An experiment for determination of translocatory gains or losses in weight of individual organs. Weight changes due to photosynthesis and respiration are determined by weighing the excised organs at the beginning and end of the experimental period. The additional effect of translocation is deduced from the weight changes of similar organs on the intact plant. (After experiment of Goodall, Ann. Botany, 10, 1946, p. 304.)*

Table 7-2. *Sources and Destinations of Translocated Material in the Tomato Plant.* (*After Goodall,* Ann. Botany, N.S., **10**, *1946, p. 328.*)

SOURCE OF MATERIAL	PERCENTAGE OF TOTAL TRANSLOCATE SUPPLIED	DESTINATION OF MATERIAL	PERCENTAGE OF TOTAL TRANSLOCATE RECEIVED
Cotyledons	11	Roots	48
Oldest leaf	23	Stem	38
2nd oldest leaf	32	Youngest leaf	1
3rd oldest leaf	32	2nd youngest leaf	2
4th oldest leaf	2	3rd youngest leaf	3

ported from the three most mature leaves of the eight-leaved plants used. The younger leaves not only did not export material, but actually received it from the older, more photosynthetically active leaves. Almost half the total photosynthate exported from the leaves was destined, however, for the roots, while another third or more remained in the stems themselves (Table 7-2).

The translocation of sugars and other solutes from the leaves is ordinarily obscured during the day by the photosynthetic production of new materials. It can readily be shown, however, that translocation proceeds during the day just as it does during the night. In Goodall's

Table 7-3. *Translocation in Tomato Plants During Day and Night. Plants Bearing a Total of Eight Leaves.* (*After Goodall,* Ann. Botany, N.S., **10**, *1946, p. 328.*)

SOURCE OF TRANSLOCATED MATERIAL	PERCENTAGE OF 24-HOUR TOTAL TRANSLOCATED FROM EACH LEAF DURING:	
	DAY	NIGHT
Cotyledons	74	26
Oldest leaf	105	—5
Second oldest leaf	94	6
Third oldest leaf	64	36

DESTINATION OF TRANSLOCATED MATERIAL	PERCENTAGE OF 24-HOUR TOTAL TRANSLOCATED TO EACH ORGAN DURING:	
	DAY	NIGHT
Roots	93	7
Stems	77	23
Youngest leaves	74	26

experiments, for example, although translocation took place during the night, the bulk of movement of materials, roughly three fourths of the total, occurred during the daytime (Table 7-3).

Results similar to those outlined above for the tomato plant have been obtained, although in less detail, for many other species, and they suggest, in general, that translocation of materials from the leaf is induced by, and follows as a result of, the photosynthetic accumulation of

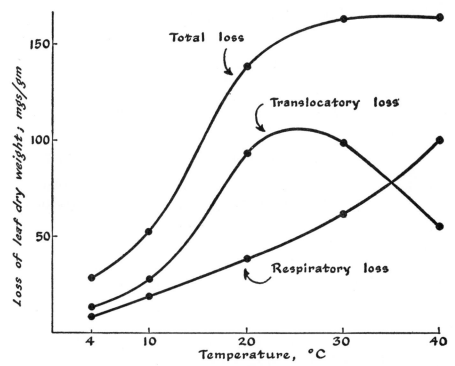

Figure 7-5. *Translocation from leaves of bean as influenced by the temperature to which the entire plant is subjected. (After Hewitt and Curtis, Am. J. Botany, 35, 1948, p. 749.)*

sugars in the leaf. In many, if not most, species a preponderance of translocation appears to take place during the daylight hours, when the gradient in sugar concentration from leaves to the receiving organs tends to be greatest.

A second factor affecting the translocation of materials from the leaf is the temperature to which the plant is subjected. Figure 7-5 depicts the amounts of material translocated in bean plants maintained at a series of different temperatures. Translocation is greatly impeded at low temperatures but rises to a maximum between 20° and 30° C, only to decrease again at still higher temperatures. These relations are complex and are compounded of the separate responses of leaf, stem, petiole, and root to changing temperatures. Thus at low temperatures the consumption of sugars in the root is slowed more than translocation to the root. Hence sugars accumulate in the root, deterring further transport to that organ. At high temperatures, on the contrary, sugars are rapidly used in the respiration of both root and leaf, and the leaf has but little material to export. Superimposed on these relations is the direct influence of temperature on the transport mechanism itself. The

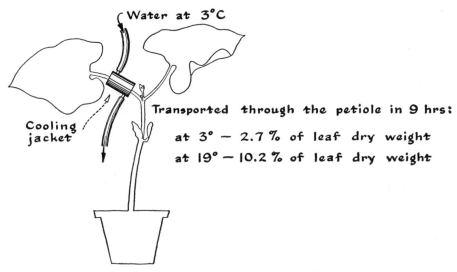

Water at 3°C

Cooling
jacket

Transported through the petiole in 9 hrs:

at 3° — 2.7 % of leaf dry weight

at 19° — 10.2 % of leaf dry weight

Figure 7-6. *Measurement of the direct effect of temperature on transport through the petiole. (Data from Curtis and Herty,* Am. J. Botany, *23, 1936, p. 530.)*

responses of transport tissue to changing temperature have been studied by surrounding a stem or petiole with a jacket through which water may be circulated to maintain a temperature different from that of the remainder of the plant. Low-temperature treatments applied in this way greatly impede translocation (Fig. 7-6).

Translocation is also inhibited in stems from which oxygen is excluded or to which chemical inhibitors of respiration are supplied. This implies that respiratory activity on the part of the phloem tissue is somehow essential to the maintenance of translocation. These facts, together with the inhibitory effect of low temperature, indicate the participation of chemical and biological, rather than purely physical, processes in the translocation of sugars. As might be expected on this basis, translocation is abolished if the phloem of a portion of stem is killed by heat, for example by scalding with a jet of steam. Nutrients accumulate above the portion of stem which has been scalded, just as though the stem had been girdled. Girdling by steam is therefore a useful experimental method for the inhibition of transport in herbaceous stems, particularly those containing internal phloem, which cannot be girdled by the ringing procedure described above for woody stems.

The Transport Elements

Whereas the transport pathways in the xylem are the dead vessels and tracheids, those of the phloem are the living sieve tube elements. The individual conducting cells of the phloem are arrayed in orderly files to form the sieve tubes, the constituent elements of which are connected one to the next by protoplasmic strands. Each sieve tube element has associated with it a smaller companion cell, the two units being derived by longitudinal division of a common mother cell. Sieve tubes and companion cells are of course not the only types of cells found in the phloem. In addition, there are greater or lesser numbers of parenchymatous cells, fibers, and other cell species. The phloem, like the xylem, forms a continuous vascular system throughout the plant, and mature sieve tubes may extend to within a few tenths of a millimeter of the growing point of root or shoot, as well as to the tips of the veins of leaves. It is apparent, therefore, that translocation through the phloem can, from the structural standpoint, take place between any and all portions of the plant.

The individual cellular elements of the sieve tube are separated one from another by end walls, which, by reason of the numerous pores which perforate them, are known as the sieve plates (Fig. 7-7). The pores, normally on the order of 0.5 to 5μ in diameter, are filled with protoplasm, which connects with the protoplasm of adjacent sieve tube elements. Protoplasmic strands, or *plasmodesmata,* also connect sieve tubes with laterally adjacent neighboring cells, and in turn connect these cells with all the other living cells of the plant.

The nucleated protoplasm of the young sieve cell is distributed in a thin layer over the wall and surrounds a well-defined vacuole, as in parenchymatous cells. As the sieve cell matures, however, the nucleus disappears, and the boundary between protoplasm and vacuole gradually becomes indistinct, until at maturity the cell contents grade uniformly from a less dense central portion to a more densely protoplasmic surface layer (Fig. 7-7). It is in this condition that the sieve tubes are maximally active in translocation. Finally, in senescence, formation of additional cell wall material or callus on the sieve plate chokes off the

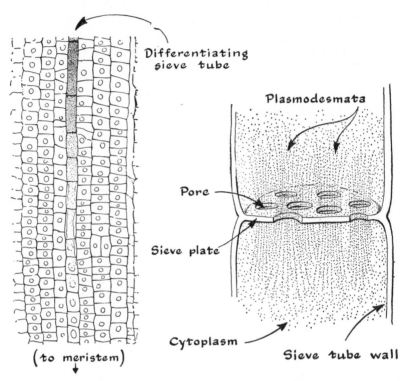

Differentiating sieve tube

Plasmodesmata

Pore

Sieve plate

Cytoplasm

Sieve tube wall

(to meristem)

Stages in the differentiation of the sieve elements

A portion of a mature sieve tube

Figure 7-7. *Development and structure of the sieve tube of to-bacco. Left, successive stages in development of sieve tube in a longitudinal section of tobacco root tip. Right, mature and functional sieve tube of tobacco primary phloem. (After Esau,* Hilgardia, 13, *1941, p. 479.)*

plasmodesmata, and this is followed in short order by the death and disintegration of the protoplasm.

The sieve cell at functional maturity possesses a curious mixture of the attributes of living and near-dead matter. Protoplasmic streaming, typical of many active cells, has not been demonstrated in functional sieve elements. Mature sieve tubes can be plasmolyzed only with difficulty or not at all, a fact which suggests that they may be highly permeable to solutes, as senescent cells often are. Even though the protoplasm of mature and functional sieve tubes possesses characteristics often associated with senescence, the presence of this protoplasm is, as we have already seen, essential to the function of sieve tubes in translocation.

The pathway of translocation is thus the sieve tubes, long interconnecting vessels filled with a mixture of cytoplasmic and vacuolar materials. How do these units function, and in what way are sugars and other solutes driven through them? We shall now turn our attention to the mechanism of phloem transport.

Phloem Transport as a Pressure Flow

Many contradictory ideas continue to prevail concerning the mechanism by which phloem transport is accomplished. Much of the experimental evidence which we possess supports, or is in agreement with, the concept that translocation through the sieve tubes is a *pressure flow*, driven by a difference in hydraulic pressures between the supplying and receiving organs of the plant. We shall first discuss translocation in terms of pressure flow and shall then return to a consideration of alternative mechanisms.

In a pressure flow, a liquid is driven through a pipe or other conductor under the influence of a pressure gradient. If the liquid happens to contain dissolved solute molecules, these molecules will be passively borne along by the flowing stream of solvent. According to the pressure flow view, sugars and other solute molecules are moved through the phloem as a flowing stream of aqueous solution. The force which drives the flow is regarded as due to differences in turgor pressure between the cells of the supplying and receiving organs.

The concept of phloem transport as a pressure flow was first formulated by the German plant physiologist Ernst Münch in 1930. The forces which result in pressure flow can be visualized from a model system proposed by Münch and shown in Figure 7-8. Suppose that an osmotic cell containing solutes is placed in water. Water will enter the cell in response to the difference between the internal and the external osmotic concentrations, and will rise in the tube of the osmometer until the hydraulic pressure on the cell contents equals the osmotic pressure. In a second osmotic cell, containing a solution of lower osmotic pressure than the first, the solution will rise in the osmometer tube to a lesser height. Suppose, now, that the tubes of the osmometer are joined (Fig. 7-8). Water will enter the cell of higher osmotic concentration and pass

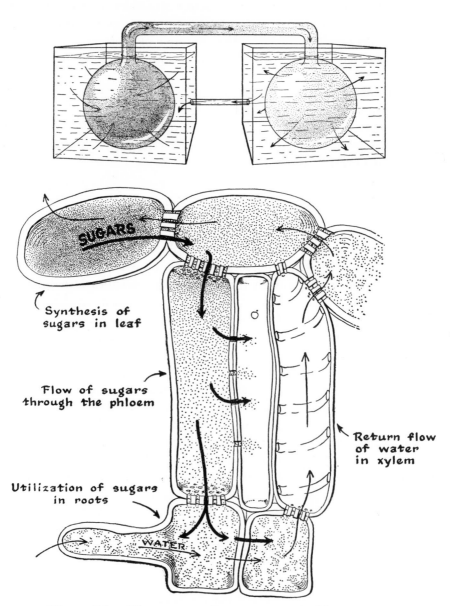

Figure 7-8. *The pressure flow concept of phloem transport.* Top, *a model system in which solute is moved by pressure flow from an osmometer containing a high concentration of solute to one containing a lower concentration.* Bottom, *application of this concept to the plant.*

through the connecting tube to the cell of lower osmotic concentration. If the cells are rigid and cannot increase in volume, and if their membranes are permeable only to water but not to the dissolved solute, water will be expressed from the second cell. In this case, a circulation of water will take place from the outer bath, through the cell of higher concentration to that of lower concentration, into the second bath, and back into the first bath by way of the connecting tube. Models of this kind have actually been made, and it has been shown that, as expected, movement of solution through the connecting tube continues until the osmotic concentrations of the two cells are equalized. If, however, one could arrange for continuous formation of solute in the supplying cell and continuous removal of solute from the receiving cell, the pressure flow between them should be capable of continuing indefinitely.

In the concept of phloem transport as a pressure flow mechanism (Fig. 7-8), the cells of the supplying organs are regarded as the supplying osmometer, whereas the cells of the receiving organs constitute the receiving osmometer. The protoplasmic contents of the cells of the supplying organs are connected through the plasmodesmata to the contents of the sieve tubes, and thence through further plasmodesmata to the protoplasmic contents of the cells of the receiving organs. The plasmodesmata and the sieve tubes play the role, then, of tubes connecting osmotic cells. All of the cells of the plant are supplied with water through the xylem, which represents the bath common to the supplying and receiving organs.

We may thus view the events which lead to translocation by pressure flow as taking place in somewhat the following way: The photosynthetic formation of sugars in the leaf mesophyll results in a high osmotic concentration in these cells. This results in water uptake and increased turgor, or hydraulic pressure, on the cell contents. A solution containing sugar and other solutes is therefore expressed from these cells through the plasmodesmata, and ultimately reaches the sieve tube. The pressure exerted by the mesophyll cells drives the solution through the sieve tube and finally into the protoplasm of the receiving cells. Here, sugars are being consumed by respiratory, growth, or storage processes. Both the osmotic concentration of these cells and particularly their turgor pressures are maintained at a low level. It should be stressed again that it is this gradient in hydraulic or turgor pressure which must be available to drive the pressure flow. The requirement essential to pressure flow is that the turgor pressure of the receiving organs be smaller than that of the supplying organs. Thus, nutrient-containing solution might conceivably flow into a growing fruit under pressure, despite a higher osmotic concentration in the receiving fruit cells, provided that the fruit cells retain a low turgor pressure by continued expansion. In general, however, osmotic gradients and turgor gradients within the plant appear to coincide.

Among the most elementary of the observations which are in agreement with the concept of phloem transport as a pressure flow is the fact that the sieve tubes are, in fact, under pressure. This is to be contrasted with the xylem, which, as we have seen in Chapter 5, is under actual tension during active transpiration. When incisions are made into the active phloem, solution is exuded under pressure from the cut sieve tubes. Species differ greatly in the amount and rapidity of this flow, because of such secondary matters as the clogging of the cut tubes or sieve plates by the rapid movements which occur within the sieve elements after incision. Nevertheless, the locust (Robinia) and certain oaks deliver quite large volumes of exudate after incision of the phloem. Since the volume exuded is much larger than the volume of the cells immediately adjacent to the cut, it is clear that solution has been transported from considerable distances within the plant. Phloem exudate is characteristically rich in sugars, containing on the order of 5 to 20 per cent of these materials. Smaller amounts of nitrogen-containing materials, including proteins (Chap. 11), and minerals are also found in the sap. In general, also, the osmotic concentration of phloem exudate is greater near the supplying organs and smaller in the neighborhood of receiving organs such as the roots. Table 7-4 gives data from a typical study and shows that a gradient in osmotic concentration equivalent to roughly 1 atm per meter exists between the supplying leaves and receiving tissues of the cambium at the base of the tree. The osmotic concentration gradients within the sieve tubes themselves are, however, smaller—usually about 0.1–0.5 atm per meter.

The rates of normal flow within the sieve tube can be calculated from a knowledge of (1) the total amount of solute which passes from supplying to receiving organ in a definite time, (2) the concentration of this solute in the sieve tube contents, and (3) the total cross-sectional area of sieve tubes in the connecting tissues. All of these quantities have been measured in several instances, and it has been calculated that movement of solution through the sieve tubes may be from 10 to 100 cm per hour in different species and under varied circumstances. These rates are well within the limits which have been calculated as physically possible on the basis of the known pressure gradients in, and physical properties of, the sieve tube contents. Similar rates of conduction within the sieve tubes have been directly meas-

Table 7-4. *Osmotic Pressure of Cell and Sieve Tube Contents in Various Portions of a Tree,* Castanea vesca. (*Modified after Pfeiffer, Flora, N.S., 32, 1937, p. 38.*)

PORTION OF PLANT	OSMOTIC CONCENTRATION OF CELL CONTENTS, ATM
Upper leaves	17.6
Sieve tube exudate	
7 meters above ground	15.5
4 meters above ground	14.0
1 meter above ground	12.4
Growing cambium 1 meter above ground	9.6

ured by the use of indicator substances which are swept along in the translocation stream, as described in the following section.

The Movement of Indicator Substances

The movement of sugars, which constitute the bulk of the mobile sieve tube contents, is accompanied by the movement of other materials which may make up only a very small proportion of the total solutes. Among the materials whose movement appears to be dependent on the translocation of the sugars are compounds native to the plant, such as the plant hormones (Chap. 15), and compounds foreign to the plant, such as virus molecules (Chap. 11), molecules experimentally marked with isotopic elements, and the synthetic plant growth substance 2,4-D (Chap. 16). In all of these instances the material moves through the phloem in the direction of sugar movement and at similar rates, from 10 to 100 cm per hour. The compound 2,4-D, for example, is readily taken up by the leaf and translocated to the phloem of the leaf veins. The movement of the material out of the leaf depends, however, upon whether or not sugar translocation is taking place. If 2,4-D is applied in minute amounts to leaves of plants which have been depleted of sugars by long sojourn in darkness, the chemical is not transported. Exposure of the leaf to light to permit photosynthetic sugar formation, or artificial feeding of the darkened leaf with sugar, both result in rapid translocation of sugars from the leaf, and bring about prompt and simultaneous movement of the 2,4-D. The same principles hold true with respect to radioactive phosphate, which, when applied to the leaf, moves downward through the plant only in association with sugar transport. These facts appear understandable on the basis that many kinds of transportable solute molecules may be carried by the moving phloem stream, even though the pressure flow is primarily governed by the major solute, which is ordinarily sugar. Since such materials as 2,4-D or radioactive phosphate are very readily followed in their progress through plant tissues, they may be, and are, used as indicators for revealing the direction and rate of solute flow from leaves and through vascular tissues.

Other Views on the Mechanism of Phloem Transport

Although most facts concerning phloem transport appear to be satisfactorily encompassed by the concept of pressure flow, other suggestions have been made as to the forces which might drive solute movement. The principal alternative views have been those which regard solute movement in the phloem as a *diffusional* flow, possibly speeded by the active participation of the cytoplasm. In a diffusion process, as we have seen in Chapter 4, solute molecules move through the solvent from regions of higher concentration to regions of lower concentration. No movement of the solvent is involved, and individual solutes may even move in opposite directions, since the movement of each substance is determined by the concentration gradient of that substance alone. Since the rates at which substances might move through the sieve tube by diffusion alone are very much lower than the translocation rates actually observed, it is necessary to assume that the purely diffusive portion of the translocation process is restricted to short distances, possibly only to passage across the sieve plates. Within each sieve tube element the transport of materials could then be hastened by circulation or streaming of the protoplasmic contents. The combined diffusion-protoplasmic streaming concept of phloem transport was particularly well formulated by the American plant physiologist O. F. Curtis in the years between 1935 and 1950.

It would seem that a clear decision between pressure flow and diffusion as the motive force of translocation might be made on the basis of experiments designed to determine whether or not solvent and solute flow together in the sieve tube. According to the concept of pressure flow, solvent and solute must flow together as a solution. According to the concept of diffusion, on the other hand, solutes diffuse through the solvent, and the movements of the two are independent. This critical experiment, which might be done by following simultaneously the movements of isotopically marked water and sugar within the phloem, has not, however, been done. Attention has centered, rather, on attempts to discover whether or not two different solutes might simultaneously move in opposite directions in the sieve tube, each in accordance with its own concentration gradient. It has not yet proved possible, however, to establish unequivocally the occurrence of simultaneous and opposite movement of two substances by normal phloem transport. On the contrary, our information on the movement of indicator substances suggests that, in general, solutes move together and in the same direction in the sieve tubes, as is required by the concept of pressure flow.

The diffusion concept of translocation requires the participation of protoplasmic streaming. This fact alone makes it unlikely that diffusion can contribute appreciably to phloem movement, since, as outlined above, protoplasmic streaming does not appear to occur in the functional sieve tubes of most species. The extended discussions of the past, and the extensive anatomical and physiological experimentation which these discussions have brought forth, all point to pressure flow as the principal mechanism of phloem transport.

Transport of Solutes in the Xylem

The transpiration stream of the xylem carries with it a variety of solutes as it passes from root to leafy shoots. The solutes thus borne along in the transpiration stream are primarily the minerals absorbed by the root from the soil. This can be demonstrated by an experiment such as that summarized in Figure 7-9, which shows that nitrogen passes upward through the xylem in cotton plants from which the phloem has been removed by ringing. Similar experiments by the American plant physiologist Hoagland with a variety of herbaceous and woody plants have shown conclusively that over short periods of time, minerals, including the nitrate and phosphate ions, move upward essentially as rapidly through a ringed shoot as through an intact one. The xylem fluid (obtained, for example, by collecting the exudate from decapitated, bleeding stumps) contains a variety of minerals, although in low concentration. Upward movement of these minerals is generally more rapid under conditions which cause intense transpiration than under conditions of low transpiration. All of these facts point to the xylem stream as the principal upward path of mineral nutrients. There are complications, however, due to the fact that transfer of minerals from xylem to phloem occurs readily and rapidly.

An experiment designed to study the lateral transfer of solutes is shown in Figure 7-10. For this experiment, a three-branched willow plant was allowed to absorb a radioactive potassium salt through its roots, and the progress of the radioactive material through the tissues of the stem was followed. Branch *a* was left intact as a control; in branches *b* and *c* the phloem was separated from the xylem. With branch *b*, a sheet of water-impervious waxed paper was inserted between xylem and phloem, while in branch *c*, the separated tissues were placed back in contact with one another. In branches *a* and *c*, in which xylem and phloem were in direct contact, approximately equal con-

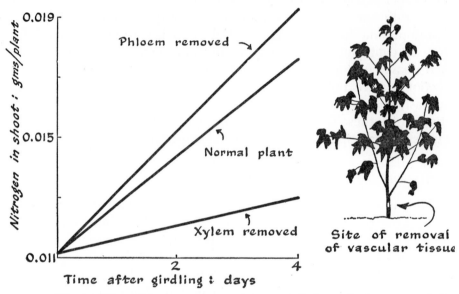

Figure 7-9. *Nitrogen movement upward through the stem of the cotton plant is not diminished by a phloem girdle. If the xylem is removed, leaving the phloem intact, nitrogen movement is greatly decreased. (After Mason, Maskell, and Phillis,* Ann. Botany, **50,** *1936, p. 37.)*

centrations of radioactive potassium were found in xylem and phloem; in branch *b*, when the two vascular tissues were separated, radioactive potassium was much more abundant in the xylem. This shows that the bulk of the potassium movement in the mature stem occurs in the xylem, but that lateral movement from xylem to phloem occurs readily.

Once minerals have entered the phloem, they are presumably subject to the usual phloem transport. It is not surprising, therefore, that the translocation of minerals into such actively growing, but slowly transpiring, regions as young leaves or elongating shoots frequently takes place in the phloem and is checked by ringing (Table 7-5).

An unresolved problem is presented by the upward movement of nitrogen in the woody stems of many trees and shrubs. In contrast with the situation in herbaceous plants such as the cotton cited above, the upward movement of nitrogen from the roots is frequently suppressed by ringing. This suggests that the movement is in the phloem.

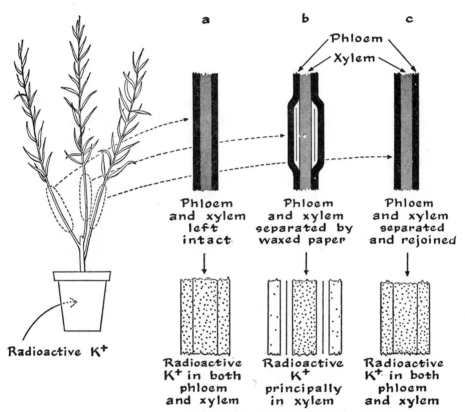

Figure 7-10. *Transport of radioactive potassium in a willow seedling. The bulk of the radioactive material moves in the xylem, but may pass to the phloem by lateral translocation.* (After Stout and Hoagland, Am. J. Botany, 26, 1939, p. 321.)

The apparent difference between trees and herbaceous forms with respect to mode of nitrogen transport may be related to differences in the chemical form in which nitrogen is translocated (Chap. 11). In any case, however, movement in the phloem in the trunk of the tree must generally be in a downward direction, bringing to the roots the sugars they require. How can the upward-moving nitrogen buck

Table 7-5. *The Influence of Ringing on the Movement of Minerals into Young, Actively Growing Shoots of the Privet* (Ligustrum *sp.*) *over a Period of Approximately Five Weeks.* (*Adapted from Curtis,* Am. J. Botany, **10,** *1923, p. 373.*)

MEASUREMENT OF:	CONTROL (NOT RINGED)		RINGED	
	INITIAL	FINAL	INITIAL	FINAL
Dry weight of shoot, gm	1.13	1.38	1.03	1.70
Total nitrogen of shoot, mg	16.4	34.5	14.1	17.4
Total ash of shoot (all minerals as oxides), mg	85.4	139.9	79.8	95.2

the downward pressure flow in the phloem? The nature of nitrogen transport in tree species is in need of considerable clarification.

Summary

The translocation of sugars and other products from the leaf to other organs of the plant takes place in the sieve tubes of the phloem. The protoplasm of the sieve tubes is connected with that of the other living cells of the plant by means of protoplasmic strands (plasmodesmata) penetrating the cell walls. It appears probable, on the basis of present knowledge, that transport through the sieve tubes takes the form of a mass flow of solution, the driving force for which is a difference in turgor pressure between the photosynthetic cells, which form and supply the translocated material, and the cells of the receiving tissues, which utilize or store their material. The turgor gradients responsible for translocation appear to have their origin primarily in differences in osmotic concentrations between the supplying and receiving tissues.

Although sugar is the solute primarily responsible for the establishment of turgor pressure gradients in the sieve tubes, other solutes, both native and foreign to the plant, may be passively borne along in the sieve tube stream. That substances may be swept along in this way in the current of the moving sugar provides support for the general concept of sieve tube transport as pressure flow.

Although the transport of sugars from the leaf continues throughout the day and night, transport during the daylight hours accounts for the bulk of material moved. Roots and growing fruits receive a large portion of the material translocated, while smaller portions go to the stem and even to young expanding leaves in which photosynthesis has not yet become fully established.

The mineral elements absorbed by roots from the soil are transported upward principally in the transpiration stream of the xylem. Minerals move readily and rapidly from xylem to phloem, and therefore mineral nutrients may enter growing organs through either or both of the vascular tissues.

QUESTIONS

1. It has been found by various investigators that organic compounds applied to a leaf are not exported from the leaf unless (a) the leaf is actively photosynthesizing or (b) sugar is applied to the leaf. Suggest a possible explanation.

2. The growth of a fruit, such as an apple, depends largely on the amount of photosynthate transported to it. How could you increase the size of an individual immature apple relative to other apples on the same tree?

3. In what ways does transport of inorganic materials differ from transport of organic materials in plants?

4. What are the probable transport mechanisms in large algae, which lack well-organized vascular systems?

5. Lundegårdh has found that suction applied to the cut end of a wheat root segment greatly increases the rate of exudation from this surface. Discuss a possible mechanism for this effect.

6. What information relative to pathways of translocation can be obtained from an experiment involving girdling?

7. Leonard has found that darkened mature leaf blades of the sugar beet translocate sugar to the petioles against a concentration gradient but cannot absorb sugars from the petiole. Can this be interpreted in terms of the pressure-flow hypothesis?

8. Can starch be translocated in the plant? Explain. Can proteins be translocated? What evidence do we have on this point?

9. Went, studying translocation and growth in the tomato plant, found that relatively low night temperatures appear to accelerate both processes. Suggest a possible reason for the apparent negative temperature coefficient for translocation.

10. How quickly could you expect material applied to the surface of the soil to appear in the terminal bud of a 1-meter high tomato plant? Explain.

GENERAL READING

Curtis, O. F., *The Translocation of Solutes in Plants.* New York: McGraw-Hill Book Co., 1935. A critical integration of the work up to 1935.

Crafts, A. S., "Movement of Assimilates, Viruses, Auxins and Chemical Indicators in Plants." *Botan. Rev.,* **5:** 471, 1939; *ibid.,* **17:** 203, 1951. A detailed survey of the literature.

PART TWO

Metabolism

CHAPTER 8

Enzymes: The Machinery
of Metabolism

Introduction

We have seen that through the process of photosynthesis, sucrose and other sugars are formed in the green tissues of the plant. From the sugars thus produced the plant is capable of manufacturing a host of other compounds, in fact, directly or indirectly, all of the various organic substances known to be present in plant tissues. Thus in the tissues of the plant, synthetic processes are continuously being carried on, and sugar and other substances are continuously being destroyed by respiration, in the dark as well as in the light. This continuous flux, the synthesis and degradation of organic material in the living organism, is known as *metabolism* (see Fig. 8-1).

We may take it as a general rule that the synthetic processes by which the plant makes new and more complex materials from simpler materials are processes which require energy. Thus, the synthesis of protoplasm, of cell wall material, or of fat from sugars formed in photosynthesis involves, in general, processes which do not proceed spontaneously but which require some external source of energy. In contrast, the degradative processes by which complex molecules are converted to simpler ones are in many cases processes which proceed with the evolution of energy. For example, a great deal of energy is evolved in the process of respiration, in which sugars are converted to carbon dioxide and water.

The basic principle of metabolism in the living organism is the utilization of energy-storage and -transport mechanisms by which energy released in respiration is made available for the driving of synthetic reactions essential to the cell economy. A portion of the

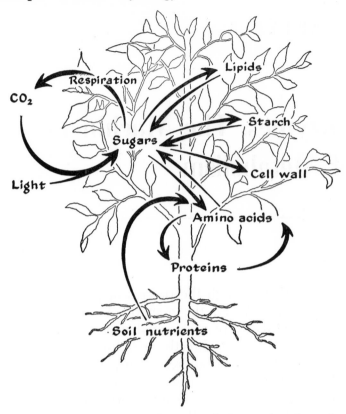

Figure 8-1. *The flux of plant metabolism. The plant, through photosynthesis, fixes CO_2 in the form of sugars. The sugars may again be degraded to CO_2 by respiration, or they may be used in the synthesis of other essential plant constituents.*

photosynthetically produced sugar is burned in respiration, and the resultant energy is used to convert an additional portion of sugar to new and essential cellular constituents (Fig. 8-2).

Enzymes Catalyze Metabolic Reactions

Some of the chemical transformations which take place in the plant are known with considerable certainty; others remain to be worked out. Those transformations which we do know have in common several features. They are reactions which proceed spontaneously even when the pure reactants are mixed together in solution outside of the living cell. Also, they are reactions which proceed with extreme sluggishness

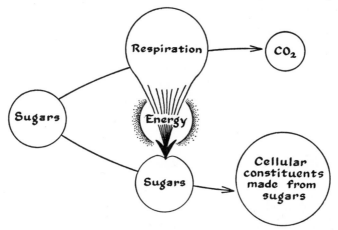

Figure 8-2. *The energy-using processes of cellular synthesis are carried on with the aid of energy liberated in respiration. Sugars serve as the starting material for cellular synthesis as well as for respiration.*

under such conditions. A solution of glucose in water at room temperature is unstable and tends gradually to take up oxygen, with the evolution of carbon dioxide. This reaction is, however, extremely slow. In the living plant cell the same reaction proceeds very rapidly. This is

Figure 8-3. *Glucose in water solution is oxidized to CO_2 in the presence of air, although this process proceeds extremely slowly (left). The living cell contains enzymes which greatly speed up the reaction (right).*

because the plant cell, in common with other living materials, contains *enzymes*, whose function it is to speed up, to catalyze, the course of particular chemical reactions (Fig. 8-3). In general there is a specific kind of enzyme for each kind of metabolic reaction, an enzyme charged with the responsibility of speeding up that particular step in the over-all metabolism. Enzymes represent, then, the machinery by means of which metabolic transformations are carried out.

The Specificity of Enzymes

The significant biological feature of an enzyme is its ability to speed up the rate of a chemical reaction. Each individual enzyme is restricted in its catalytic activity to one particular reaction or one group of related chemical reactions. Thus we have in the plant the enzyme invertase, which catalyzes the hydrolysis or cleavage of sucrose to its constituent sugars, glucose and fructose. Other sugars closely related to sucrose are not attacked by invertase; each has its own specific hydrolytic enzyme.

$$\text{Sucrose} + H_2O \xrightarrow{\text{Invertase}} \text{Glucose} + \text{Fructose}$$

HYDROLYSIS OF SUCROSE BY INVERTASE.

In other cases an enzyme may show specificity for a particular chemical linkage. The enzyme lipase, for example, catalyzes the cleavage of the ester linkages in fat without great regard for the nature of the fatty acids involved in the particular fat. Other enzymes are similarly specific as to the compounds or *substrates* they will attack. Since each enzyme is specific to one reaction or to a small group of related reactions, and since there are a great many different chemical reactions which occur in living things, there are a great many different enzymes in each cell. Several hundred individual enzymes have been recognized, and it has been estimated that each cell probably contains on the order of a thousand different kinds.

It is characteristic of an enzyme that it is not consumed during the over-all reaction. The reaction for the cleavage of sucrose, as written above, is the same whether the cleavage takes place very slowly in the absence of an enzyme or rapidly in its presence. It can be shown, also, that a very small amount of enzyme can speed up the reaction of a relatively large amount of reactant (Fig. 8-4). It has been calcu-

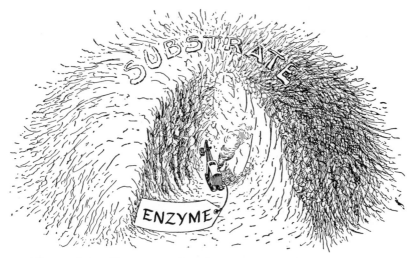

Figure 8-4. *Enzyme molecules perform feats out of all proportion to their size.*

lated that a single molecule of the enzyme catalase can effect the decomposition of approximately 5,000,000 molecules of hydrogen peroxide per minute, even at 0° C. A single enzyme molecule can,

$$2\ H_2O_2 \xrightarrow{\text{Catalase}} 2H_2O\ +\ O_2$$

Hydrogen   Water   Oxygen
peroxide

DECOMPOSITION OF HYDROGEN PEROXIDE BY CATALASE.

therefore, attack in rapid succession a great number of molecules of the substrate for which it is specific. In this way a small amount of an enzyme can bring about a chemical transformation which is out of all proportion to the quantity of enzyme present.

The Physical and Chemical Nature of Enzymes

By suitable extraction of plant material it has been possible to separate a number of enzymes from the living tissue and to isolate particular ones as individual pure chemical substances. All of the enzymes thus far isolated in pure form have been found to belong to the group of compounds known as proteins. The chemical nature of proteins will be covered more extensively in Chapter 11. Here we will discuss only some of the physical characteristics of proteins which are of importance to enzymatic activity.

The enzymatic proteins which have been isolated are substances of relatively high molecular weight. Peroxidase, one of the smaller enzyme molecules, has a molecular weight of 40,000, whereas catalase, one of the largest, has a molecular weight of, roughly, 250,000. Enzyme molecules are, therefore, larger than those of the usual simple organic substances, but are nevertheless small enough to dissolve completely in aqueous media and to yield clear, nonturbid solutions.

Enzyme proteins share with other proteins the property of extensive alteration by heat. Thus when a protein solution is boiled, even briefly, the protein becomes insoluble, precipitates out of solution, and loses all enzymatic activity; the protein is said to have been *denatured*. Agents other than heat can also bring about denaturation. Heavy metal ions such as those of lead, mercury, or silver; concentrated acids or bases; and ultra-violet light all cause denaturation of proteins and effect loss of the catalytic activity of enzymes. Use is made of heat denaturation in diagnosing the presence of an enzyme in a plant extract. We could, for instance, compare the rates of sucrose hydrolysis in the presence of boiled and unboiled extract of plant tissue. If hydrolysis proceeds rapidly in the presence of unboiled but not of boiled extract, then we may conclude that invertase is present in the tissue extract.

Protein molecules, including enzymes, behave in solution as polyvalent ions. Each molecule possesses numerous groups which yield hydrogen ions in slightly alkaline solutions and groups which yield hydroxyl ions in slightly acid solutions. Unlike many simpler substances, then, a protein is *amphoteric*, that is, capable of ionizing either as an acid or as a base, depending on the acidity of the external solution. At some particular acidity of the external solution, an acidity characteristic for each species of protein, the protein molecule possesses equal numbers of acidic and basic groups and is, therefore, an internally compensated or electrically neutral ion. Under these conditions the protein is said to be at its isoelectric point. The importance of this in relation to enzymes lies in the fact that the catalytic activity of each enzyme depends intimately on the ionic nature of the protein molecule, or on the acidity or alkalinity of the reaction medium. For each enzyme there is an optimum pH at which the enzymatically catalyzed reaction proceeds most rapidly, while at acidities greater or less than this optimum the reaction is slower. Superimposed on this effect of acidity is the fact brought out above that strong acid or alkali solutions actually denature or destroy the enzyme.

The Prosthetic Groups of Enzymes

Certain of the enzymes appear to consist solely of protein. This is true, for example, of certain of the proteolytic enzymes, which attack and degrade proteins, as well as of the amylases, which attack and degrade starch. Many other enzymes, however, consist of two portions, a protein portion and a nonprotein prosthetic group, or *coenzyme*

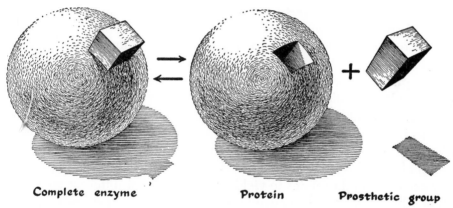

Complete enzyme   Protein   Prosthetic group

Figure 8-5. *A complete enzyme molecule is frequently made up of two parts, a protein component and a nonprotein prosthetic group. The combination of the two portions is essential for enzymatic activity.*

(Fig. 8-5). Perhaps the simplest cases of this kind are enzymes in which the prosthetic group consists of a single metal atom. The enzyme tyrosinase, which attacks the amino acid tyrosine, is made up of a protein portion combined with an atom of copper. If the copper is removed, the residual protein is enzymatically inert, as is the free copper ion. If copper is again added to the protein portion, the enzyme and its activity are reconstituted. Other copper-containing enzymes are also known, including ascorbic acid oxidase, which attacks and destroys ascorbic acid (vitamin C). The presence of copper is essential to the functioning of these enzymes in catalyzing an oxidation. The particular substrate oxidized, whether tyrosine or ascorbic acid, depends, however, on the nature of the protein portion of the enzyme.

There are individual enzymes or groups of enzymes which contain metals other than copper as essential prosthetic groups. Zinc, manganese, magnesium, and iron are all known to function as parts of various enzymes. In the case of iron, the metal is not bound directly to the protein, but is incorporated into a more complex molecule, such as an iron porphyrin, which then becomes the prosthetic group proper. Such iron porphyrin enzymes include several of the catalysts which make up essential links in the process of respiration (Chap. 10). An important fact to be borne in mind is that the heavy metals required in small amounts as minor elements for the growth of plants are essential to the plant because they form constituents of essential enzymes.

Still other enzymes possess relatively complex organic substances as their prosthetic groups. It is a striking fact that the substances first discovered as essential micro-food materials, or vitamins, for animals are now known to function in enzyme prosthetic groups. In the enzymes of higher plants, also, the vitamins of the B complex, including thiamine (vitamin B_1), riboflavin (vitamin B_2), pyridoxine (vitamin B_6), niacin, pantothenic acid, biotin, and adenine all constitute enzyme prosthetic groups or portions of prosthetic groups. For example, niacin and adenine appear together in phosphopyridine nucleotide, the prosthetic group of dehydrogenases. This prosthetic group can be combined with any one of several proteins to yield a whole series of different enzymes, all of which attack and remove hydrogen atoms from oxidizable materials. In this case, again, all enzymes which contain a phosphopyridine nucleotide as a prosthetic group are ones which remove hydrogen from the substrate. Exactly which chemical compound is attacked as substrate by each enzyme is dependent on the protein with which the phosphopyridine nucleotide is combined. Similarly, all the flavoprotein enzymes containing riboflavin bound as a portion of their prosthetic group are involved in the oxidation of substrates. The exact substrate attacked depends, again, on the protein concerned in each particular enzyme.

The Nature of Enzyme Action

Although enzymes function as catalysts, they are not altered or destroyed in the over-all reaction. The amount of enzyme needed to speed up the rate of a reaction markedly is extraordinarily small in comparison with the amount of reactant or substrate transformed. We should now ask ourselves: How is it that traces of an enzyme can accomplish such prodigious chemical results? Let us first consider what occurs in a reaction mixture containing substance *A* which is gradually and spontaneously converted to *B* in the absence of an enzyme (Fig. 8-6, *left*). If the reaction is spontaneous, substance *B* must possess a lower energy content than *A*. The rate at which *A* is converted to *B* is depend-ent not on the concentration of molecules of *A per se*, but on the number of molecules of *A* with an energy greater than a certain mini-mal amount. The molecules of substance *A* in solution have different

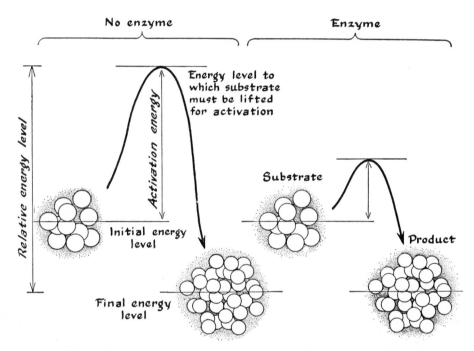

Figure 8-6. *In any spontaneous reaction the energy level of the prod-ucts is lower than the energy of the initial substrate. Before the reac-tion can occur the substrate molecule must surmount an energy bar-rier, the magnitude of which is known as the activation energy. The presence of an enzyme lowers the required activation energy*

energies, since they are continuously moving about hitting one another. When a molecule, through collision or otherwise, obtains an energy greater than the critical, it is ready to react and to be converted to the reaction product *B*. The magnitude of this energy barrier, or hump, which molecules of substance *A* must surmount before they can react and drop to the lower energy level of substance *B* is called the *activa-tion energy* of the reaction. Since molecular motions increase in inten-sity as the temperature is raised, the proportion of molecules of *A* possessing the needed activation energy increases with temperature. For this reason, reactions increase in rate with rising temperature.

Let us now look at the reaction $A \rightarrow B$ as it occurs in the presence of a specific enzyme which catalyzes the reaction. It is found that the presence of an enzyme causes a decrease in the activation energy of the reaction; that is, the energy barrier which molecules of A must surmount before descending to the energy level of B is lowered (Fig. 8-6, *right*). Because of the lowered energy of activation, a larger proportion of molecules of A attain the requisite energy per unit time,

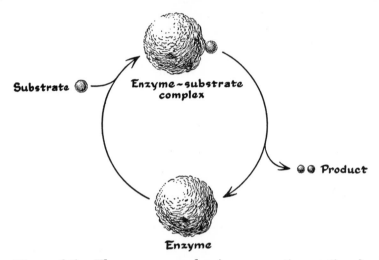

Figure 8-7. *The enzyme cycle. An enzymatic reaction is characterized by the momentary formation of an enzyme-substrate complex. In the dissolution of the complex the modified substrate is released as the product of the reaction, and the enzyme itself is regenerated.*

and the rate of reaction is increased. The chemical reactions of living organisms are carried on at rapid rates because of the lowered activation energies involved in enzymatic systems.

How does an enzyme lower the activation energy? It is believed that in many cases, perhaps in all, this is accomplished by the formation of an actual compound or complex of A and enzyme. It is the energy of activation of the new compound which is then lower than the activation energy of A itself. The complex reacts to form an enzyme-B complex, and B is then liberated with the restoration of a free enzyme which is ready to repeat the cycle (Fig. 8-7). Even though the presence of an enzyme does not alter the over-all course of reaction, it does, nevertheless, enter into reaction briefly and temporarily with its substrate.

Distribution of Enzymes in the Cell

Another important question concerning the enzymes of the plant relates to the localization and the quantities of these materials within the cell. We know that most, if not all, of the enzymes of plant cells are contained in the protoplasm, and few, if any, are located in the vacuole or in the cell wall. Some of these enzymes are present as soluble components of the cytoplasm; indeed, it seems probable that the protein of the cytoplasm is largely made up of enzymatic proteins. Many of the enzymatically catalyzed reactions of metabolism undoubtedly are mediated by these soluble enzymes of the cytoplasm.

Many other enzymes are, however, bound firmly into the structure of various of the particles which are always found in protoplasm. Thus, numerous enzymes are functionally associated in the chloroplast. These include, for example, phosphorylase, which is responsible for the synthesis of starch in the chloroplast, as well as other enzymes which are involved in the photosynthetic reaction proper. Still other enzymes are found in nonchlorophyll-containing particles, as, for instance, the mitochondria. This is true of an entire group of enzymes concerned with the respiration or oxidation of sugars. One interpretation of the presence of such particulate enzyme complexes is that closely bound and integrated enzymatic structures may be essential for carrying out metabolic processes in which several or many reactions follow one another in a closely knit series of steps. Thus, if we imagine that the product of one reaction immediately becomes the substrate for a following reaction, it may be of great importance that the two enzymes involved be associated in a correctly organized and integrated unit. Be that as it may, it is true that complex chains of reactions, such as those of respiration or photosynthesis, do have their respective enzymes bound together in particulate complexes.

Still a third type of important particle in the cell is represented by the nucleus. The proteins of the nucleus are remarkable in that they include the genic material on which the development and heredity of the organism depend. We know very little about the enzymatic relationships of the gene proteins, but we do know that in particular instances a genetic defect or mutation, that is, a chemical change in the genic material, may result in the alteration or even the loss of a particular enzyme in the protoplasm outside the nucleus. This has led to the hypothesis that genes are, in general, concerned with the production of enzymes, that they are master enzymes for making other enzymes. Whereas the enzymes of the extranuclear protoplasm are involved in the everyday metabolic process of respiration and chemical synthesis, the proteins of the nucleus would seem to be concerned with the regulation of the kinds or amounts of enzymes in the protoplasm, as well as with the passage of genetic characters from cell to cell and from generation to generation.

Summary

The manifold chemical reactions of the plant would hardly proceed at measurable rates were it not for the presence in the cell of enzymes, specific catalysts which increase the rate of chemical reaction without being altered or destroyed in the over-all course of the reaction.

Each enzyme is specific to one reaction or to a group of closely related reactions, and there are a great many, perhaps a thousand or more, different kinds of enzymes in each cell.

Many enzymes, when extracted from the cell, are able to carry out their specific catalytic action quite apart from organized living material.

Those enzymes which have been studied chemically are proteins, possessing typical protein properties in that they are readily denatured and inactivated by heat and certain other agents.

Frequently, the enzymatic protein has been found to have associated with it, as an active functional group, a smaller nonprotein prosthetic group. Among the recognized prosthetic groups are heavy metals such as iron, manganese, copper, and zinc, which we know as the minor elements of plant nutrition. In other cases the prosthetic group may be an organic substance, frequently including a member of the vitamin-B complex.

The activity of an enzyme in catalyzing a chemical change is exceedingly great, and a single enzyme molecule may catalyze the reaction of several million reactant or substrate molecules per minute. The enzyme speeds the reaction by combining with the substrate and decreasing the energy barrier, the energy of activation, which must be surmounted before substrate can be converted to product.

Despite the small quantities of each present in any individual plant cell or tissue, the enzymes are, nevertheless, the actual machinery by which the complex series of chemical reactions of metabolism are guided, integrated, and finally achieved.

QUESTIONS

1. Is the presence of an enzyme in an extract of a plant conclusive proof that such an enzyme is active in the plant? Is the absence of a given enzymatic activity in a homogenate of a plant tissue conclusive proof that this enzyme is absent from the plant? Why?

2. In what way do enzymes speed chemical reactions? How is it possible for an enzyme to effect the decomposition of many molecules of its substrate without itself being substantially altered?

3. Using your knowledge of enzymes, how could you distinguish raw from pasteurized milk?

4. Meat wrapped in bruised fig leaves becomes very tender in the course of several days. Can you suggest a possible mechanism?

5. How can a gene located in the nucleus possibly affect the production of enzymes located in the cytoplasm?

6. It has been found that certain enzymes are much less labile to heat and pH alterations when in the presence of their substrate. How can one explain this apparent protective action of substrate?

7. Certain enzymes, known as adaptive enzymes, are formed only in cells which have previously been exposed to the substrate for this enzyme. Suggest a possible mechanism for this apparent ability of a substrate to elicit the appearance of the enzyme which attacks it.

8. The economically important phloem fibers of the flax plant are best prepared free of impurities by permitting the stems to "ret," that is, to lie submerged in water until most of the nonfibrous material has disappeared. Could enzymes be involved in this retting? How could one test this hypothesis?

9. The blackening of wounded or cut potato tubers and various fruits is due to the oxidation of various phenols by the enzyme polyphenoloxidase. Since both enzyme and substrate are present in the cell, why does not blackening occur without preliminary wounding?

GENERAL READING

Advances in Enzymology, New York: Interscience Publishers, Vol. I–. 1941–. One bound volume of this review journal appears each year. It is an excellent general source of advanced critical discussions of enzymatic matters.

Baldwin, E., *Dynamic Aspects of Biochemistry*. Cambridge: University Press, 1947. An excellent picture of the role of enzymes in metabolic processes.

Northrop, J. H., Kunitz, M., and Herriott, R. M., *Crystalline Enzymes*, 2nd ed. New York: Columbia University Press, 1948. The purification and characterization of several important enzymes.

Sumner, J. B., and Myrbäck, K., *The Enzymes, Chemistry and Mechanisms of Action*. New York: Academic Press, 1950. The newest encyclopedia of enzymology.

Sumner, J. B., and Somers, G. F., *Chemistry and Methods of Enzymes*, 2nd ed. New York: Academic Press, 1947. A brief and moderately elementary discussion with descriptive material concerning the best-known individual enzymes.

CHAPTER 9

Carbohydrates: Their Nature, Functions, and Interrelations

Introduction

The sugar produced in photosynthesis may either be stored as such in the plant or may be converted to other substances. In fact, it appears probable that the great majority, perhaps all, of the many different chemical compounds in the plant are manufactured in one way or another from the sugar produced in photosynthesis. Many of the materials which go to make up the bulk of the plant—starch and the components of the cell wall—are chemically closely related to the sugar produced in photosynthesis. The bulk of the plant consists, in fact, of modified sugars, and plant growth depends on the modification of the sugar produced in photosynthesis to form the chemical compounds which make up the plant. To understand the growth and functioning of the plant, it is necessary, therefore, that we understand something of the chemical relationships among the sugars and something of the ways in which these materials are interconverted in the plant.

The Carbohydrates

The simple hexose sugars mentioned earlier belong to the general class of chemical compounds known as the *carbohydrates*. Carbohydrates are constituted, chemically speaking, of the elements carbon, hydrogen, and oxygen in the ratio of one atom each of carbon and oxygen to two atoms of hydrogen. In the hexose sugars, 6 carbon atoms, 12 hydrogen atoms, and 6 oxygen atoms are united to form the molecule; whereas in the pentose sugars, 5 carbon, 10 hydrogen, and 5 oxygen atoms are involved. Although simple sugars containing 3, 4, 5, 6, and 7 carbon atoms are known to organic chemistry, only the pentose and hexose sugars are common to, and of quantitative importance in, all higher plants.

The simple sugars, and the hexose sugars in particular, are of functional importance not only as the principal materials utilized in respiration (Chap. 10), but also as the raw materials from which the plant synthesizes its wealth of other organic materials. The molecules of simple sugars may be united to form more complex derivatives, such as the disaccharides (two molecules of simple sugar linked together), trisaccharides (three molecules), tetrasaccharides (four molecules), or polysaccharides (many molecules). Among the disaccharides of higher plants the most important is sucrose, which, as we have seen, is perhaps the principal sugar of translocation. The polysaccharides, on the other hand, possess both metabolic and structural functions. Thus the polysaccharide starch constitutes a major form of sugar storage in a great number of species. Starch forms the reserve food of many seeds, roots, and tubers; it is stored during growth of the organ and reutilized during germination of the seed or sprouting of the tuber. The principal components of the cell walls of higher plants are also polysaccharides. These materials, including particularly cellulose, are chiefly responsible for the rigid mechanical properties of plant tissues.

Organic Chemistry of the Hexose Sugars

To understand the functions of carbohydrates in the plant, it will first be necessary to survey briefly the organic chemistry of the simple

Carbon atom				
1	$HC=O$	CH_2OH	$HC=O$	$HC=O$
2	$HCOH$	$C=O$	$HOCH$	$HCOH$
3	$HOCH$	$HOCH$	$HOCH$	$HOCH$
4	$HCOH$	$HCOH$	$HCOH$	$HOCH$
5	$HCOH$	$HCOH$	$HCOH$	$HCOH$
6	CH_2OH	CH_2OH	CH_2OH	CH_2OH
	D-Glucose	D-Fructose	D-Mannose	D-Galactose

sugars themselves. The hexose sugar glucose (dextrose) possesses a chemical structure in which 5 of the 6 carbon atoms are linked to hydroxyl, or —OH, groups. The remaining and apical carbon atom (carbon atom number 1) is involved in an aldehydic, or $-C{\overset{O}{\underset{H}{\diagup}}}$, group. This aldehydic group is readily oxidized by reagents which are themselves reduced in the process. Thus, oxidation of glucose with cupric hydroxide results in the production and deposition of red cuprous oxide. Glucose is therefore a reducing sugar, and cupric hydroxide a standard reagent for the detection of such compounds. Fructose resembles glucose in structure, with the difference that it contains a subterminal ketonic, or $\overset{|}{\underset{|}{C}}=O$, group at carbon atom number 2 rather than an apical aldehydic group. Since the ketonic group of fructose is also readily oxidized, fructose is, like glucose, a reducing sugar.

The spatial configuration of the hydroxyl groups about the individual carbon atoms is of great importance in the structure of the sugars. This orientation is depicted in the structural formulas above by the orientation of each hydroxyl group relative to the longitudinal axis of the sugar molecule. The naturally occurring hexose, mannose, differs from naturally occurring glucose only in orientation of the hydroxyl group about the second carbon atom, while naturally occurring galactose differs from glucose only in orientation of the hydroxyl group about carbon atom number 4.

Glucose itself may exist in two steric forms designated as D-glucose and L-glucose, respectively, and differing in configuration about the fifth carbon atom. The same is true of fructose, mannose, and galactose. Only the D-form of each of these sugars, however, is ordinarily found in nature.

Configurational differences in molecular structure, such as those between D- and L-glucose, result not only in appreciable chemical differences between otherwise similar compounds but also in marked differences in physical behavior and in biological properties. D-Glucose is readily utilized as a substrate for respiration by plant tissues, while D-galactose, D-mannose, and even L-glucose are utilized much more sluggishly or not at all.

Of the great number of possible stereoisomers of the hexose sugars, only a small number are formed as plant products. The four hexose sugars—glucose, fructose, mannose, and galactose—appear to be present in every living plant. Of these, only D-glucose and D-fructose ordinarily occur dissolved in molecular form in the cytoplasm or vacuole of the plant. D-Mannose and D-galactose are found in the plant only in the form of derivatives and particularly as component sugars of polysaccharides of the cell wall. Still other hexose sugars occur scattered through the plant kingdom, generally bound with other materials in the form of rare or unusual compounds.

The Pentose Sugars

There are four pentose, or 5-carbon, sugars which appear to be ubiquitous and important components of plant material. None of these four sugars is found, however, dissolved as such within the plant, but all occur as derivatives bound in larger molecules. Two of the pentoses, D-xylose and L-arabinose, occur in the plant as constituents of polysaccharides of the cell wall, the xylans and arabans, respectively. D-Xylose is sterically related to D-glucose; that is, it is identical with

$$
\begin{array}{cc}
\text{HC}=\text{O} & \text{HC}=\text{O} \\
\text{HCOH} & \text{HCOH} \\
\text{HOCH} & \text{HOCH} \\
\text{HCOH} & \text{HOCH} \\
\text{CH}_2\text{OH} & \text{CH}_2\text{OH} \\
\text{D-Xylose} & \text{L-Arabinose}
\end{array}
$$

D-glucose but for the absence of the sixth, or terminal, atom. L-Arabinose is similarly related to D-galactose. Neither of these sugars is utilizable in respiration, and neither appears in any reserve polysaccharide; they seem to be purely structural materials.

The pentose sugar D-ribose is found in the plant, as well as in all other living things, as a component of certain respiratory enzymes (Chap. 10) and as a constituent of certain nucleic acids (Chap. 11).

$$
\begin{array}{cc}
\text{HC}=\text{O} & \text{HC}=\text{O} \\
\text{HCOH} & \text{HCH} \\
\text{HCOH} & \text{HCOH} \\
\text{HCOH} & \text{HCOH} \\
\text{CH}_2\text{OH} & \text{CH}_2\text{OH} \\
\text{D-Ribose} & \text{2-Desoxy-D-ribose}
\end{array}
$$

The sugarlike compound desoxyribose, which is related to ribose but which lacks a hydroxyl group at the second carbon atom, is likewise a universal constituent of living matter, being found in the cell nucleus.

Ring Structure of the Sugars

The open-chain structure of sugars depicted above applies primarily to solutions of these substances. In their derivatives, including both starch and the polysaccharides of the cell wall, sugars occur in a ring or cyclic structure, the exact nature of the ring depending on the sugar involved. In glucose, for example, a 6-membered ring may be formed

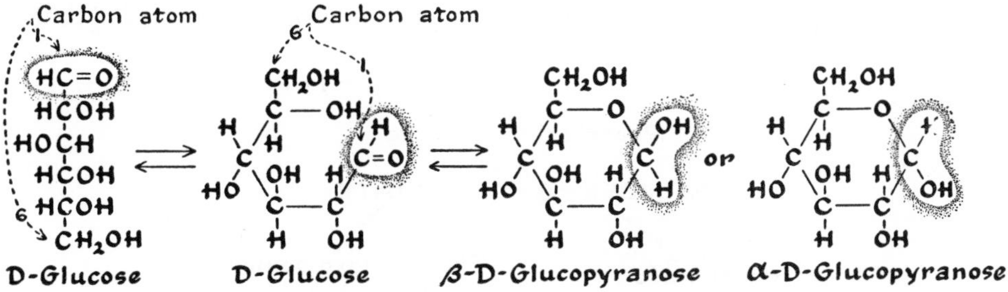

FORMATION OF THE 6-MEMBERED GLUCOPYRANOSE RING.

by formation of an oxygen bridge between the terminal aldehydic carbon atom and the fifth carbon atom. With the closing of this 6-membered, or pyranose, ring, a new hydroxyl group is formed at the aldehydic end of the molecule, as is shown in the above diagram. Since this new hydroxyl group may have either of two possible orientations with regard to the remainder of the molecule, there are two forms of the cyclic pyranose D-glucose, forms which are known as α and β respectively. This same hydroxyl group is involved in the formation of many of the derivatives of D-glucose, which may be derivatives either of α-D-glucose, as starch, or derivatives of β-D-glucose, as cellulose. Here, again, a simple steric difference in molecular configuration confers on the two compounds a wide difference in chemical, physical, and biological properties.

Phosphate Derivatives of the Simple Sugars

From the standpoint of metabolism, perhaps the most important derivatives of the simple sugars are those in which one or more groups of the sugar are combined with phosphoric acid. *Phosphorylation*, as it is called, appears to be the first step in many of the metabolic transformations to which the sugars are subject. The participation of phosphorylated sugar derivatives in metabolic processes was first demonstrated by the English biochemists Harden and Young, who in 1905 found that phosphorylation constitutes an important initial step in the fermentation of sugar by yeast. In the respiratory oxidation of the hexoses also, phosphorylated sugars, rather than free sugars, form the actual substrate.

We know today of four principal phosphorylated hexoses, two involving glucose and two involving fructose. The two glucopyranose derivatives are glucose-1-phosphate, in which phosphoric acid is bound through the hydroxyl group of carbon atom number 1 (that

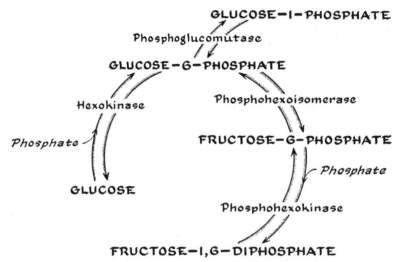

Figure 9-1. *The stepwise formation of fructose-1,6-diphosphate from glucose. Four different enzymes are involved in the interconversion of glucose and the four important phosphorylated sugars shown above.*

formed on the aldehydic carbon by ring closure), and glucose-6-phosphate, in which phosphoric acid is bound through the hydroxyl group of the terminal carbon atom number 6. The two well-known fructose derivatives are fructose-6-phosphate and fructose-1,6-diphosphate. These four phosphorylated hexoses bear an intimate metabolic relationship to one another, since they are readily interconverted by enzyme systems of the plant. Thus glucose-6-phosphate and fructose-6-phosphate are converted one to another by the enzyme phosphohexoisomerase, and this enzymatic mechanism represents, so far as is known, the sole manner in which glucose and fructose may be interconverted. Other enzymes, whose names are given in Figure 9-1, catalyze the formation of glucose-6-phosphate from glucose, the conversion of glucose-6-phosphate to glucose-1-phosphate, and the conversion of fructose-6-phosphate to fructose-1,6-diphosphate. This last compound is, as we shall see in Chapter 10, the actual substrate for respiration, and all hexose sugars must first be converted to fructose-1,6-diphosphate before they are subject to further respiratory breakdown. Glucose-1-phosphate, on the other hand, is the starting material used by the plant in the synthesis of other di- and polysaccharides.

Sucrose

The principal disaccharide of higher plants is sucrose, which is produced both directly as a product of photosynthesis and indirectly from simple sugars in many nonphotosynthetic tissues. Sucrose is of interest not only to the plant but also to man, and crops such as sugar cane and sugar beet are grown for their yield of sucrose, which may, in the case of sugar cane, reach the extraordinarily high value of five tons of the pure chemical per acre per year.

In sucrose, as in all disaccharides, two simple sugar molecules are bound together through a linkage formed by elimination of the elements of one molecule of water. Thus sucrose has the empirical formula $C_{12}H_{22}O_{11}$. On treatment with warm dilute acid or with the enzyme invertase, sucrose is hydrolytically cleaved. In the hydrolysis (see p. 176) the elements of one molecule of water are taken up, and one molecule each of glucose and fructose are liberated. Sucrose is not a reducing sugar; that is, it does not, for example, reduce cupric ions and hence does not possess either the free aldehydic group of glucose or the free ketonic group of fructose. In fact, it is precisely these two groups which are involved in the glucose-fructose bond in sucrose, as is shown in the

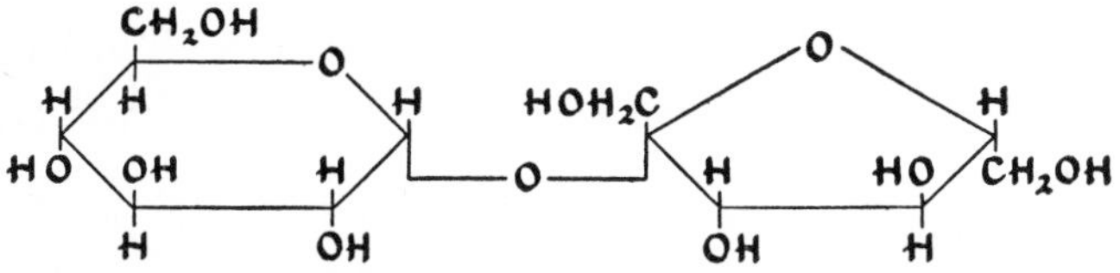

CHEMICAL STRUCTURE OF SUCROSE.

accompanying diagram. It may be noted also that whereas the glucose unit possesses a 6-membered pyranose ring structure, the fructose unit occurs as a 5-membered, or furanose, ring.

The Formation of Sucrose

We have seen that sucrose is formed as an early product of the photosynthetic reaction (Chap. 2). In addition, however, many plant tissues have the ability to form sucrose when they are supplied with simple hexose sugars. This fact has made it possible to analyze more closely the way in which sucrose and possibly other disaccharides are formed. When leaves of barley or clover are cut from the plant and placed in a moist container in the dark, they rapidly use up their sucrose supply, and their content of both sucrose and hexose sugars drops to a low level. If, however, during the dark period the leaves are floated on a solution containing glucose, the glucose is taken up, and sucrose appears in large amounts. It is clear, therefore, that the plant possesses mechanisms for the conversion of glucose to fructose (the phosphohexoisomerase system described above) and for the union of glucose and fructose to form sucrose.

The mechanism of this synthesis in a higher plant has not yet been elucidated, but important work bearing on the problem has been carried out with a sucrose-forming bacterium, *Pseudomonas saccharophila*. This organism contains an enzyme which may be extracted and purified and which is capable of catalyzing the union of glucose-1-phosphate and fructose with the formation of sucrose and inorganic phosphate.

$$\text{Glucose-1-phosphate} + \text{fructose} \underset{}{\overset{\text{sucrose}}{\underset{\text{phosphorylase}}{\rightleftharpoons}}} \text{sucrose} + \text{phosphoric acid}$$

This enzyme sucrose phosphorylase, discovered at Berkeley in 1944 by Hassid, Doudoroff, and Barker, likewise catalyzes the reverse reaction, that is, the phosphorolytic breakdown of sucrose to glucose-1-phosphate and fructose. In the presence of the enzyme, then, an equilibrium is established between these four materials, and, depending on the relative concentrations of the reactants, sucrose will be synthesized or degraded.

This general type of reaction mechanism is quite possibly similar to that which occurs in the higher plant. It is to be contrasted with the hydrolytic cleavage of sucrose in the presence of the enzyme invertase, by which sucrose is degraded to glucose and fructose. In the hydrolytic reaction catalyzed by invertase, the equilibrium is far over toward the side of hydrolysis, and it is not possible to bring about any detectable synthesis of sucrose from glucose and fructose in the presence of the enzyme. The hydrolytic reaction is, therefore, applicable only to sucrose breakdown and apparently cannot be used by the organism for sucrose synthesis. The phosphorolytic reaction, on the other hand, can be used by the organism for either synthesis or breakdown of sucrose, as conditions warrant.

Starch

The principal reserve carbohydrate of the higher plant is starch. This material is stored in large amounts in many seeds, where it is called upon as a source of nutriment for the seedling at the time of germination. Starch is similarly stored in many fleshy tubers and roots, where it provides a source of food for the development of new tissues

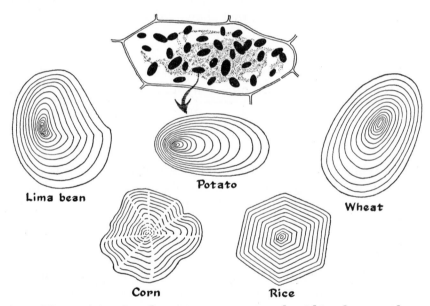

Figure 9-2. *Starch grains are scattered within the cytoplasm of the cell. The starch in each grain is deposited in numerous more or less concentric layers.*

when growth is resumed after a dormant period. Starch is accumulated also in woody twigs, where it serves as the energy source for growth of buds in the spring, and in the chloroplasts of many leaves during the course of photosynthesis. In all of these varied tissues, starch is stored in the form of grains, small granules which vary in different species from one to many microns in diameter, and which are microscopically distinguishable as to species of origin by their various shapes (Fig. 9-2). In many species the grains are characteristically layered into regions of denser and less dense starch. This layering is absent in plants grown under conditions of constant light and temperature. The normal layering is due to the fact that denser, more highly refracting starch is deposited during the day, while less dense starch is deposited during the night.

Starch, as we now know, is made up of long chains of glucose residues linked together by oxygen bridges of the type found in the disaccharide maltose, in which the terminal, or number 1, carbon atom of each residue is linked through an oxygen atom to the fourth carbon atom of the following glucose residue. All of the glucose residues of starch possess the 6-membered, or pyranose, ring structure, and the linkages between them are of the α configuration. In basic outline the chemical structure of starch is that shown below.

CHEMICAL STRUCTURE OF STARCH.

Starch, while it is often considered as a single material, is actually made up of two distinguishable components, amylose and amylopectin. Amylose is more soluble in water than is amylopectin, and may be separated from amylopectin merely by allowing starch grains to stand in water for prolonged periods. Under these conditions amylose dissolves in, and diffuses out into, the solution, while the less soluble amylopectin remains behind. This difference in physical behavior is due to a fundamental difference in chain structure between the two forms of starch (Fig. 9-3). In amylose the chains are unbranched and may contain 300 to 1000 glucose residues in a single long molecule. In amylopectin, on the contrary, the chains are much branched. Many short branches, containing, on the average, eighteen glucose residues, are coupled into other chains at intervals of roughly eight glucose residues, the whole forming a highly ramified structure of very high molecular weight. The branch points in amylopectin involve linkages of a different nature than those of the glucose residues in the chains themselves. The number 1 carbon atom of the terminal residue of the branch chain is bonded through an oxygen atom to the number 6 carbon atom of the glucose residue at the branch point of the main chain. These chemical differences between amylose and amylopectin are reflected in differences in their behavior toward enzymatic attack, as we shall see below.

One last point of interest in starch structure is the fact that in amylose the long chain of glucose residues is wound up in a helix, each turn of

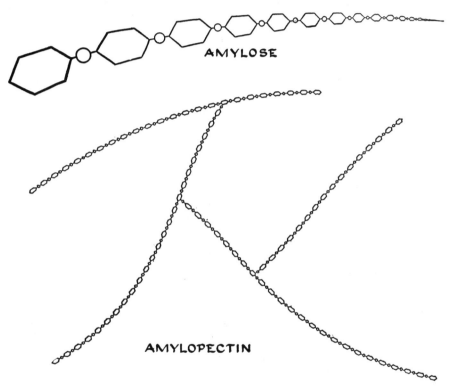

AMYLOSE

AMYLOPECTIN

Figure 9-3. *The contrasting arrangement of glucose residues in the structures of amylose and amylopectin.*

the helix consisting of six glucose residues (Fig. 9-4). A similar helical structure may also characterize the much shorter chains of amylopectin. In the well-known iodine reaction of starch, in which starch yields an intensely blue complex in the presence of iodine, it appears that the iodine molecule is accommodated within the helical coil of glucose residues, one I_2 molecule being bound for each complete loop of the helix (Fig. 9-5).

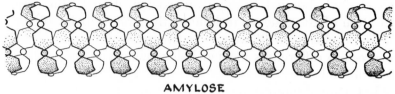

AMYLOSE

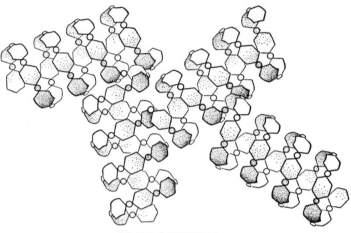

AMYLOPECTIN

Figure 9-4. *Helical arrangement of the glucose residues in amylose and amylopectin. There are six glucose residues in each turn of the helix.*

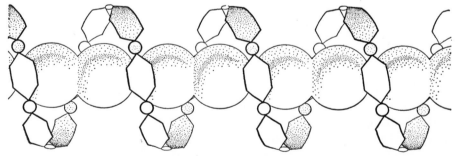

Figure 9-5. *In the blue starch-iodine complex, the iodine molecules occupy the center of the helix. Amylose takes up one diatomic iodine molecule for each six glucose residues. (Adapted from Rundle and Baldwin,* J. Am. Chem. Soc., **65,** *1943, p. 555.)*

The Synthesis of Starch

The synthesis of starch from glucose-1-phosphate is accomplished through the intervention of the enzyme starch phosphorylase (Fig. 9-6). The Canadian biochemist Hanes, who first described the enzyme,

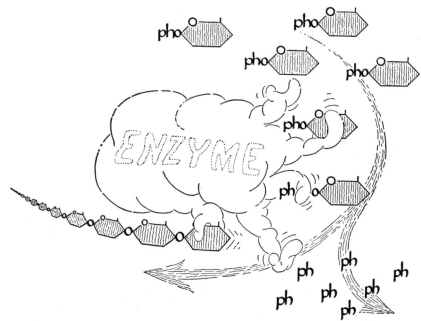

Figure 9-6. *The synthesis of starch by starch phosphorylase. The enzyme makes the 1-4 linkages of starch by using the energy of the phosphate bond in glucose-1-phosphate.*

found it readily in pea seeds and in potato tubers, but it is also present in a wide variety of other plant tissues, including the starch-accumulating cells of the green leaf. In the presence of the enzyme starch phosphorylase, an equilibrium is established between glucose-1-phosphate, amylose, and inorganic phosphate.

$$\text{Glucose-1-phosphate} \underset{\text{phosphorylase}}{\overset{\text{starch}}{\rightleftharpoons}} \text{amylose} + \text{H}_3\text{PO}_4$$

If the reaction mixture initially contains much glucose-1-phosphate and no inorganic phosphate, starch is produced. If, however, the reaction mixture initially contains much starch and inorganic phosphate, starch will be degraded to glucose-1-phosphate until equilibrium is established. Thus this enzyme catalyzes either the synthesis or the phosphorolytic breakdown of starch, depending on the prevailing circumstances. In general, the presence, or production in the plant, of much glucose-1-phosphate will favor the production of starch, and it can actually be shown that treatment of excised tissues of seedlings or leaves with glucose-1-phosphate does result in starch formation in the tissue. On the other hand, the depletion of glucose-1-phosphate by translocation away from the organ, or by transformation to other compounds, might be expected to result in starch degradation. In this way, the starch of plant tissues is kept readily responsive to the needs of the organism, being formed or utilized as conditions require.

Starch Hydrolysis: The Amylases

Long before the role of starch phosphorylase in synthesis and phosphorolysis of starch was appreciated, other starch-attacking en-

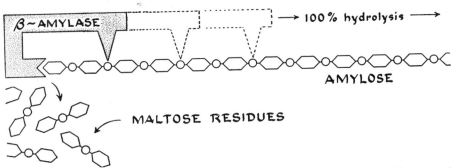

Figure 9-7. *The enzyme β-amylase attacks starch by splitting off successive units of the disaccharide maltose. The unbranched amylose molecules are completely converted to maltose by this enzyme.* (*After Hassid and McCready, J. Am. Chem. Soc., 65, 1943, p. 1159.*)

zymes, the amylases, were known to be present in many plant tissues. It was, in fact, the discovery of the starch-digesting power of what we now know as amylase which led Kirchoff to his discovery of the existence of enzymes in 1814. Two enzymes, α- and β-amylase, occur very widely throughout the plant world, but have been studied particularly in the germinating seeds of cereals, especially barley. Dormant seeds of barley contain the enzyme β-amylase, which attacks amylose according to the reaction shown in Figure 9-7. In this reaction the amylose molecule is quantitatively cleaved to the disaccharide maltose.

The reaction does not involve the uptake of phosphoric acid, as does the cleavage of starch by starch phosphorylase, and the splitting is a purely hydrolytic one involving the uptake of one molecule of water for each molecule of maltose produced. Although β-amylase possesses the ability to speed the cleavage of starch to maltose, it is not able to bring about the production of detectable amounts of starch from maltose. In the plant, then, β-amylase must function purely as a degradative, hydrolytic enzyme.

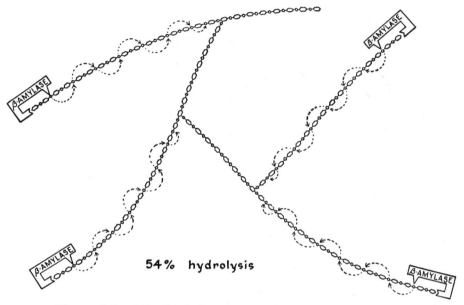

54% hydrolysis

Figure 9-8. *The hydrolysis of amylopectin by β-amylase. β-Amylase removes only the short branch chains of amylopectin, since it is unable to attack the glucose residues which are involved in branch formation. (After Hassid and McCready,* J. Am. Chem. Soc., **65,** *1943, p. 1159.)*

β-Amylase converts only the short branch chains of amylopectin to maltose and is unable to cleave the branch point linkage of the much-branched amylopectin molecule. The action of β-malt amylase on amylopectin results, therefore, in the production of maltose and of a residual fragment or dextrin which represents the amylopectin molecule from which the free branches have been pruned (Fig. 9-8).

α-Amylase, unlike β-amylase, is not present in dormant barley seeds but appears during germination of the seed. Although α-amylase, like β-amylase, is a hydrolytic enzyme, it differs from the latter in its mode of attack on amylose in that the products of α-amylase cleavage are the so-called *dextrins,* short chains of glucose molecules possessing, in general, from six to twelve glucose residues. Thus α-amylase quickly degrades starch but only to relatively large fragments (Fig. 9-9).

In summary, starch is formed in the plant through the action of the

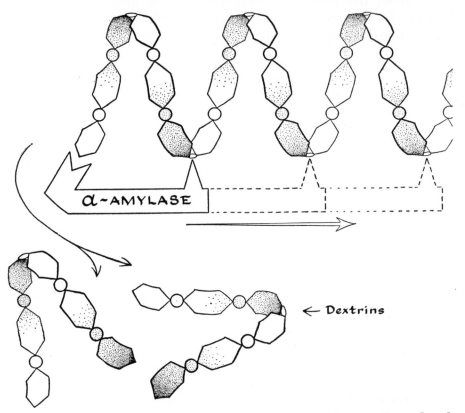

Figure 9-9. *α-Amylase hydrolyzes starch to large polysaccharide fragments or dextrins. Many of the dextrins produced contain six or twelve glucose residues and represent, therefore, one or two complete turns of the starch helix.*

enzyme starch phosphorylase. Starch may, however, be degraded by either of two processes, the phosphorolytic cleavage by starch phosphorylase or the hydrolytic cleavage by the amylases. Amylases are present in particularly high concentration in starchy seeds, where rapid starch utilization is a characteristic feature of the germination process. Starch phosphorylase, on the other hand, is quite probably present in all tissues which synthesize or utilize starch.

Inulin

Certain species of plants do not produce starch as a reserve material but rather accumulate the polysaccharide inulin, of which fructose is the basic repeating unit. A well-known example of a plant containing inulin is the Jerusalem artichoke (*Helianthus tuberosus*), whose tuber

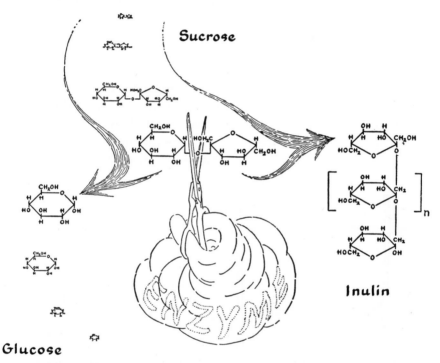

Figure 9-10. *Inulin, a polysaccharide of higher plants, is composed of chains of fructose residues. Judging by analogy with related fructose polysaccharides of bacteria, inulin may be formed from sucrose in the manner depicted above.*

is a rich source of the carbohydrate. Several genera of the Compositae, such as Taraxacum, Parthenium, and Dahlia, also contain inulin as their reserve carbohydrate. In all of these plants, inulin is stored, just as starch is stored, either in the leaves as a photosynthetic product or in reserve organs, such as tubers or fleshy roots.

The inulin molecule consists of polysaccharide chains in which the fructose residues are linked together by oxygen bridges between the number 1 carbon atom of each residue and the number 2 carbon atom of the succeeding residue. The chains thus formed are shorter than those of starch, consisting of roughly 28 hexose residues. The metabolism of inulin has not been investigated as thoroughly as that of starch, and enzymes which deal with inulin synthesis and degradation are not known in the higher plant. Evidence obtained from microorganisms suggests, however, that inulin may be formed from sucrose by a mechanism involving the utilization of the fructose portion of the disaccharide for polysaccharide formation, and liberation of the glucose portion (Fig. 9-10).

The Cell Wall

The walls of plant cells have in common many chemical features, such as the presence of cellulose, pectic substances, and other typical cell wall constituents. The microscopic morphology of the cell wall exhibits, however, a wide diversity of structure in different types of cells. A cross section through the wall separating two typical young

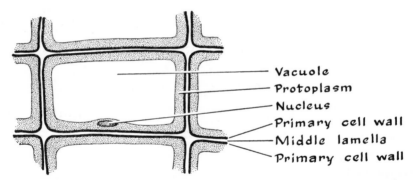

Figure 9-11. *Arrangement of the layers which make up the primary cell wall. The cytoplasm of each cell is bounded by a thin, cellulose-containing primary cell wall layer. Adjacent cells are cemented together by the middle lamella, which is composed primarily of pectic substances.*

parenchymatous cells, such as is shown in Figure 9-11, reveals a central middle lamella flanked on each side by the thin primary wall, which is in contact with the cytoplasm of the cell. The walls of mature wood fibers contain these same cell wall layers, as well as additional layers of the secondary wall, layers which are interposed between the primary wall and the cytoplasm of the cell.

Differentiation of the cell wall into these various layers is related to the physiology of cell growth. The wall of an actively growing cell possesses only middle lamella and primary wall. In some types of cells, no additional cell wall material is formed, and the primary wall is the sole covering of the cell throughout its life. This is true of many parenchymatous cells, as well as of sieve tubes and latex vessels. On the other hand, the cessation of growth in length may be followed by the deposition of new layers of secondary cell wall, particularly in woody cells such as fibers, tracheids, and vessels.

Cellular Growth and Cell Wall Growth

The division of the cell into two daughter cells is accomplished by the formation of a new wall which separates the daughter nuclei produced by mitotic division. The middle lamella is first laid down, appearing during the final phase of nuclear division as local thickenings in the region of the cell plate. The primary walls are then laid down upon the middle lamella. The middle lamella and primary wall differ, however, in their chemical constitution, as we shall see below.

The primary cell wall and the middle lamella have relatively little mechanical strength, and both are actually expanded in area during growth of the cell. As the cell expands during active cell growth, it would become thinner were it not for the fact that new cell wall material is being continuously deposited. This continuous deposition of cell wall material results in the maintenance of an essentially constant thickness during cell expansion. The primary wall is not in itself a barrier to the inward or outward passage of solutes, for water, mineral salts, and even complex organic materials can move freely back and forth across the cell wall through the many pores which are present in the latticelike structure. In addition, the protoplasm of cells in tissues such as the parenchyma of leaves, stems, and roots is continuous from cell to cell by virtue of protoplasmic strands, the plasmodesmata, which pass through pores in the primary wall.

The cells of various tissues may exhibit great differences in morphol·ogy. The cells of the cortex of stem or root grow primarily in a longitudinal direction, as is appropriate for cells of elongated cylindrical organs. Other cells, as for example the nearly spherical cells of the fleshy parenchyma of fruits, grow in all directions, that is, they expand in a spherical fashion. Whether the cell enlarges asymmetrically or symmetrically, its growth is related to the arrangement of the cellulose units in the cell wall.

We shall see that cellulose consists of long chains of linked glucose residues. In cells which elongate primarily in a longitudinal direction, the chains of cellulose run circumferentially in the surface of the cell and surround the cell like barrel hoops in a direction at right angles to the long axis of the cell, as depicted in Figure 9-12. In cells which expand spherically, the cellulose chains are tangential to the surface of the cell but are oriented in a random fashion and run in all directions in the surface of the cell wall. The morphology of cellular growth is,

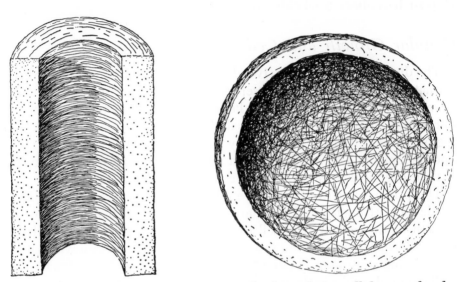

Figure 9-12. *Arrangement of the long-chain cellulose molecules which form the basis of primary cell wall structure in two cell types. Left, transverse orientation of cellulose molecules in primary walls of an elongating cell. Right, random orientation of cellulose molecules in primary walls of a cell which is growing into a more or less spherical shape. (After Frey-Wyssling,* Ber. deut. botan. Ges., **55,** *1937, p. 132.)*

therefore, reflected in the submicroscopic arrangement of cell wall constituents.

After cessation of longitudinal growth, formation of secondary cell wall layers may commence, and in fibers it is common to find, as shown in Figure 9-13, one, two, three, or more layers of cell wall material deposited upon the primary cell wall. These layers are, then, intercalated between the cytoplasm of the cell and the primary cell wall. The secondary cell wall layers, which are laid down after cessation of growth in length, may be very massive, and it is in fact these massive secondary cell wall thickenings which form the bulk of the material in the fibers of commerce, such as cotton, flax, ramie, and hemp. The layers of the secondary cell wall do not necessarily possess chemical composition identical with that of the primary cell wall. For example, lignin, which is a typical constituent of the secondary cell wall, is absent from, or present only in minute amounts in, the primary cell wall, and is formed and laid down by the cell only after cessation of growth in length.

Just as the chemical composition of secondary walls is more varied than that of primary walls, so, also, the submicroscopic arrangement of cellulose in secondary walls presents a diversity not found in the pri-

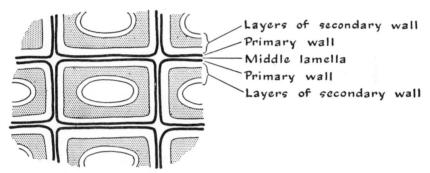

Figure 9-13. *Arrangement of layers in a typical secondary cell wall. The layers of the secondary wall are deposited inside the primary wall after cessation of growth in size. In many instances the secondary wall is composed of three principal layers. (Redrawn by permission after Bailey,* Ind. Eng. Chem., *30, 1938, p. 41.)*

mary wall. Most frequently the cellulose chains of secondary walls are so arranged that they ascend the fiber in long spirals, such as shown in Figure 9-14. These spirals may be so steep as to be nearly parallel to the long axis of the fibers, or they may be so flat as to be nearly at right angles to this axis; many of the possible intermediate situations have also been found and reported. The orientation of cellulose chains in the various layers of a single secondary wall may, in fact, differ greatly. These various dispositions of the cellulose chains are reflected in the tensile strength and other mechanical properties of the fiber. Fibers such as those of ramie, which possess an orientation of cellulose chains nearly parallel to the fiber axis, have high tensile strength but can be stretched very little before breaking occurs. On the other hand, in fibers like those of cotton, in which the chains are principally in spirals

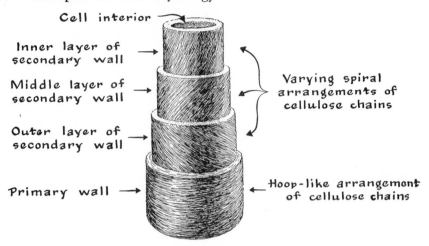

Figure 9-14. *Arrangement of cellulose chains in the successive cell wall layers in a typical fiber cell with a heavy deposition of secondary wall. The outermost layer is the primary wall and possesses transverse orientation. The three inner layers are the outer, middle, and inner layers of the secondary wall. These layers possess various spiral arrangements of their cellulose molecules. (Adapted from Lüdtke, from Frey-Wyssling,* Die Stoffausscheidung der Höheren Pflanzen, *Julius Springer [Berlin], 1935, p. 100.)*

which make a large angle with the fiber axis, tensile strength is lower, but the fiber may be stretched much more without breakage.

Cellulose

The cell walls of the higher plant are typically made up of a mixture of a number of kinds of polysaccharides and polysaccharide derivatives. In the cell walls of woody tissues, nonpolysaccharide material, especially lignin, may also be incorporated into the structure of the wall.

The characteristic component of the cell wall is cellulose, which occurs in nearly pure form in the walls of fibers such as those of cotton, flax, hemp, and ramie—the raw material of textiles. Cellulose is also a major constituent of essentially all the higher plant cell walls which have been investigated. The physical properties of cell walls—their tensile strength, elasticity, and plasticity—depend in large measure on the cellulose which they contain. Through the work of many individuals, notably the organic chemists Haworth and Meyer and the plant physiologists Sponsler and Frey-Wyssling, a rather complete picture not only of the chemical structure of cellulose, but also of its organization in the cell wall, has been achieved, largely in the years since 1920.

Cellulose, as we now know, is made up of long chains of glucose molecules held together by β oxygen linkages between carbon atoms 1 and 4, a type of linkage characteristic of the disaccharide cellobiose. These chains are like those of amylose in that they are unbranched, but,

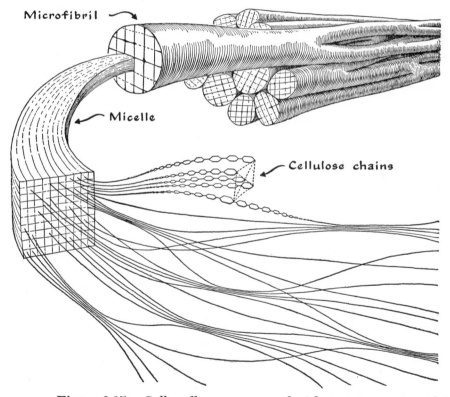

CHEMICAL STRUCTURE OF CELLULOSE.

Figure 9-15. *Cell walls are composed of long interwoven and interconnected strands, the microfibrils, which are large enough to be seen in the electron microscope. The microfibril is in turn composed of smaller units, the micellar strands. Each strand is made up of many long-chain cellulose molecules.*

unlike amylose, they are not coiled; on the contrary, they occur in the cell wall in an extended form, each chain containing 1000 or more glucose residues. The glucose chains of cellulose are, in turn, packed neatly together into crystalline bundles or micelles, each micelle being about 120 glucose residues long. Each chain participates in the formation of several such crystalline micelles, the chains fraying out into noncrystalline regions and reuniting with other chains to form new crystalline regions. In this way, the submicroscopic crystalline units of the cell wall are bound together by noncrystalline cellulose. The micellar units of the cell wall are further organized into larger units, the microfibrils, each of which may contain many micellar bundles of cellulose chains. The organization of the cellulose of the cell wall into micelles and microfibrils is illustrated in Figure 9-15. The micelles of cellulose in the cell wall are separated by relatively small spaces of noncrystalline cellulose or of actual pores. The larger microfibrils are separated by much larger spaces. It is in these spaces that much of the noncellulosic material of the cell wall is deposited.

Noncellulosic Cell Wall Components

Cell walls commonly contain a variety of polysaccharides in addition to cellulose, including derivatives of the hexose sugars mannose and galactose, as well as derivatives of the pentose sugars xylose and arabinose. The mannose-containing polysaccharides, or mannans, are usual constituents of the cell walls of hardwoods, and resemble cellulose in general structure. Galactans, made up of chains of linked galactopyranose residues, may be either branched, as in the wood galactans, or unbranched, as in galactan of the cell walls of the lupine seed.

The pentose-containing polysaccharides, xylans and arabans, also made up of chains of sugar residues, are general constituents of woody cell walls and are particularly characteristic of wood and of the straws of cereals.

The hemicelluloses, still another group of cell wall constituents, are found in all woody tissues and make up a large fraction of the total cell wall material of cereal straws, pasture grass leaves, oat hulls, corn cobs, and wood. The hemicelluloses, unlike the polysaccharides proper, contain both a sugar component, xylose or arabinose, and a nonsugar component, glucuronic or galacturonic acid. The latter materials belong to the group of uronic acids, substances which may be thought of as having been derived from hexose sugars by oxidation of the terminal (sixth) carbon atom to the acidic carboxyl group. The

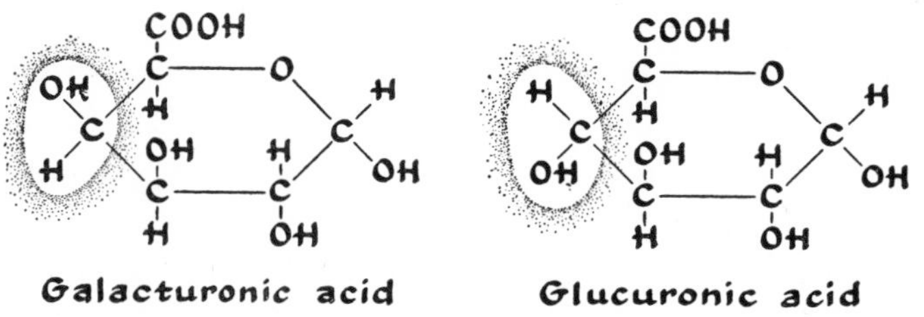

Galacturonic acid   Glucuronic acid

GALACTURONIC AND GLUCURONIC ACIDS. THE DIFFERENCE BETWEEN THESE TWO MOLECULES RESIDES IN THE CONFIGURATION OF THE NUMBER 4 CARBON ATOM, ENCIRCLED IN THE DIAGRAM.

structures of the polyuronide hemicelluloses are still unknown, but they are quite possibly complex and undoubtedly involve extensive branching.

Pectic Substances

Still another group of cell wall material is constituted by the pectic substances, derivatives of pectic acid, which in turn is made up of long chains of linked galacturonic acid residues. The galacturonic acid residues all possess the 6-membered pyranose ring structure, and the basic chain structure of the pectic substances is therefore that shown below.

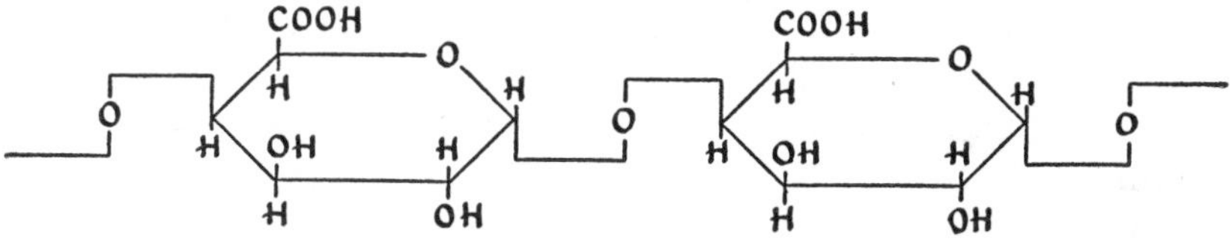

CHAIN STRUCTURE OF PECTIC ACID.

In pectic acid the carboxyl groups are free and hence able to combine with available cations such as calcium, in which case the insoluble calcium pectate is precipitated. In pectin and protopectin, which are both derivatives of pectic acid, the carboxyl groups are masked and are, in fact, esterified with methyl alcohol. Thus the chain structure of pectin and protopectin is as shown below.

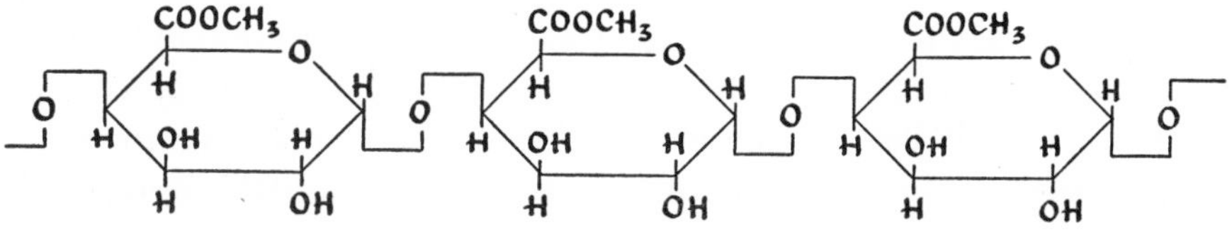

STRUCTURE OF PECTIN AND PROTOPECTIN SHOWING LINKAGE OF GALACTURONIC ACID RESIDUES INTO LONG CHAINS AS WELL AS ESTERIFICATION OF CARBOXYL GROUPS BY METHYL ALCOHOL.

In the living plant, protopectin is almost exclusively confined to the cell wall. Pectin, however, is found dissolved in the plant juices and is presumably present in the protoplasm of the cell. Pectic acid, in the form of its salts, calcium and magnesium pectate, appears to make up much of the middle lamella of the cell wall and is hence responsible for the adhesion of adjacent cells. When the pectate of the middle lamella is removed, for example through precipitation of its calcium with oxalate or by hydrolysis with the appropriate enzyme, pectinase, the cells of the tissue concerned tend to separate from one another.

The interconversions of pectic materials in the cell wall are of particular importance in the process of maturation and senescence of fruit. In the apple, protopectin of the primary cell wall and pectates of the middle lamella are accumulated during the growth of the fruit. Little soluble pectin is present in the immature fruit. The process of maturation, by which the fruit softens and attains edible maturity, is accompanied by the conversion of protopectin to soluble pectin and particularly by the loss of pectate from the middle lamella. It is this latter process which is, in a large measure, responsible for the actual softening of the fruit. As dissolution of protopectin and pectates continues, the fruit becomes oversoft and senescent.

Pectin holds a modest but gratifying interest for man in its role as the solidifying agent for fruit jams and jellies. When small amounts of pectin are dissolved in solutions of concentrated sugar at an acid pH, the whole sets to a rigid gel. This property of pectin forms the basis of the jam and jelly art. In the past the maker of jam or jelly has relied on the soluble pectin content of the mature (but neither underripe nor overmature) fruit. The natural acidity of the fruit suffices also in many instances to achieve an appropriate pH, and the making of jelly then depends primarily on the addition of sufficient sugar. Today, purified pectin prepared from citrus or apple fruits is available to insure against failures caused by the use of excessively green or ripe fruit.

Lignin

Mature woody cell walls are characterized by their content of lignin, which may make up from a few per cent to half or more of the total weight of the cell wall. Lignin is deposited in the submicroscopic spaces between the units of cellulose and of the other cell wall constituents. Unlike the other wall constituents, lignin is not chemically a carbohydrate or carbohydrate derivative and its chemical structure is, in fact, not clearly understood at the present time. This is because lignin cannot be removed from the cell wall except by very drastic treatment which degrades the material and alters its chemical nature. Lignin is one of the most resistant of plant products as far as both chemical attack and attack by microorganisms are concerned. Thus, when woody material is incorporated into the soil and subjected to decomposition by the soil bacteria, the lignin remains long after the other cell wall components have been decomposed. Lignin or ligninlike substances are, therefore, important components of the soil organic matter. Lignin is, however, dissolved by sodium bisulfite, which converts it to water-soluble sulfite-containing derivatives. This process is one of those used in the removal of lignin from wood in the manufacture of paper pulp, where its presence causes paper to yellow rapidly.

Summary

The sugars or carbohydrates play a principal role in both the metabolism and structure of plants. Certain sugars, particularly sucrose, are formed as the direct products of photosynthesis. This sucrose may be translocated from the leaves to other organs, either to the growing regions of the plant, where it may be used directly as the substrate for growth and respiration, or to depots where it is stored for future use.

Although many plants store carbohydrate in the form of sucrose, still a greater number deposit their reserve carbohydrate in the form of larger, more complex, and more insoluble molecules, the polysaccharides. Starch, in particular, serves as the reserve carbohydrate of a great number of plant species and is formed in such organs as leaf, stem, tuber, or seed, where it is deposited during conditions favorable to photosynthesis.

Through a wide variety of transformations, sugars and their phosphorylated derivatives yield directly or indirectly the other multitudinous chemical constituents of the plant. In particular, the cellulose and other cell wall constituents are polysaccharides or closely related materials. In contrast to starch and the other reserve sugars, the polysaccharides of the cell wall, once laid down, are generally lost to metabolism and cannot be drawn upon by the plant.

The cell wall of the higher plant is typically composed of a particular array of materials, including: (1) cellulose; (2) noncellulosic polysaccharides, such as mannans, galactans, xylans, and arabans; (3) the polyuronide hemicelluloses; (4) the pectic substances, protopectin and salts of pectic acids; and (5) lignin.

In the primary cell wall of young growing cells, lignin is ordinarily absent. In the secondary layers of the heavily thickened cell walls of mature cells, not only lignin but other materials may be present. By and large, however, it is the polysaccharides and related substances which are characteristic of cell wall composition.

QUESTIONS

1. A nonphotosynthetic plant tissue is fed glucose and converts it to sucrose. Write a sequence of reactions showing the probable intermediate steps involved in this synthesis.

2. What characteristics distinguish the carbohydrates as a group from other substances?

3. Distinguish between: (a) monosaccharide and disaccharide, (b) reducing and nonreducing sugars, (c) pentose and hexose, (d) glucose and fructose, (e) D- and L-glucose, (f) pyranose and furanose sugars.

4. What is known about the synthesis and degradation in plants of (a) sucrose, (b) starch?

5. On the basis of chemical structure, explain why cellulose occurs as long fibers, whereas starch occurs as rounded grains.

6. How do the amylases differ from starch phosphorylase in their action?

7. How can one account for the fact that some plants store sucrose, while others may store starch? Starting with sucrose, how could one produce starch *in vitro*?

8. Mannose and galactose are found in plants only in the form of derivatives or highly polymerized mannans and galactans. What might this indicate about the possible pathway of biosynthesis of these compounds?

9. What changes in the cell wall occur during fruit ripening?

10. How can one chemically separate lignin from cellulose? Starch from lignin? Cellulose from pectin?

GENERAL READING

Bonner, J., *Plant Biochemistry*. New York: Academic Press, 1950. A detailed discussion of the state of our knowledge concerning the chemical processes in plants. This will be found a useful reference for Chapters 9–13.

Frey-Wyssling, A., "Physiology of Cell Wall Growth." *Ann. Rev. Plant Physiol.*, 1: 169, 1950. A good, modern treatment of primary cell wall structure and growth.

Hassid, W. Z., and Putman, E. W., "Transformation of Sugars in Plants." *Ann. Rev. Plant Physiol.*, 1: 109, 1950. A brief review of modern work on the synthesis of sucrose, starch, and related substances.

Onslow, M. W., *The Principles of Plant Biochemistry*. Cambridge: Cambridge University Press, 1931. Chapters I and II have much interesting information on the chemistry and physiology of plant carbohydrates.

Pigman, W. W., and Goepp, R. M., Jr., *Chemistry of the Carbohydrates*. New York: Academic Press, 1948. A mine of information on all aspects of the carbohydrates but useful particularly as a reference work.

CHAPTER 10

Respiration and the Mechanism of Biological Oxidations

Rationale of Respiration

In the process of respiration, sugars or sugar derivatives are oxidized to carbon dioxide and water by the living cell. The over-all reaction for the oxidation of glucose or other hexose sugars in respiration can be written as follows:

$$C_6H_{12}O_6 + 6\,O_2 \longrightarrow 6\,CO_2 + 6\,H_2O$$

OXIDATION OF HEXOSE TO CO_2 AND H_2O.

In this reaction six molecules of oxygen are taken up and six molecules each of CO_2 and H_2O are formed for each molecule of sugar burned. A great deal of energy is liberated in this oxidative process. This is in agreement with our common experience, since we know that sugar may be burned to CO_2 and H_2O with the evolution of heat by merely warming the material in air to a critical combustion temperature. In the living organism, however, combustion of sugar at the relatively low temperatures typical of biological systems is made possible by the interaction of a series of enzymes which catalyze the process.

In the biological oxidations of respiration the liberated energy appears in part as heat, but a further part is conserved through storing and transporting processes. It is this latter source which the cell taps to carry on its many energy-consuming processes. With energy derived from respiration the plant cell is able to do chemical work in synthesizing energy-rich materials such as fat and hydrocarbons, osmotic work in the uptake and accumulation of salts, and mechanical work such as is involved in growth. The photosynthetically formed sugars represent, then, stored energy. This stored energy is made available through the process of respiration.

Production of Heat in Respiration

The transfer of energy from the energy-producing reactions of respiration to the energy-using reactions of the cell is not completely efficient, and a portion of it inevitably appears as heat, as shown in Figure 10-1. In fact, under some conditions, a very large part of the total res-

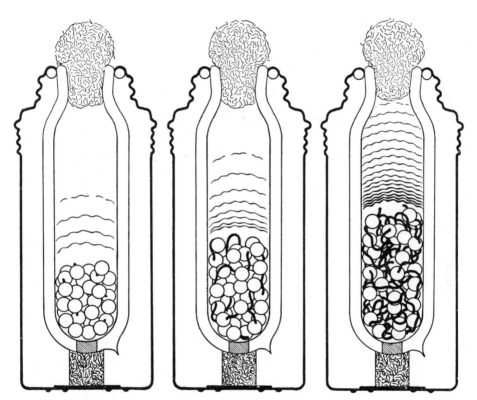

Figure 10-1. *Respiration is an energy-producing process, and this energy is in part liberated as heat.*

piratory energy may be liberated as heat. The production of heat during respiration is simply demonstrated by seeds which are allowed to germinate in a closed container such as a thermos bottle. Over a period of a few hours the temperature in the thermos bottle will rise as much as several degrees. The same experiment may be done more quantitatively by noting the heat loss from respiring tissue in a calorimeter, an instrument for measuring heat exchange. If the amount of oxygen consumed and the amount of CO_2 liberated by the plant material are simultaneously determined, we may calculate the total substrate burned and compare the amount of energy liberated by respiration with the amount of heat which actually appears. Experimentally this has shown that even in rapidly growing seedlings a large portion of the total energy liberated in respiration immediately appears as heat, while only the relatively small remainder is used in chemical, osmotic, mechanical, or other forms of work.

The Respiratory Quotient

We have seen above that when sugars are burned in respiration, one molecule of CO_2 is evolved for each molecule of O_2 taken up during the process. The ratio of CO_2 evolved to O_2 consumed, $\dfrac{CO_2}{O_2}$, is known as the *respiratory quotient*, or *R.Q.*, of the process. The R.Q. during combustion of sugar is therefore 1. The R.Q.'s of respiring plant tissues are often found experimentally to approach unity very closely. In other cases, however, the R.Q. may deviate from 1 considerably. This is in part because materials other than sugars may be consumed in respiration. Fats may be burned, especially in the germination of seeds which contain fat as a reserve material. Fats are poorer in oxygen and richer in hydrogen than the sugars, and correspondingly more oxygen is needed for the combustion of fat to CO_2 and H_2O. This is shown below for the combustion of a fatty acid, stearic acid, to CO_2 and H_2O.

$$C_{18}H_{36}O_2 + 26\,O_2 \longrightarrow 18\,CO_2 + 18\,H_2O \qquad R.\,Q. = 0.7$$

OXIDATION OF A FATTY ACID (STEARIC ACID) TO CO_2 AND H_2O.

The R.Q. of this reaction is approximately 0.7, and, in general, the R.Q.'s for the respiration of fats are less than 1. The R.Q. for the respiration of substances richer in oxygen than sugar is greater than 1. The R.Q. for the complete respiration of malic acid, a common plant constituent and respiratory substrate, is 1.33, as shown below.

$$C_4H_6O_5 + 3\,O_2 \longrightarrow 4\,CO_2 + 3\,H_2O \qquad R.Q. \approx 1.33$$

OXIDATION OF MALIC ACID TO CO_2 AND H_2O.

The concept of the respiratory quotient is important because it tells us something about the nature of the compounds which serve in a particular plant or plant tissue as the substrate for respiration. Sugars are by no means the only substrate for this process; fats, organic acids, and other materials may all contribute to respiration. In many cases, also, it is probable that respiration may represent the simultaneous utilization of a mixture of several different substances, so that the measured R.Q. represents an average or over-all gas exchange for the combustion of the entire complex of materials.

Measurement of Gas Exchange

The measurement of respiratory gas exchange may be made in any of several different ways, and new methods are still being devised. Perhaps the simplest and most straightforward measurement makes use of direct methods of gas analysis. Suppose we place a plant or plant part in a closed container in an atmosphere of known volume and composition, such as air (Fig. 10-2). Let us now permit respiration to proceed for a measured time. A portion of the O_2 will have been used up, and in its stead CO_2 will have appeared. By a suitable device (gas pipette) we may remove the gas, or a sample of known size, from the closed chamber, transfer it to a gas-analysis apparatus, and determine directly the concentrations of O_2 and CO_2. In such an apparatus the volume of the whole sample is first determined in a gas burette at measured temperature and pressure. The gas is then passed into a chamber containing a concentrated alkali, for example KOH. In this chamber, CO_2 is removed by reaction with the alkali to form carbonate. The gas may now be passed back into the gas burette, measured again, and its original CO_2 content estimated from the decrease in volume of the gas. Then the gas may be passed into a chamber containing an oxygen absorbent, such as alkaline pyrogallol. From the decrease in volume after this absorption, the content of O_2 in the sample can also be determined. We can now calculate (1) the O_2 consumed by the tissue (initial O_2 content of chamber minus final O_2 content), and (2) the CO_2 evolved by the tissue. This method, while direct, is cumbersome and has largely given way to more rapid methods.

Most measurements of gas exchange in respiration are now made by manometric methods (Fig. 10-3). In these methods the tissue is allowed to respire in a closed vessel, and the pressure changes within the vessel are measured by sensitive manometers, in which the rise or fall of a liquid level in a capillary indicates, respectively, decrease or increase of pressure. A decrease of pressure within the vessel is of course due to the uptake of O_2 by the tissue. This decrease is, however,

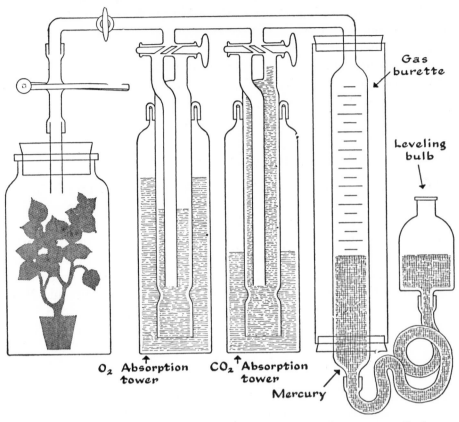

Gas
burette

Leveling
bulb

O_2 Absorption
tower

CO_2 Absorption
tower

Mercury

Figure 10-2. *A schematic representation of the way in which respiration may be followed by gas analysis. Left, a plant is allowed
to respire in a closed container filled with air. After respiration has
proceeded for a measured length of time, a sample of gas may be
sucked into the gas burette at the right. First, the volume of the gas
is measured. The gas is then driven into one of the central towers,
where the CO_2 is removed by alkali. The gas is now returned to the
gas burette and the volume again measured. Oxygen is removed by
returning the gas to the second tower, which contains alkaline pyrogallol. From the changes in volume after CO_2 and O_2 removal, the
proportion of each in the gas about the respiring plant can be determined.*

offset by the CO_2 given off, which tends to increase pressure. To cir-
cumvent this difficulty it is a frequent practice to measure the respiration of identical samples of tissue simultaneously in two vessels. In the
first vessel a small open chamber or well, containing concentrated KOH,

is provided. This removes all CO_2 as it is liberated, keeps CO_2 pressure at a constant low level, and permits the measurement of pressure changes caused by O_2 consumption alone. In the second vessel, no KOH is provided, and the difference between O_2 uptake and CO_2 evolution may be determined. These two values permit calculation of both

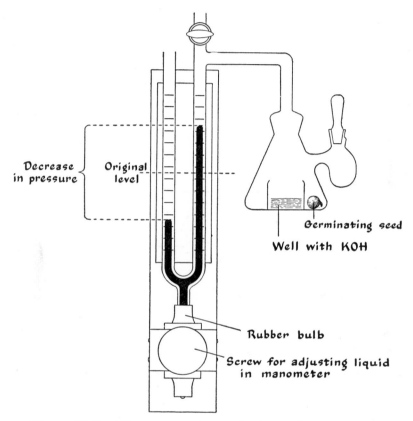

Decrease in pressure

Original level

Germinating seed

Well with KOH

Rubber bulb

Screw for adjusting liquid in manometer

Figure 10-3. *The manometric methods for the study of respiration depend on measuring the changes in gas pressure which occur when an object is allowed to respire in a closed container. Right, vessel to accommodate tissue. At left, manometer for determination of pressure changes caused by O_2 uptake and CO_2 evolution.*

O_2 uptake and CO_2 evolution. Since the apparatus needed for this manometric type of gas-exchange determination is relatively simple, it is possible for the experimenter to have several pairs of units and to make comparisons of respiration under various circumstances in a single experiment.

In much of the earlier work on plant respiration, O_2 uptake was not measured at all, and attention was confined to the determination of CO_2 evolved. This is most commonly done by passing a stream of CO_2-free air over the respiring plant or tissue (Fig. 10-4). CO_2 is given off to the gas stream by the respiring tissue. The effluent gas stream is next conducted into, and allowed to bubble up through, a tower filled with

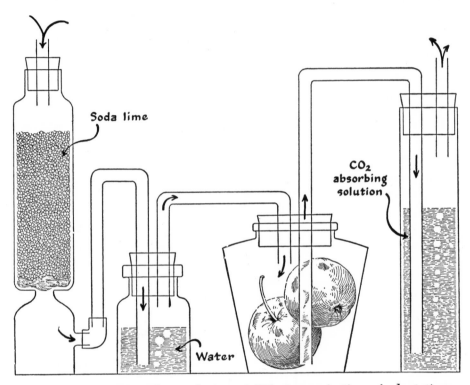

Soda lime

CO_2 absorbing solution

Water

Figure 10-4. *The evolution of CO_2 in respiration of plant tissues can be followed by an arrangement in which a stream of air, freed of CO_2 by the soda-lime tower and humidified by passage through water, is passed over the tissue and through a tower containing a known quantity of alkali. By titration of the residual alkali the amount of CO_2 evolved by the tissue can be determined.*

CO_2-absorbing solution. This solution may be simply dilute KOH, which is partly used in fixation of the CO_2 as K_2CO_3. The residual KOH may be determined by titration. If $Ba(OH)_2$ is used as the reagent, the $BaCO_3$ which is precipitated may be filtered off and weighed. Because of its adaptability to large vessels, the flowing gas-stream technique is still widely used in experiments on entire plants. It should be noted, however, that this method does not permit ready determination of oxygen consumption, so that information concerning the respiratory quotient is not obtained.

Many different methods have been used in the past to express the respiratory rate of gas exchange of tissues. Some workers have expressed amounts of gas as volumes, others as weights. There is now quite general agreement that the amount of gas be expressed as cubic millimeters (mm^3) measured at standard conditions of $0°$ C and 1 atm pressure. Very commonly, rates are given in cubic millimeters of gas consumed or evolved per unit weight of tissue per hour.

Respiratory Rates of Tissues and Organs

The various organs of a higher plant differ in their rates of respiration, as shown in the data of Table 10-1. In general, leaves show a higher level of respiratory activity than roots, stems, or fruits, and the leaves contribute very largely to the gas exchange of the plant as a

Table 10-1. *Respiration Rates of Various Tissues and Organs.*

PLANT	ORGAN	RATES OF OXYGEN UPTAKE MM³/GM FRESH WT/HR
Carrot	Root	25
	Mature leaf	440
Fraxinus nigra	Stem:	
(ash tree)	Phloem	154
	Cambium	233
	Sapwood	47
	Heartwood	15
Spinach	Leaf	515
Apple	Flesh	30
	Skin	95
Barley	Seed, soaked 15 hr:	
	Embryo	715
	Endosperm	76

whole. The various tissues of a given organ also show great differences in respiratory rate, as shown in Table 10-2 for the woody stem of Fraxinus, the ash tree. The cambium shows greater respiratory rate than either the phloem or the tissues of wood when compared on a total fresh weight basis. This is in part because of the increasing dilution of the older woody tissues with inert cell wall material. If the comparison is made on the basis of gas exchange per unit of nitrogen, these differences are very much less. Rate of respiration per unit of actual proto-plasm is, therefore, much more nearly a constant than is respiration per unit of total weight.

Although the total respiration carried on by a plant or plant part

Table 10-2. *Rate of Respiratory Gas Exchange in Various Tissues of the Stem of Fraxinus. (After Goodwin and Goddard, Am. J. Botany, 27, 1940, p. 235.)*

| TISSUE OF STEM | RATE OF RESPIRATORY GAS EXCHANGE | |
	MM^3 O_2/GM FRESH WT/HR	MM^3 O_2/MG N/HR
Phloem	167	112
Cambium	220	120
Outer sapwood	78	130
Inner sapwood	31	76
Heartwood	15	38

increases as the plant grows, the rate of respiration per unit weight decreases continuously. This is brought out for the sunflower in Figure 10-5. The increase of weight with age is due, in large measure, to the accumulation of inert nonrespiratory materials. Thus, if the respiratory rate is based on the amount of actual protein or even nitrogen in the tissue, it is constant or may increase somewhat with age. This probably signifies that total respiration per cell remains constant with age, or even increases as a result of the production of additional respiratory enzyme protein.

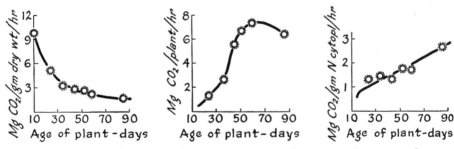

Figure 10-5. *Rate of respiration as a function of age, as demonstrated by the sunflower. Left, respiration rate per unit of dry weight decreases with increasing age of plant. Center, respiration rate per whole plant rises to a maximum and then falls off again. Right, respiration rate per unit of plant nitrogen increases steadily with age. (Data from Kidd, West, and Briggs, Proc. Roy. Soc. B., 92, 1921, pp. 368, 384.)*

Factors Which Influence Rate of Respiration

The factors which affect the respiratory rate of gas exchange may be roughly divided into (1) external or environmental factors and (2) internal factors, which depend on the genetic makeup of the plant.

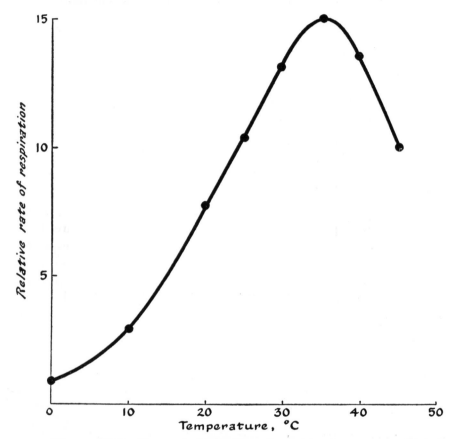

Figure 10-6. *Rate of respiration of germinating pea seedlings as affected by temperature. (Calculated from data of Fernandes, Rec. trav. botan. néerland., 20, 1923, p. 188.)*

Temperature is one important environmental factor affecting respiration. Respiration is generally very slow at temperatures close to 0° C; it increases gradually with rising temperature, and reaches a maximum rate in the region of 30° to 40° C (Fig. 10-6). Like many biological processes which depend on complex chemical reactions, respiratory rate increases some two- to fourfold for each 10° C rise in temperature over this range. At temperatures beyond this optimum, the respiratory rate again decreases because of the destructive effects of higher temperatures on the enzymatic systems of the cell.

A second important environmental factor is the partial pressure of oxygen which prevails in the atmosphere surrounding the respiring tissue. In general, respiration is decreased by oxygen pressures smaller than that of air (0.2 atm) and drops off very sharply at oxygen pressures of less than 0.05–0.1 atm (Fig. 10-7). The relation of oxygen

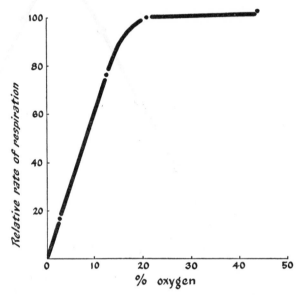

Figure 10-7. *Oxygen tension may limit the rate of respiration if it falls below the 20 per cent present in normal air. For the experiment above, O₂ pressure was varied by mixing oxygen and nitrogen in different proportions. (After Steward, Berry, and Broyer, Ann. Botany, 50, 1936, p. 354.)*

pressure to respiration has a particularly important implication in the growth of roots. Roots must respire vigorously if they are to grow and take up minerals from the soil. This vigorous root respiration is dependent on high oxygen pressures in the space surrounding the roots. When roots are poorly aerated, as in waterlogged or heavy soils, growth of the plant may be restricted.

Many environmental factors affect the rate of plant respiration indirectly through effects on the amount of respiratory enzymes or substrate present in the tissue. Nitrogen-deficient plants exhibit reduced respiratory rates. Since such plants contain much respirable carbohydrate, it is possible that the nitrogen deficiency may result in a decrease in the amount of respiratory enzyme system present in the plant. Similarly, plants grown in low light intensity for long periods of time may exhibit low rates of respiration simply because of a lack of respirable materials.

Metabolic Pathway of Respiration

We have seen that respiration results in the biological oxidation of certain materials, particularly the sugars. This oxidation results in the disappearance of sugar, the uptake of O_2, and the production of CO_2 and water. The conversion of sugar and O_2 into CO_2 and water does not take place in one gigantic step, but rather through a long series of carefully integrated reactions. In this process, the sugar is converted to smaller and smaller fragments, and a great number of individual oxidations contribute to the observed over-all reaction of respiration. These many steps in the respiratory process have been worked out in great detail, particularly in the past twenty years, and the accumulation of this body of knowledge constitutes one of the most spectacular developments in modern biology. It appears also that the respiratory processes of higher plants, animals, and microorganisms are probably basically quite similar. Although we know less about the respiration of higher plants than about that of animal tissues or microorganisms, the many points of similarity have given us a good general picture of the process as it occurs in the plant world.

In the process of respiration, hexose is first converted to the phosphorylated sugar fructose diphosphate (Chap. 9). This 6-carbon material is then cleaved into two fragments, each containing three carbon atoms, and the two fragments are metabolized through a series of steps to the 3-carbon compound pyruvic acid. The production of pyruvic acid from hexose constitutes the initial phase of respiration, a phase known as *glycolysis*. The initial or glycolytic phase can take place anaerobically, in the absence of oxygen. The pathway involved is common to fermentation (anaerobic breakdown of sugar) and to respiration (aerobic breakdown of sugar). The terminal phase of respiration is the conversion of pyruvic acid to carbon dioxide and water. This phase is strictly aerobic and does not, of course, take place in fermentation. The first step in the final destruction of pyruvic acid is the conversion of this 3-carbon compound to a 2-carbon derivative. The 2-carbon derivative is next fed into a metabolic cycle in which it is combined

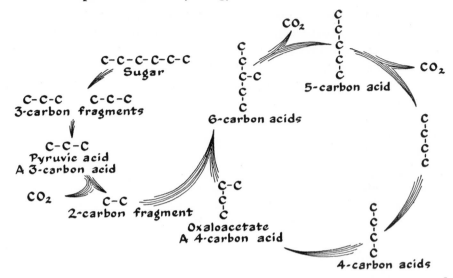

Figure 10-8. *The pathway of carbon atoms in respiration. The 6-carbon sugars are converted to the 3-carbon pyruvic acid and hence to a 2-carbon compound. These 2-carbon fragments combine with a 4-carbon acceptor to form a 6-carbon molecule, which is then degraded stepwise with the evolution of CO_2 to reform the 4-carbon acceptor.*

with a 4-carbon acceptor molecule and degraded through a series of steps by which the 4-carbon acceptor molecule is reformed (Fig. 10-8).

Conversion of Hexose to Pyruvate

In the first, or anaerobic, phase of respiration, sugar is converted to pyruvic acid. This most important series of reactions involves the phosphorylated sugars, rather than the sugars themselves. The phosphorylated sugar glucose-6-phosphate is formed from glucose in the simultaneous presence of the enzyme hexokinase and the complex substance adenosine triphosphate (ATP). (Fig. 10-9). ATP acts in this reaction as the donor of a special type of phosphate group, symbolized as ~Ph. The phosphate group is bodily transferred to glucose, the ATP being simultaneously converted to adenosine diphosphate (ADP). For the reaction to continue indefinitely it is essential that ADP be reconverted to ATP. (This reaction does indeed take place at later stages in respiration, as we shall see later in this chapter.) The glucose-6-phosphate is readily interconverted to glucose-1-phosphate, and, indeed, glucose-6-phosphate may be formed in the plant from the glucose-1-

phosphate which arises through the phosphorolytic degradation of starch or sucrose (Chap. 9). In the presence of the enzyme phospho-hexoisomerase, glucose-6-phosphate is transformed to fructose-6-phosphate, and this substance is again phosphorylated by a second molecule of ATP to fructose-1,6-diphosphate. As we have seen in Chapter 9, these four phosphorylated hexoses are common to plant materials.

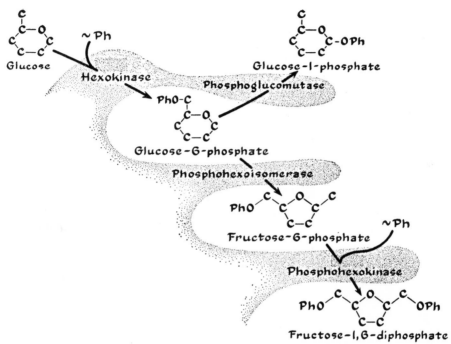

Figure 10-9. *The initial steps of respiration involve the conversion of sugar to fructose diphosphate. The hexose sugar glucose receives a phosphate group from adenosine triphosphate in the presence of the enzyme hexokinase. The glucose-6-phosphate thus formed is converted to fructose-6-phosphate and thence to fructose-1,6-diphosphate in the presence of other specific enzymes and an additional molecule of phosphate. These reactions are all reversible.*

At the stage of fructose diphosphate the first actual cleavage of sugar to smaller molecules takes place. In the presence of the enzyme aldolase, fructose-1,6-diphosphate is split in the center to yield two 3-carbon-atom fragments, glyceraldehyde-3-phosphate and dihydroxyacetone phosphate. Dihydroxyacetone phosphate does not itself participate further in respiration but is converted to glyceraldehyde-3-phosphate through the action of the enzyme isomerase (Fig. 10-10).

The next reaction in this series is the conversion of glyceraldehyde-3-phosphate to 3-phosphoglyceric acid. This is actually an energy-releasing oxidation, in which the aldehyde group of glyceraldehyde is converted to the acidic carboxyl group of glyceric acid, and in which an enzyme specific for the reaction, phosphoglyceraldehyde dehydrogenase, participates. This reaction entails the uptake of inorganic phos-

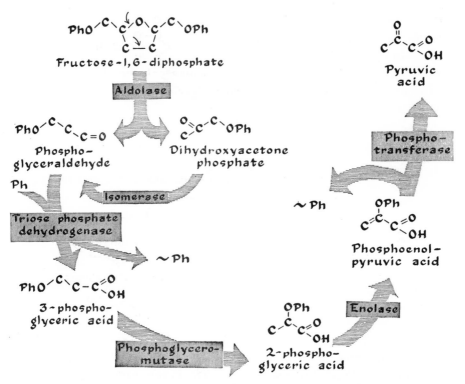

Figure 10-10. *With the production of pyruvic acid from fructose diphosphate the initial phase of respiration is completed. Each fructose diphosphate molecule yields two molecules of pyruvic acid as the result of the series of reactions shown above. At least six different enzymes are involved in the several steps of the process.*

phate, which forms ATP from ADP with the aid of energy liberated in the oxidation. The mechanism of this reaction will be discussed later in this chapter under "Phosphorylative Coupling."

Next, the 3-phosphoglyceric acid is converted to 2-phosphoglyceric acid, a simple shift in position of the phosphate group which takes place in the presence of the enzyme phosphoglyceromutase. The 2-phosphoglyceric acid, in turn, loses a molecule of water in the presence of the enzyme enolase to become phosphoenolpyruvic acid. This compound now loses its phosphate to become pyruvic acid. The loss of phosphate from phosphopyruvic acid occurs, however, in the presence of a specific enzyme and of ADP, the phosphate group of phosphopyruvic acid serving to reconstitute ATP from ADP.

The formation of pyruvic acid completes the initial, or anaerobic, phase of respiration. Each molecule of hexose which passes through the system yields, of course, two molecules of pyruvic acid. Each molecule of hexose used requires two molecules of ATP for the formation of fructose-1,6-diphosphate. We have seen, however, that the production of each molecule of pyruvic acid results in the formation of two molecules of ATP, so that four molecules of ATP are produced per hexose utilized. Thus a surplus of two ATP molecules remains for other cellular uses.

Fermentation

Many lower organisms as well as many tissues of higher organisms have the ability to degrade sugars and other substrates in the absence of oxygen. The energy liberated in such anaerobic respiration, or *fer-*

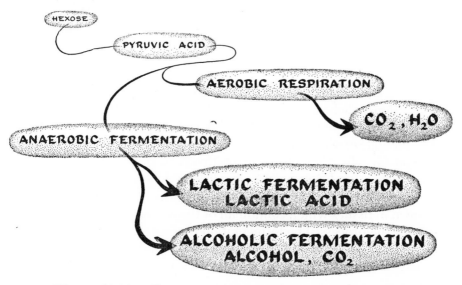

Figure 10-11. *The processes of aerobic respiration and fermentation are both dependent on the initial production of pyruvic acid formed from hexose. In fermentation, which occurs only if oxygen is not available to the tissue or organism, pyruvic acid is reduced directly to lactic acid or indirectly to other reduced products such as alcohol.*

mentation, can serve to support the growth of certain organisms. The fermentative degradations of sugars are, however, much less efficient, from the standpoint of energy yield per unit of sugar consumed, than is aerobic respiration proper. In fermentations the pyruvic acid produced in the initial phase of carbohydrate breakdown is reduced rather than oxidized. In the simplest case, that of lactic acid fermentation, pyruvic acid is reduced to lactic acid (Fig. 10-11). We have seen earlier that during the initial breakdown of carbohydrate, phosphoglyceraldehyde is oxidized to phosphoglyceric acid. In lactic acid fermentation the reduction of pyruvic acid to lactic acid is achieved by the simultaneous oxidation of phosphoglyceraldehyde to phosphoglyceric acid. Lactic acid fermentation, while common among microorganisms such as the milk-souring lactic acid bacteria, is not usual in higher plant tissues. Many higher plant tissues do, however, possess the ability to carry out alcoholic fermentation, which is similar to yeast fermentation. In alcoholic fermentation, pyruvic acid first loses a molecule of CO_2 to become acetaldehyde. This reaction, a decarboxylation, is catalyzed by

$$CH_3\overset{O}{\underset{}{C}}-\overset{O}{\underset{OH}{C}} \xrightarrow{\text{Carboxylase}} CH_3\overset{O}{\underset{H}{C}} + CO_2$$

Pyruvic acid   Acetaldehyde

DECARBOXYLATION OF PYRUVIC ACID TO ACETALDEHYDE AND CO_2.

the enzyme carboxylase. Acetaldehyde is next reduced to ethyl alcohol. This reaction is achieved by the simultaneous oxidation of phosphoglyceraldehyde to phosphoglyceric acid, so that here again, as in lactic acid fermentation, there is no net oxidation or uptake of oxygen in the process as a whole. Alcoholic fermentation is carried on by many plants or plant tissues under anaerobic conditions, where respiration is suspended. In the presence of O_2, however, fermentation does not take place even in tissues which contain all of the requisite enzymatic mechanisms for the process. The fermentation process is actually suppressed in the presence of oxygen and is carried out by higher plant tissues only when external conditions make respiration impossible.

Respiration as an Oxidative Process

We have already seen that the biological oxidations of respiration take place primarily in connection with the oxidation of pyruvic acid. We now know a great deal about the actual chemical mechanisms by which these biological oxidations of respiration occur. Before we discuss the reactions of the living organism, a clear understanding of the nature of oxidative processes is necessary.

In the simplest form of oxidation, a compound actually takes up oxygen and becomes a new compound richer in oxygen than the original. This type of oxidation is illustrated by the oxidation of carbon monoxide to carbon dioxide in the presence of oxygen. Actual addition

$$CO + \tfrac{1}{2}O_2 \longrightarrow CO_2$$

OXIDATION OF CARBON MONOXIDE TO CO_2 BY OXYGEN.

(1)

of oxygen to the substrate is not, however, an essential feature of oxidation. In the oxidation of hydroquinone, hydrogen atoms are removed from the substrate to yield the oxidation product benzoquinone. The

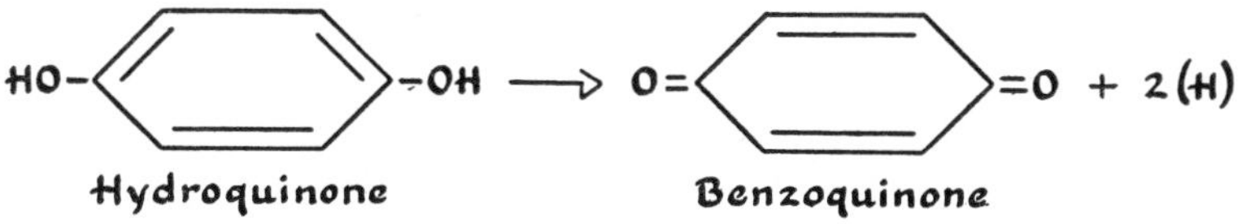

OXIDATION OF HYDROQUINONE TO BENZOQUINONE BY REMOVAL OF HYDROGEN ATOMS.

(2)

hydrogen atoms which are removed from the substrate, represented by 2(H) in Equation 2, must necessarily be taken up by some other material, an acceptor or oxidant, which is then itself reduced. Oxygen could, for example, be the oxidant, in which case the oxidation of hydroquinone would be written as follows:

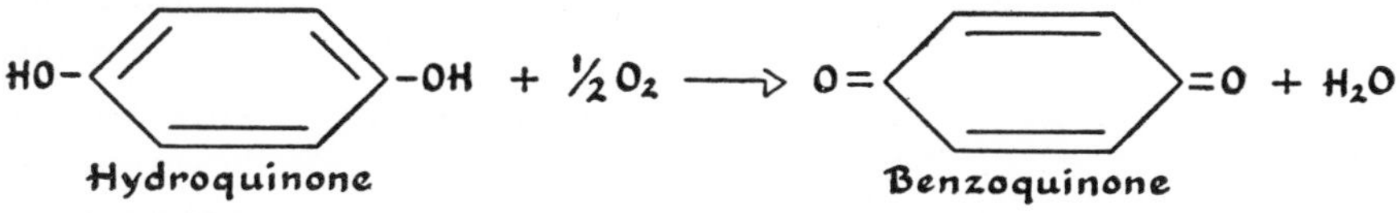

OXIDATION OF HYDROQUINONE TO BENZOQUINONE BY OXYGEN.

(3)

Substances other than oxygen may act as hydrogen acceptors in the oxidation of hydroquinone. No matter whether the hydrogen acceptor is oxygen or some other substance, the mere removal of hydrogen atoms from the substrate constitutes its oxidation. A great many of the biological oxidations of respiration are of this type.

A still more general type of oxidation is that typified by the oxidation of ferrous iron to ferric iron. Here, one electron is removed from the ferrous iron and transferred to some suitable electron acceptor.

$$Fe^{++} \longrightarrow Fe^{+++} + (e)$$

OXIDATION OF FERROUS TO FERRIC IRON BY REMOVAL OF ONE ELECTRON.

(4)

The electron acceptor or oxidant may be oxygen, in which case the complete reaction is as follows:

$$2Fe^{++} + \tfrac{1}{2}O_2 + 2H^+ \longrightarrow 2Fe^{+++} + H_2O$$

OXIDATION OF FERROUS TO FERRIC IRON BY OXYGEN.

(5)

Again, the essential feature of the oxidation is the removal of electrons, and the reaction is an oxidation of the iron whether the oxidant is oxygen or some other electron acceptor.

It should be noted that the three types of oxidation described above —addition of oxygen, removal of hydrogen, and removal of electrons— are, in actuality, closely related. In all three cases, oxidation of the substrate consists of the removal of electrons from the substance which undergoes oxidation. These electrons may be removed from the carbon atom to the carbon-oxygen bond (Equation 1); they may be removed together with protons as hydrogen atoms (Equation 2); or, finally, they may be removed as electrons (Equation 4). We may think of biological oxidation as the removal of electrons from substrate. These electrons are then passed on through a series of acceptors until finally they are combined with hydrogen ions and oxygen to form water.

Sequence of Steps in Biological Oxidations

In the respiratory oxidations carried out by living material, hydrogen atoms are ordinarily removed two at a time from the substrate by enzymes belonging to the group of dehydrogenases (see Fig. 10-12). The dehydrogenases are themselves reduced in the process. The reduced dehydrogenases, however, are reoxidized not by molecular oxygen but by enzymes belonging to the flavoprotein group. In this reaction the flavoprotein is itself reduced, only to be reoxidized by an enzyme or substrate belonging to the general group of the intermediate carriers. The reduced intermediate carrier is finally reoxidized by a terminal oxidase, an enzyme which is itself reoxidized by molecular oxygen. Thus in the typical respiratory oxidation, the hydrogen atoms (or electrons) removed from substrate are handed on from enzyme to enzyme through five successive steps before the final uptake of oxygen and formation of water. In the oxidation of a single hexose molecule this entire procedure must be repeated twelve times, since twelve atoms of oxygen are taken up in the over-all reaction.

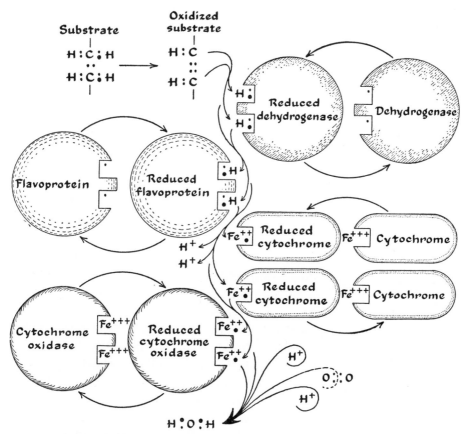

Figure 10-12. *The pathway of electrons in respiration. In many oxidative reactions of respiration, electrons are removed from substrate together with protons as hydrogen atoms. These hydrogen atoms are first taken up by a dehydrogenase. They are then handed on to a flavoprotein. The electrons pass from flavoprotein to cytochrome, and at this step the protons are liberated as hydrogen ions. Reduced cytochrome is reoxidized by cytochrome oxidase, which in turn is reoxidized by O_2.*

The Oxidative Enzymes

Each group of enzymes involved in the respiratory oxidations has certain outstanding chemical characteristics which distinguish it from all other enzymes. These characters concern primarily the non-protein prosthetic groups, or coenzymes (Chap. 8). Many dehydro-genases have in common a particular type of prosthetic group; the flavoproteins share a second and different type; and the intermediate carriers and terminal oxidases still another.

The Dehydrogenases

The dehydrogenase enzymes characteristically remove pairs of hydrogen atoms from substrate molecules, as exemplified below by the oxidation of malic acid. Characteristically, also, these enzymes consist

OXIDATION OF MALIC ACID BY MALIC DEHYDROGENASE.

of two portions: a protein portion, which is different for each individual dehydrogenase; and a nonprotein coenzyme, which is common to many enzymes of the group. The coenzyme phosphopyridine nucleotide contains as its active group nicotinic acid, known in animal nutrition as niacin, the pellagra-preventive vitamin. The coenzyme is, however, a complex material involving adenine, ribose, and phosphoric acid residues in addition to nicotinic acid. Certain of the dehydrogenases possess a coenzyme containing two molecules of phosphoric acid, diphos-phopyridine nucleotide (DPN), while others make use of a coenzyme containing three molecules of phosphoric acid, triphosphopyridine nucleotide (TPN). In all cases, however, the coenzyme is essential to the activity of the enzyme, since either coenzyme or protein alone is inactive. In all cases, also, oxidation of substrate by the enzyme involves actual reduction of the phosphopyridine nucleotide coenzyme. Reoxidation of the reduced coenzyme is carried out by enzymes of the following group.

Flavoproteins

The flavoproteins are so called because in purified form they are yellow, a color which is due to the riboflavin present in the nonprotein prosthetic group. As with the dehydrogenases, it is the prosthetic group which is active in oxidation, the riboflavin itself being capable of reversible oxidation and reduction. In all cases, however, the riboflavin-

Reduced DPN + Flavoprotein ⇌ Oxidized DPN + Reduced flavoprotein

REOXIDATION OF REDUCED DPN BY FLAVOPROTEIN.

containing prosthetic group must be attached to an appropriate protein to function as an oxidative catalyst. At least a dozen different flavoprotein enzymes are known in nature. Of greatest importance to respiration are those which act specifically in the reoxidation of the reduced phosphopyridine nucleotides. Such flavoproteins, or diaphorases, are, in turn, reoxidized by enzymes of the cytochrome group.

Cytochromes

The cytochromes are enzymes which function as intermediate carriers between flavoproteins or certain other systems and the terminal oxidase. Although several cytochromes have been distinguished, only one, cytochrome C, has been studied extensively in the higher plant. Cytochrome C contains as its prosthetic group an iron-containing porphyrin nucleus, the porphyrin being similar in general structure, although not in detail, to those of leaf chlorophyll or blood hemoglobin. The porphyrin nucleus is tightly bound to the protein portion of the

Reduced .·. 2 oxidized ⟶ Oxidized + 2 reduced + 2H+
flavoprotein cytochrome C ⇌ flavoprotein cytochrome C

REOXIDATION OF REDUCED FLAVOPROTEIN TO CYTOCHROME C.

enzyme, and in turn binds at its center the iron, which is the functional group. In oxidized cytochrome C, the iron is present in the ferric, or trivalent, state. Reduction of cytochrome C is achieved by the transfer of one electron to the iron atom, which results in the formation of the ferrous or divalent form. In cases such as the oxidation of reduced flavoprotein by cytochrome C, a hydrogen atom is removed from the reduced riboflavin, an electron is transferred to the iron atom of cyto-chrome, and a hydrogen ion is liberated to the reaction medium.

The Terminal Oxidase

Reoxidation of reduced cytochrome C is achieved by the enzyme cytochrome oxidase, which carries out the reaction shown below, in which electrons from ferrous cytochrome, hydrogen ions, and molecular oxygen are combined to form water. Cytochrome oxidase is ordi-

$$\underset{\text{cytochrome C}}{\text{2 reduced}} + \tfrac{1}{2}O_2 + 2H^+ \xrightarrow[\text{oxidase}]{\text{Cytochrome}} \underset{\text{cytochrome C}}{\text{2 oxidized}} + H_2O$$

REOXIDATION OF REDUCED CYTOCHROME C BY CYTOCHROME OXIDASE.

narily associated with insoluble particles in the cell, and it has not yet proved possible to purify and characterize this enzyme in detail. It does, however, appear to be an iron-containing enzyme.

Polyphenoloxidase

Many plant tissues exhibit an injury response characterized by dark-ening of the damaged portions, a response which is usually enzymatic and due to oxidations catalyzed by the enzyme polyphenoloxidase. This enzyme is involved in the oxidation of phenols to the corresponding quinones, as shown in the reactions below, in which R may represent

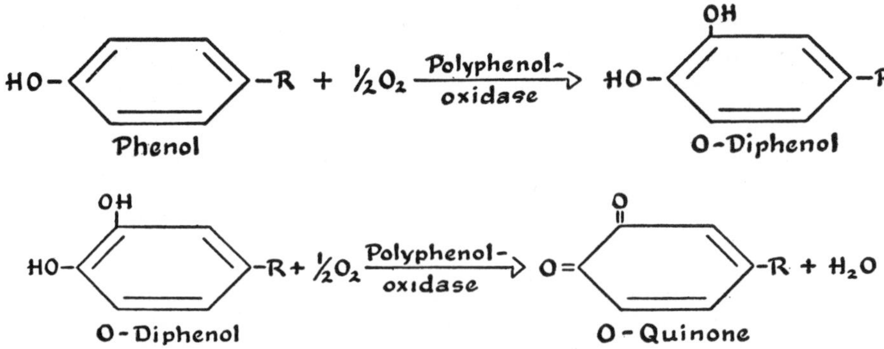

OXIDATION OF PHENOLS BY POLYPHENOLOXIDASE.

any one of a large number of radicals, including, for example, —COOH or —CH$_2$CHNH$_2$COOH. The quinones produced are often further oxidized and polymerized to characteristic brown pigments, which are responsible for the actual color changes observed after injury of plant tissues. Polyphenoloxidase, unlike cytochrome oxidase, is a copper protein and is present in many, although not in all, plant tissues. There is much evidence that it may play the role of a terminal oxidase in potato tubers, some leaves, and perhaps in other tissues. In such cases a suitable phenol would presumably assume the role of intermediate carrier which cytochrome C assumes in tissues containing cytochrome oxidase as the terminal oxidase.

Catalase and Peroxidase

These two enzymes, like cytochrome C of universal occurrence in tissues of higher plants, contain iron porphyrins as their prosthetic groups. Both catalase and peroxidase possess the ability to oxidize a

$$H_2O_2 \xrightarrow{\text{Catalase}} H_2O + \tfrac{1}{2}O_2$$

DECOMPOSITION OF H_2O_2 BY CATALASE.

variety of substrates using hydrogen peroxide as the oxidant. Catalase is further able to decompose H_2O_2 to water and molecular oxygen in the absence of additional substrate. Many phenols and other aromatic

$$HO-\langle \ \rangle-OH + H_2O_2 \xrightarrow{\text{Peroxidase}} O=\langle \ \rangle=O + 2H_2O$$

Hydroquinone · Benzoquinone

OXIDATION OF HYDROQUINONE BY PEROXIDASE IN THE PRESENCE OF H_2O_2.

substances are attacked by these enzymes in the presence of H_2O_2. We do not as yet have, however, a clear picture of their function in the economy of the plant.

Enzymatic CO₂ Evolution: Carboxylases

The evolution of CO_2 in the respiratory process is brought about by a group of enzymes, the carboxylases, which have as their substrates keto acids, containing the $R-\overset{O}{\overset{\|}{C}}-COOH$ configuration. Thus pyruvic acid is subject to decarboxylation by pyruvic carboxylase, with the formation of CO_2 and acetaldehyde (see p. 232). This decarboxylation is typical of alcoholic fermentation but is not a part of aerobic respiration, which involves decarboxylation of other more complex keto acids, such as oxalosuccinic and α-ketoglutaric (see below). Carboxylases are typified in many instances by the presence of a derivative of thiamine (vitamin B_1) as the prosthetic group. This derivative, thiamine pyrophosphate, is known as cocarboxylase.

The Plant Acids

Plant tissues, as well as tissues of other organisms and the cells of lower organisms, typically contain varying amounts of certain simple organic acids, commonly known as the *plant acids*. Several of these, such as malic acid, citric acid, isocitric acid, succinic acid, and fumaric acid, are very well known and important constituents of plant tissues. Less well known but probably equally important are *cis*-aconitic acid,

```
  COOH        COOH        COOH        COOH        COOH
  HCH         HCH         HCH         HCH         HCH
HOC-COOH      C-COOH    HC-COOH     HC-COOH       HCH
  HCH         CH        HOCH          C=O          C=O
  COOH        COOH        COOH        COOH         COOH
  Citric     cis-Aconitic  Isocitric  Oxalosuccinic  α-Ketoglutaric
   acid        acid        acid        acid          acid


  COOH        COOH        COOH        COOH
  HCH         CH          HCH         HCH
  HCH         CH          HCOH        C=O
  COOH        COOH        COOH        COOH
  Succinic    Fumaric      Malic     Oxaloacetic
   acid        acid        acid        acid
```

STRUCTURES OF THE PLANT ACIDS.

oxaloacetic acid, and α-ketoglutaric acid. The chemical structures of these compounds show that citric, *cis*-aconitic, and isocitric acids contain six carbon atoms and three acidic carboxyl (—COOH) groups. Fumaric, malic, and succinic acids all contain four carbon atoms and two carboxyl groups. Oxaloacetic and α-ketoglutaric acid, containing four and five carbon atoms, respectively, are dicarboxylic acids (two

—COOH groups), characterized by the $R\!-\!\overset{\displaystyle O}{\overset{\|}{C}}\!-\!COOH$ or α-keto-con-

figuration in which a carbonyl group $-\overset{\displaystyle .O}{\overset{\|}{C}}-$ is situated adjacent to a carboxyl group.

Although these acids are of widespread occurrence in plant tissues, it is only relatively recently that we have gained an understanding of their function in, or the ways in which they are synthesized by, the plant. We now realize that the plant acids are intermediates in the respiratory oxidation of pyruvic acid. The pathway of pyruvic acid through the various plant acids to CO_2 and water is known as the *citric acid* or *Krebs cycle*, after the English biochemist, H. A. Krebs, who first formulated and proposed the mechanism.

The Krebs Cycle

The oxidation of pyruvic acid to CO_2 and water is achieved in many organisms, including the higher plants, by a cyclic series of steps in which pyruvic acid is combined with oxaloacetic acid to yield a 6-carbon acid with the evolution of one molecule of CO_2 (Fig. 10-13). The 6-carbon acid thus formed, which appears to be citric acid, is then degraded stepwise, through a cycle including isocitric acid, α-ketoglutaric acid, and succinic acid, until, finally, oxaloacetic acid is itself reformed. For each molecule of pyruvic acid oxidized by one passage through the cycle, three molecules of CO_2 are evolved and five atoms of oxygen are consumed, just as would be expected according to the usual concept of the complete oxidation of pyruvic acid:

$$CH_3\overset{O}{\overset{\|}{C}}-\overset{O}{\overset{\|}{C}}\diagdown_{OH} + \tfrac{5}{2}O_2 \longrightarrow 3\,CO_2 + 2\,H_2O$$

Pyruvic acid

THE COMPLETE OXIDATION OF PYRUVIC ACID.

We might thus regard the biological oxidation of pyruvic acid as a process in which pyruvic acid is coupled to an acceptor to form a larger molecule, which is then snipped away piecemeal until the original acceptor molecule is reformed.

The initial reaction of the Krebs cycle is the degradation of pyruvic acid to a 2-carbon fragment, which then combines with oxaloacetic acid to form the 6-carbon citric acid. In the second step of the Krebs cycle, citric acid is converted to isocitric through *cis*-aconitic acid as an intermediary, a process catalyzed by the enzyme aconitase and involving simple removal and addition of water. Isocitric acid is attacked by the enzyme isocitric dehydrogenase to form an intermediate, oxalosuccinic acid, which next undergoes decarboxylation to form α-ketoglutaric acid. The latter is now decarboxylated and oxidized to succinic acid. Succinic

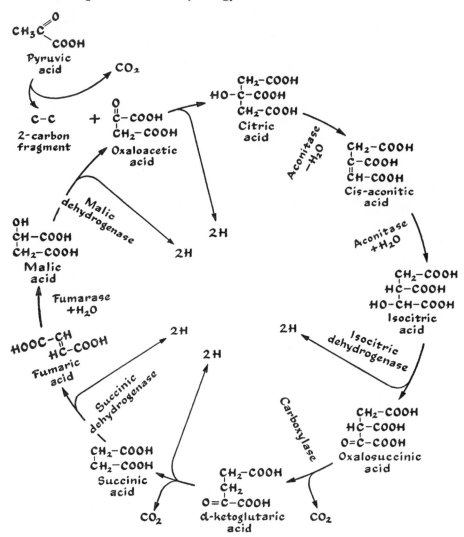

Figure 10-13. *The individual steps involved in the oxidation of pyruvic acid through the Krebs cycle.*

acid, in turn, is oxidized to fumaric acid by the enzyme succinic dehydrogenase, a reaction which consists of the removal of two hydrogen atoms from the succinic acid molecule. Enzymatic addition of water to fumaric acid by the enzyme fumarase results in the formation of malic acid, while oxidation of malic acid by the DPN-containing malic dehydrogenase results in the final reformation of oxaloacetic acid.

In summary, the reactions of the Krebs cycle can be put together in cyclical form as shown in Figure 10-13. With each complete revolution of the cycle, one molecule of pyruvic acid is burned to CO_2 and H_2O. In each oxidative step, two electrons are removed from substrate, passed through the enzyme chain to terminal oxidase, and thus combined with oxygen and hydrogen ions to form water.

Experimental Implications of the Krebs Cycle

It is not possible within the limits of this book to bring forward and evaluate the great mass of experimental work on which the concept of the cyclic oxidation of pyruvic acid is based. There are, however, three basic experiments which have been widely used in investigations

COOH
|
CH$_2$
|
COOH
Malonic
acid

COOH
|
CH$_2$
|
CH$_2$
|
COOH
Succinic
acid

on the mechanism of pyruvate oxidation, the results of which are interpretable on the basis of the Krebs cycle. The first two are concerned with the use of the specific inhibitor malonic acid, which inhibits the oxidation of succinic acid to fumaric acid by the enzyme succinic dehydrogenase. Malonic acid resembles succinic acid in structure but with the difference that it contains three, rather than four, carbon atoms. Since malonic acid so closely resembles succinic acid, it is

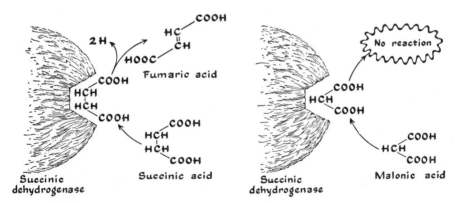

Figure 10-14. *Malonic acid inhibits the oxidation of succinic to fumaric acid by formation of a complex at the reactive site of the enzyme succinic dehydrogenase. This blocks the occupation of the reactive site by succinic acid.*

capable of combining with the active spots of the enzyme to form an inhibitor-enzyme complex. Since this complex cannot be oxidized, and since the enzyme involved in inhibitor-complex formation cannot combine with succinic acid, the enzymatic oxidation of succinic acid, the true substrate, is inhibited (Fig. 10-14).

When respiring plant tissues are treated with malonic acid, their

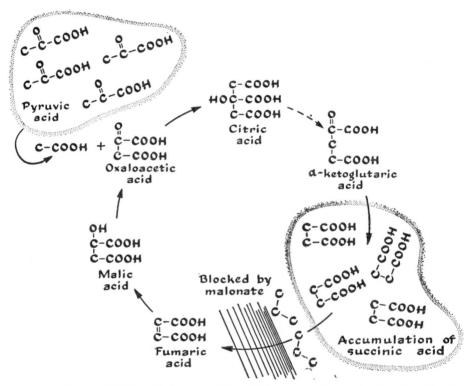

Figure 10-15. *Malonic acid inhibits normal respiration by blocking the oxidation of succinic acid.*

respiration is inhibited, a result indicating the participation of succinic dehydrogenase in the respiratory mechanism. It can be shown by direct analysis that in malonic acid-poisoned tissues, succinic acid accumulates, as would be expected, since the enzyme for removal of succinic acid, succinic dehydrogenase, is inhibited (Fig. 10-15). The accumulation of succinate is greatly increased if α-ketoglutaric acid, citric acid, or other of the acids of the cycle are added to the malonic acid-inhibited tissues. In other words, these acids are converted as far as the succinic acid stage and accumulate as succinic acid in the malonic acid-inhibited tissue.

A second basic experiment shows that in malonic acid-poisoned tissue, the formation of oxaloacetic acid is blocked or largely blocked. Pyruvic acid cannot, therefore, be oxidized by malonate-poisoned tissue, because no acceptor for pyruvic acid is present. If oxaloacetic acid or a precursor of oxaloacetic acid, such as malic or fumaric acid, is added to malonic acid-inhibited tissue, the ability of the tissue to oxidize pyruvic acid is restored.

Finally, experiments with isotopically tagged pyruvic acid molecules, in which the pyruvic acid contains one or more of its carbon atoms tagged with radioactive C^{14} or the stable isotope C^{13}, show that during the oxidation of pyruvic acid its carbon atoms are actually incorporated into the acids of the Krebs cycle.

The Utilization of Energy Liberated in Respiration

It has been pointed out earlier that the primary function of respiration is to provide energy for the energy-consuming reactions of the cell—the synthetic, organizational, mechanical, osmotic, and similar activities of the organism. Though there is still much work to be done, biochemists have in recent years begun to understand the mechanisms

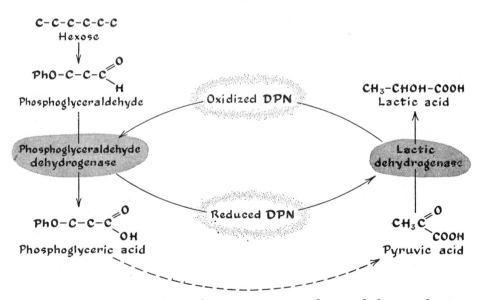

Figure 10-16. *An oxidative reaction may be coupled to a reduction through a common coenzyme.*

by which oxidative energy liberated in respiration is transferred and made available to energy-consuming processes. These mechanisms are of two kinds—oxidative coupling and phosphorylative coupling.

In oxidative coupling the energy released in oxidation of substrate is stored in an intermediate until it can be used directly in carrying out the reduction of some other cellular constituent. Simple and well understood cases of this kind of coupling are found in the fermentations, for example, the lactic acid fermentation. We have seen earlier that in the initial phase of hexose breakdown a single oxidative step intervenes, namely, the oxidation of phosphoglyceraldehyde to phosphoglyceric acid. The enzyme for this oxidation is phosphoglyceraldehyde dehydrogenase, which contains DPN as its active group. In the oxidation, DPN is itself reduced. As the result of hexose breakdown, pyruvic acid is formed, and, for lactic acid fermentation to occur, this pyruvic acid must be reduced to lactic acid. The enzyme for the pyruvic-lactic reaction, lactic dehydrogenase, has as its active group DPN, just as does phosphoglyceraldehyde dehydrogenase. The two enzymes differ, of course, in the nature of their protein apoenzymes, but they have in common the nature of their coenzyme or active group. In lactic acid fermentation, then, the reduced DPN produced in oxidation of phosphoglyceraldehyde is utilized in the reduction of pyruvic to lactic acid, the DPN being itself reoxidized in the process. We might visualize this process as shown in Figure 10-16. The essence of oxidative coupling is that the hydrogen atoms removed in oxidation of one substrate may be stored on a coenzyme such as DPN and used directly for reduction of a second substance. Such oxidative coupling takes place not only in lactic acid fermentation but also in alcoholic fermentation, where acetaldehyde is reduced to ethyl alcohol. It no doubt also occurs in certain instances of aerobic metabolism.

Phosphorylative Coupling

The most general and important mode of energy transport in living systems appears to occur through the intervention of particular phosphorylated compounds. The key materials in this type of energy transfer are three adenine derivatives: adenylic acid, adenosine diphosphate, and adenosine triphosphate. Adenine, a nitrogenous base belonging to the chemical group of purines, is linked in all of these materials with the sugar ribose to form adenosine. In adenylic acid, a phosphoric acid molecule is esterified with the ribose portion. Adenosine diphosphate (ADP), as the name implies, contains two phosphoric acid

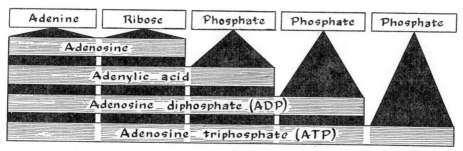

| Adenine | Ribose | Phosphate | Phosphate | Phosphate |

Adenosine

Adenylic acid

Adenosine diphosphate (ADP)

Adenosine triphosphate (ATP)

THE COMPOSITION OF ADENOSINE TRIPHOSPHATE.

residues, the first being linked to ribose as in adenylic acid, while the second is linked to this first phosphate residue. In adenosine triphosphate (ATP) still a third phosphoric acid residue is linked to the two present in ADP.

When ATP is hydrolyzed with acid or with an appropriate enzyme, the terminal phosphate is removed, with the liberation of a relatively large amount of energy—12,000 cal per mol. With ADP, also, hydrolysis and removal of the terminal phosphate result in the liberation of approximately 12,000 cal of energy per mol. The phosphate of adenylic acid is, however, less readily hydrolyzed and yields only a relatively small amount of energy—approximately 3000 cal per mol. The terminal phosphates of ATP and ADP are, therefore, referred to as *energy-rich phosphates* as contrasted with those such as the sugar phosphate of adenylic acid.

In the oxidative reactions of respiration, phosphorylated compounds such as ATP are formed, and part of the energy liberated in the oxidation is stored as energy of the phosphate bond. The energy-rich phosphate groups may be subsequently used as the source of energy for synthetic reactions. A simple example of such energy coupling is that of the formation of starch from glucose. The formation of the glucosidic bonds in starch requires an external source of energy. This energy is derived from respiration through the intervention of the energy-rich phosphate of ATP, as shown in Figure 10-17.

The adenosine triphosphate generated in respiration is used in the phosphorylation of hexose to glucose-6-phosphate. In the presence of the enzyme phosphoglucomutase, glucose-6-phosphate is transformed to glucose-1-phosphate. Glucose-1-phosphate in the presence of starch phosphorylase is converted to starch, with the simultaneous liberation of inorganic phosphate. The energy needed for the formation of the glucosidic linkage in starch is thus derived directly from the energy of the phosphate linkage in glucose-1-phosphate. This is, in turn, derived from the energy of the phosphate bond in glucose-6-phosphate. The glucose-6-phosphate has been formed at the expense of the energy-rich phosphate bond generated in respiration and stored as ATP bond energy.

The way in which respiratory oxidation is linked with the production of energy-rich phosphate was first worked out in detail for the phosphoglyceraldehyde system by Otto Warburg in 1939, and his findings still constitute the best understood example of the mechanism involved. In this complex of reactions, the phosphoglyceraldehyde first takes up inorganic phosphate to become a 1,3-diphosphoglycer-

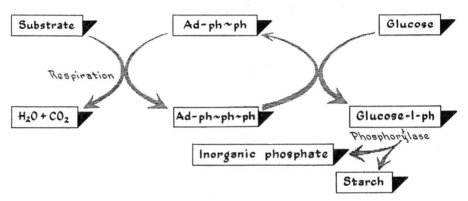

Figure 10-17. *Respiratory energy, transported in the form of energy-rich phosphates, may be used to carry on synthetic reactions such as the formation of glucose-1-phosphate, the precursor of starch.*

aldehyde. This reaction involves but little energy change, and the diphosphate is formed spontaneously. Oxidation of the 1,3-diphosphoglyceraldehyde by the appropriate dehydrogenase next results, however, in the formation of 1,3-diphosphoglyceric acid. In this new compound, phosphate is attached to the newly formed carboxyl group, and such carboxyl phosphates are of the energy-rich type. In the presence of a specific transphosphorylating enzyme, the carboxyl phosphate of 1,3-diphosphoglyceric acid is transferred to ADP, with the formation of ATP (Fig. 10-18).

In summary, inorganic phosphate is taken up by phosphoglyceraldehyde at a low-energy level. The diphosphoglyceraldehyde is next oxidized, so that in the oxidation product phosphate is held at a high-energy level. To put it another way, a portion of the energy liberated in the oxidation has been conserved in formation of the energy-rich phosphate bond. Two other features of this reaction deserve special emphasis: (1) Inorganic phosphate is a necessary component of the oxidative system; the reaction cannot ordinarily proceed in the absence of phosphate. (2) ADP, which acts as a final receptor for the energy

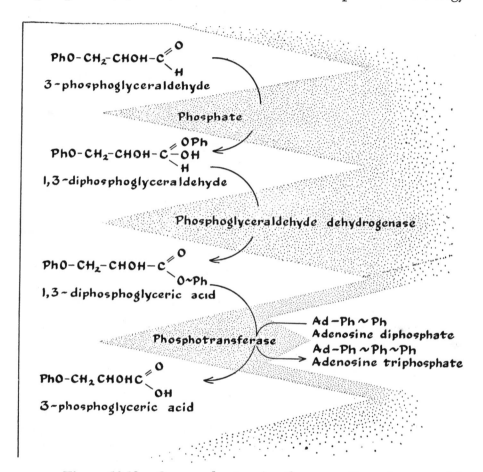

Figure 10-18. *One mechanism for the generation of energy-rich phosphate involves the oxidation of phosphoglyceraldehyde.*

released in the reaction, is a necessary component of the oxidative system. In the absence of this energy acceptor the oxidation cannot proceed. In other words, oxidation of phosphoglyceraldehyde is compulsorily coupled with phosphate uptake and energy-rich phosphate production.

If, for example, a tissue has built up much energy-rich phosphate and has only a little work in progress to deplete the store, then the tissue may become short of acceptor for energy-rich phosphate, and the respiration rate would necessarily slow down. In tissues which utilize their energy-rich phosphate rapidly, fresh acceptor is rapidly being renewed, so that respiration may proceed at a rapid rate. Thus the compulsory coupling of oxidation to phosphorylation serves as a mechanism by which respiratory rate can be geared by the organism to energy demand.

There are other respiratory reactions known to be coupled with the production of energy-rich phosphates. One has been alluded to in the discussion of phosphoenolpyruvic acid earlier in this chapter. Certain of the steps in the Krebs cycle are linked with energy-rich phosphate production. It is estimated that some twenty to thirty energy-rich phosphate bonds are generated in the course of the degradation of each

Figure 10-19. *Energy-rich phosphate is the connecting link between the energy liberated in respiratory oxidations and the varied kinds of biological work which must be done by living organisms.*

mol of hexose. Thus of the total 678,000 calories liberated in the complete oxidation of one mol of hexose, about 300,000 calories are probably conserved in the form of energy-rich phosphate and are available for other purposes. Among the syntheses which we know to be powered by energy-rich phosphates are those of starch and sucrose. It is possible, also, that they may be needed for the production of phosphorylated sugars to be used in the synthesis of cell wall polysaccharides, although we have as yet no specific indication of this requirement. Work on animal tissues and microbial cells has indicated that ATP also supplies energy for synthesis of fatty acids and of amide linkages similar to those of proteins. There are undoubtedly many other synthetic systems of the organism which can receive their energy in the form of energy-rich phosphate.

The concept of phosphorylative coupling is presented in Figure 10-19. Here, respiration is represented as a cycle which produces energy-rich phosphate. This energy-rich phosphate is, in turn, transmitted to, and used as a source of energy by, the machinery which carries out the varied kinds of cellular work.

Summary

Respiration is the oxidation or burning of sugars or other substrates to form carbon dioxide and water, with the uptake of oxygen from the air. Respiration takes place, so far as we know, in all living plants, plant organs, and plant tissues, although the rate of the process depends greatly on temperature and other environmental conditions as well as on the age and condition of the tissue. Through the process of respiration, energy is liberated and made available to the manifold energy-using reactions of the plant. Thus the synthesis of new chemical materials, the uptake of inorganic ions, growth, and the very maintenance of the living condition all depend on energy derived from respiration. The way in which energy liberated in respiration is transferred and made available to the energy-using processes of the plant can only be described in general outline, but we have begun to appreciate that such energy transfer is in many instances carried on by the mediation of particular energy carriers, the energy-rich phosphates.

The biological combustion of sugar to carbon dioxide and water is a process involving a great many, perhaps fifty or more, individual chemical steps, each requiring the presence of its own appropriate enzyme. The process as a whole may, however, be divided into two major portions: an initial portion in which each hexose sugar molecule is converted to two molecules of pyruvic acid, and a final portion in which pyruvic acid is converted to CO_2 and water. Characteristic of the initial, or glycolytic, phase of respiration is the fact that phosphate derivatives of the sugars are involved. Characteristic of the final phase, the Krebs cycle, is the participation of the simple plant acids as intermediates in the process by which pyruvic acid is oxidized and dismembered.

QUESTIONS

1. How may one demonstrate the release of energy during the respiration of plants? Is the energy measured by this method capable of doing useful work within the plant?

2. What are the relative rates of photosynthesis and respiration in a well-illuminated turgid green leaf? What is the evidence for this answer?

3. Of what use is the information furnished by the respiratory quotient?

4. The storage life of apples may be prolonged by enriching the atmosphere surrounding them with CO_2. What is a possible mechanism for this effect?

5. In what way does fermentation differ from respiration? Through what common steps do the two processes proceed?

6. Discuss the various meanings which can be applied to the term *oxidation*. What have all oxidations in common?

7. Which of the various oxidases found in plants seem to function terminally in respiration? What is the evidence for this?

8. What experimental facts indicate the operation of an organic acid cycle in plants?

9. In what ways may the energy liberated during respiration be harnessed for the performance of useful biochemical work?

10. How could one increase the respiration rate of roots in a flooded soil?

11. Certain organisms can ferment glucose anaerobically, but will abruptly shift to an aerobic respiration when brought into contact with oxygen. Suggest a possible mechanism.

12. What errors are implicit in any determination of respiratory quotient by manometric methods?

13. How does knowledge of the intermediary metabolism of carbohydrate oxidation aid in our understanding of the possible mechanism of photosynthesis?

GENERAL READING

Goddard, D. R., "The Respiration of Cells and Tissues," in Höber, R., *Physical Chemistry of Cells and Tissues*, Sec. 6. Philadelphia: Blakiston Co., 1945. A lucid description of respiration as a general biological process.

————, and Meeuse, J. D., "Respiration of Higher Plants." *Ann. Rev. Plant Physiol.*, 1: 207, 1950. A critical review of recent advances in the study of respiration.

Lardy, H. A., ed., *Respiratory Enzymes*. Minneapolis: Burgess Publ. Co., 1949. Deals primarily with respiratory enzymes of animal tissues but useful to the plant physiologist.

Stiles, W., "Respiration," Parts I and II. *Botan. Rev.*, 1: 249, 1935; *ibid.*, 12: 165, 1946. The more botanical and ecological aspects of plant respiration.

CHAPTER 11

Nitrogen: Its Metabolism and Economy in Plant and Nature

The Role of Nitrogen in the Plant

The element nitrogen accounts for roughly 1 to 5 per cent of the dry weight of the plant leaf and a lower, but still important, proportion of the dry weight of other vegetative tissues. Nitrogen combines with carbon-containing materials in the plant to form a great many different organic compounds. These materials contain, on the average, approximately 16 per cent nitrogen, so nitrogen-containing compounds make up from 5 to 30 per cent of the total dry weight of the plant tissue.

In addition to its role as a contributor to the bulk of plant tissue, nitrogen is significant as a component of many important plant compounds. Nitrogen is found in many of the vitamins that serve as functional groups of enzymes; in the purines, such as adenine (Chap. 10), important in respiration and in the structure of nucleic acids; and in the alkaloids (Chap. 13). But even more important is that portion of the plant nitrogen which is combined in the structure of the proteins, which, as we have seen in Chapter 8, constitute the enzymatic machinery for the conduct of cellular metabolism. It is because nitrogen is an essential and characteristic constituent of the proteins that the nitrogen economy of the plant is of special interest and importance to plant physiology.

Nitrogen is not only essential to the structure and welfare of the plant but is also an indispensable ingredient of the food of animals. The nitrogen which is found in, and which forms essential components of, the animal body comes originally from plants. Plants, in fact, act as converters, transforming the nitrogen of the soil into forms suitable for the nutrition of animals.

We shall first consider the uptake and metabolism of nitrogen by the plant and then proceed to a consideration of the plant in relation to the nitrogen economy of nature.

Forms of Nitrogen Available to Plants

When we grow plants in nutrient solution, we usually supply nitrogen either as a salt of the nitrate ion or, less frequently, as a salt of the ammonium ion. Calcium and potassium nitrates, $Ca(NO_3)_2$ and KNO_3, respectively, are good sources of nitrogen for most higher plants. Similarly, ammonium sulfate, $(NH_4)_2SO_4$, is sometimes used as a nitrogen source in nutrient solutions. Both nitrate and ammonium ions are also present in soils, but the ammonium salts are rapidly converted to nitrate by the bacterial process of nitrification. Nitrate, therefore, is undoubtedly the principal form in which nitrogen is taken up by plants from the soil. Certain amino acids such as glutamic and aspartic acids, the amides asparagine and glutamine, and urea have also been shown to serve as suitable sources of nitrogen for one or another species of higher plants.

Most of the nitrogen of the earth is present not as soil nitrogen but as molecular N_2 in the atmosphere. This nitrogen cannot be utilized by most species of higher plants, but is assimilated and used as a source of nitrogen by a number of types of microorganisms which either live free in the soil or inhabit special tissues, nodules found on the roots of plants belonging to the legume family. The capacity of nodulated leguminous plants to utilize molecular N_2 as a source of nitrogen places the legumes in a special position with regard to their nitrogen nutrition, a matter which will be reserved for discussion later in this chapter.

Nitrate Reduction

Although nitrate is taken up by, and often stored in, the roots of the plant, the absorbed nitrate is ultimately converted into ammonia before it is incorporated into the amino acids and other nitrogenous plant constituents. The conversion of nitrate to ammonia represents a substantial reduction, since eight atoms of hydrogen are needed to reduce one nitrate ion to the level of ammonia. We do not know

$$HNO_3 + 8H \longrightarrow NH_3 + 3H_2O$$

THE REDUCTION OF NITRATE TO AMMONIA.

exactly which enzyme or enzymes transport the hydrogen needed for reduction of nitrate, but we do know that this hydrogen must ultimately come from the oxidation of substrate in respiration. Thus, if plants which have been deprived of nitrogen for several weeks are suddenly supplied with nitrate, their rate of respiratory CO_2 production is greatly increased, as would be expected if nitrate reduction does depend on respiratory dehydrogenations in the general way shown in Figure 11-1.

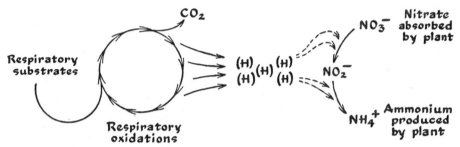

Figure 11-1. *Nitrates absorbed through the roots must be reduced to ammonia before the nitrogen can be utilized by the plant for synthesis of its nitrogenous constituents. The H atoms needed in this reduction come from the oxidative processes of respiration. Over-all respiration may therefore be increased by the application of nitrate.*

It seems quite probable that nitrite, NO_2^-, is an intermediate in the reduction of nitrate to ammonia. When nitrogen-depleted tomato plants are suddenly supplied with nitrate, both nitrate and nitrite appear in the tissues. Nitrite is not, however, found in any detectable quantity in the tissues of normal plants, so it must be further converted at a rapid rate.

Although nitrite appears to be an intermediate in nitrate reduction, we do not as yet know what other compounds intervene between nitrite and the final production of ammonia.

The reduction of nitrate to ammonia is carried out by most of the plant roots which have been studied. In some species, the apple tree for instance, nitrate reduction is, in fact, ordinarily carried on exclusively in the roots, and nitrogen is transported to the other organs in the form of compounds such as the amino acids. In many plants, however, a portion of the absorbed nitrate is reduced in the roots, while a further portion is transported to the leaves and there reduced. This is true of wheat and tomatoes.

It is an interesting fact that ammonia itself does not ordinarily accumulate to any great extent in the plant. This is significant, since even rather low concentrations of ammonia are injurious to plant tissues. Our next problem, then, is to trace the way in which ammonia is incorporated into organic compounds and particularly into amino acids.

The Amino Acids

Proteins are large and complex molecules, with molecular weights far greater then those of the simple compounds of organic chemistry. We have seen (Chap. 8) that there are a great many different kinds of proteins, proteins which differ not only in molecular weight and other physical properties but also in enzymatic activity. All proteins, however, are constructed from similar building blocks, the amino acids. There are some twenty-two different amino acids which occur in nature as components of proteins, as well as several others which are not protein constituents. Some particular kinds of proteins contain all of these twenty-two different amino acids, while others may lack one or more of them. For each protein, however, there is a fixed and definite proportionality between the constituent amino acids.

With but few exceptions, the naturally occurring amino acids have in common the structure shown below, a structure in which a terminal carboxyl group is joined to a second carbon atom, which in turn has an —NH$_2$, or amino, group. This amino group is usually attached to

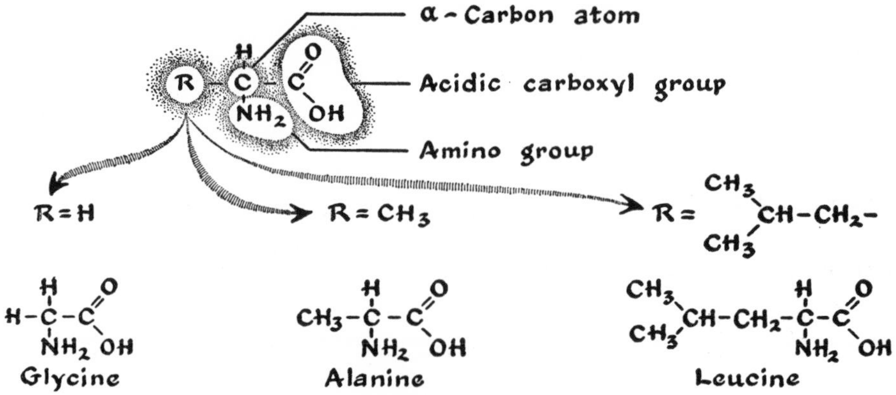

THE STRUCTURE OF AMINO ACIDS.

the α-carbon atom, that nearest the carboxyl group, and such amino acids are therefore termed α-amino acids. Amino acids differ among themselves in the nature of the groups, other than the amino group, which are also attached to the α-carbon atom. This variable group is designated as R in the structure above. In the simplest amino acid, glycine, R is merely a hydrogen atom. Glycine is therefore an amino acid which contains only two carbon atoms. In alanine, which is a 3-carbon-atom amino acid, R is a —CH₃, or methyl, group. R may, however, vary greatly among the twenty-two amino acids which are recognized as constituents of plant proteins. The structures of these amino acids are shown in Table 11-1.

Table 11-1. *Names and Structures of Some Important Amino Acids Known to Occur in Proteins.*

NAME	STRUCTURE	NAME	STRUCTURE
Glycine	NH_2CH_2COOH	Proline	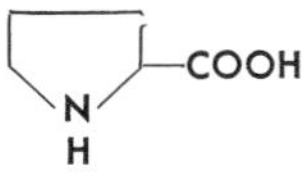 —COOH
Alanine	CH_3CHNH_2COOH	Hydroxyproline	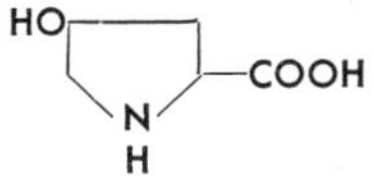 HO— —COOH
Valine	$\begin{array}{c}CH_3\\CH_3\end{array}$CHCHNH₂COOH	Cystine	$(-SCH_2CHNH_2COOH)_2$
Leucine	$\begin{array}{c}CH_3\\CH_3\end{array}$CHCH₂CHNH₂COOH	Cysteine	$HSCH_2CHNH_2COOH$
Isoleucine	$\begin{array}{c}C_2H_5\\CH_3\end{array}$CHCHNH₂COOH	Methionine	$CH_3SCH_2CH_2CHNH_2COOH$
Norleucine	$CH_3(CH_2)_3CHNH_2COOH$	Aspartic acid	$HOOCCH_2CHNH_2COOH$
Serine	$HOCH_2CHNH_2COOH$	Glutamic acid	$HOOCCH_2CH_2CHNH_2COOH$
Threonine	$CH_3CHOHCHNH_2COOH$	Hydroxy-glutamic acid	$HOOCCH_2CHOHCHNH_2COOH$
Phenyl-alanine	—CH₂CHNH₂COOH		
Tyrosine	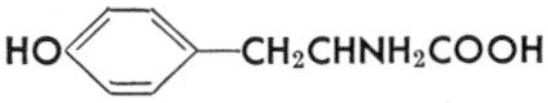 HO——CH₂CHNH₂COOH	Lysine	$NH_2CH_2(CH_2)_3CHNH_2COOH$
Tryptophane	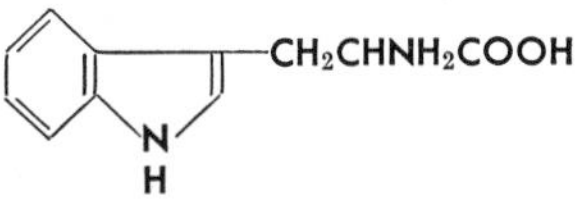 —CH₂CHNH₂COOH	Arginine	$\begin{array}{c}NH_2\\HN\end{array}$CNHCH₂(CH₂)₂CHNH₂COOH
		Histidine	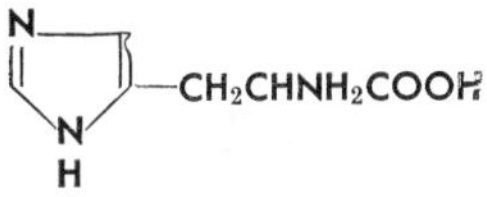 —CH₂CHNH₂COOH

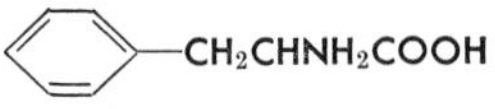

Several additional points concerning the chemistry of these compounds are noteworthy. In the first place, the amino acids listed in Table 11-1 are, with the exception of the simplest, glycine, capable of existing in the isomeric D and L forms. However, the naturally occurring amino acids are largely, and possibly entirely, of the L configuration. Attention should be directed also to the structure of glutamic and aspartic acids. These are dicarboxylic amino acids and are related in structure to α-ketoglutaric and oxaloacetic acids, respectively. The substances glutamine and asparagine, which have been of particular interest to plant physiologists, are also related to glutamic and aspartic acids, being their amides. Thus in glutamine the hydroxyl of one carboxyl group of glutamic acid is replaced by an —NH₂ group to form

the $-\overset{\overset{\text{O}}{\|}}{\text{C}}-\text{NH}_2$, or amide, group.

Although the plant is capable of synthesizing all of the amino acids it requires, the animal organism must ingest some of these in the intact form. Such amino acids, for which the animal is completely dependent on plants, are referred to as the essential amino acids.

The Formation of Amino Acids

Perhaps the principal reaction by which ammonia is taken up into organic combination in the plant is through reaction with α-ketoglutaric acid to form glutamic acid. This reaction is an enzymatic one and proceeds only in the presence of the enzyme glutamic dehydrogenase, for which DPN (Chap. 10) is the coenzyme. In this reaction, ammonia first reacts spontaneously with α-ketoglutaric acid to form small amounts of α-iminoglutaric acid. This material is next acted upon by reduced glutamic dehydrogenase, which transfers two hydrogen atoms to the α-iminoglutaric acid to form glutamic acid and oxidized glutamic dehydrogenase.

INCORPORATION OF AMMONIA INTO α-KETOGLUTARIC ACID TO FORM GLUTAMIC ACID.

It is evident that continued synthesis of glutamic acid by this reaction will demand a continued source of α-ketoglutaric acid. Such
a source is readily available, since it is continuously produced in the
cell as an intermediate in respiration. A continued source of reduced
DPN for the formation of reduced glutamic dehydrogenase is likewise
assured, since reduced DPN is produced in cellular respiration.

Although the synthesis of glutamic acid by the route outlined above
is by no means the sole manner in which ammonia is introduced into
organic combination in the plant, it is probably a major pathway, as
has been indicated by experiments in which ammonia-containing
isotopic N^{15} has been supplied to plants and found to be rapidly and
extensively converted to glutamic acid.

Transamination

Glutamic acid can serve as a donor of amino groups to other compounds to form still other amino acids. This process, in which the
amino group of glutamic acid is transferred bodily to other α-keto acids

| Glutamic acid | Oxaloacetic acid | | α-Ketoglutaric acid | Aspartic acid |

TRANSAMINATION REACTION BETWEEN GLUTAMIC ACID AND OXALOACETIC
ACID.

to form new amino acids, is known as *transamination*. A simple example
of enzymatic transamination is that which occurs between glutamic
acid and oxaloacetic acid to produce α-ketoglutaric acid and aspartic acid. Through the transamination reaction, ammonia and oxaloacetic acid can be effectively combined to form aspartic acid by the mediation of a small amount of α-ketoglutaric acid. Glutamic acid can
also tranfer its amino group to pyruvic acid to form the amino acid
alanine. This reaction likewise is enzymatic and requires a transaminase
which is different and separable from that required for the glutamic-
aspartic reaction. It is possible that still other amino acids may be
made from glutamic acid by analogous transaminations with the appropriate α-keto acids.

An interesting aspect of the transamination reaction is the fact that the enzymes responsible contain a derivative of the vitamin pyridoxine as the prosthetic group. This vitamin derivative, pyridoxal phosphate, appears to be the prosthetic group of the transaminase enzymes, not only in the higher plant, but in all living creatures.

The Proteins

Proteins contribute to living material many of its physical, chemical, and biological properties. Much of the protein of the living cell is enzymatic, and it is the function of the enzymes to mediate the metabolism typical of living matter. The reproductive and genetic characteristics of living matter are determined by certain specialized proteins of the nucleus which make up the substance of the chromosomes.

Proteins are constructed of amino acid residues linked together through their α-amino and carboxyl or acid groups, as shown below.

The linkage —HN—C— (with O double-bonded to C) is called a *peptide bond*, and chains of amino acids bound in such linkages are called *peptides*. If the chain is very short and contains but two amino acids linked through a peptide bond,

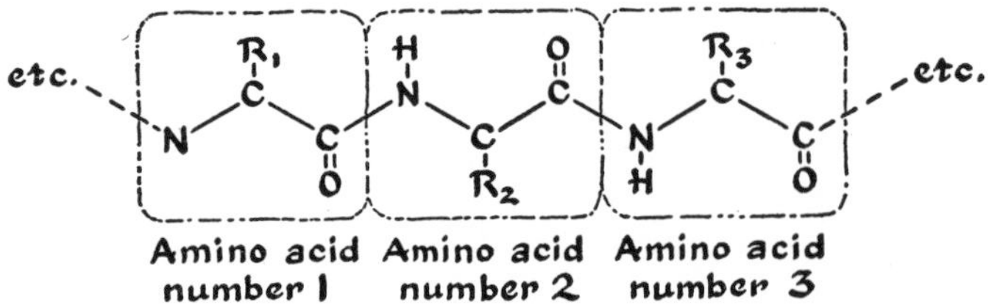

Amino acid number 1   Amino acid number 2   Amino acid number 3

LINKAGE OF AMINO ACIDS INTO PEPTIDE CHAINS.

it is referred to as a *dipeptide;* whereas if it contains three amino acids linked through two peptide bonds, it may be termed a *tripeptide*. In the structure of a protein, many amino acids are linked into very long *polypeptide* chains. Even the smallest of protein molecules contains roughly a hundred amino acids linked together, while many of the plant proteins we shall discuss contain 300–3000 residues linked together into a single large molecule. It is clear, therefore, that even in a protein which contains twenty or more different kinds of amino acids, some or all of these must be repeated many times in the structure of a single protein molecule.

Proteins may be split into their individual amino acid components by hydrolysis of the interconnecting peptide bonds. This hydrolysis may be brought about by heating the protein in alkaline or acid

HYDROLYSIS OF PEPTIDE CHAINS.

solution or by treatment with a proteolytic enzyme or enzymes. The individual amino acids in the protein hydrolyzate can be accurately determined, so that we may characterize a protein by its over-all composition of amino acids. We do not, however, have any adequate way of determining fully the order in which these residues occur along the peptide chain of the original protein. Nor do we have a satisfactory way of determining and describing in detail the manner in which the peptide chains of the protein are arranged in space. It is probable, however, that in most proteins the component chains are not straight, but are coiled up and folded over to form complex three-dimensional structures with characteristic protuberances and indentations on the surface.

Denaturation of Proteins

Perhaps the most characteristic reaction of a protein is that of *denaturation*. If we prepare a solution of a native protein, for example a water extract of a seed, and if we heat this solution to a temperature of 50–100° C, a voluminous precipitate of protein appears (Fig. 11-2). This protein will not go back into solution when the reaction mixture has cooled, and it will have lost all enzymatic and other biological properties. The original or native protein has been altered and is said to have undergone denaturation.

Denaturation can be brought about by agents other than heat. A strong acid or base; heavy metal ions such as lead, mercury, or silver; and various organic compounds can cause denaturation of protein

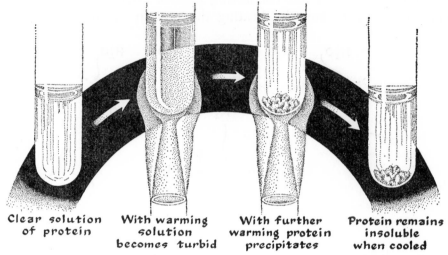

Clear solution | With warming | With further | Protein remains
of protein | solution | warming protein | insoluble
| becomes turbid | precipitates | when cooled

Figure 11-2. *Heat causes proteins to coagulate and irreversibly precipitate from solution.*

and are for this reason highly deleterious to living cells. Denaturation is an ever-present possibility, and must be guarded against by the plant physiologist who wishes to prepare native, undenatured proteins from plant tissues.

Separation of Proteins from One Another

A mixture of proteins such as occurs in a plant juice or extract may be separated by any of several methods. The best-known and most frequently applied method is that of fractional precipitation with high concentrations of a neutral salt, generally ammonium sulfate. Many proteins are insoluble in ammonium sulfate solutions. Some proteins are precipitated by relatively low concentrations of the salt, as for example by one-third saturated solutions. Other proteins are precipitated only at higher concentrations. By successive additions of ammonium sulfate to a protein solution it is possible to separate a protein mixture into a series of fractions of increasing solubility in the salt solution. The precipitated protein fractions are not denatured or harmed by the treatment and may be taken up and again dissolved in water or other solution.

Precipitants other than ammonium sulfate can also be employed; successive additions of acetone to aqueous protein solutions are sometimes successful for protein separations. Physical methods such as electrophoresis and ultracentrifugation are also tools which may be applied in the separation of protein mixtures. In electrophoresis, use is made of the fact that protein molecules are ordinarily ionized in solution, so that when an electric current is passed through a protein solution, a portion of the current flow is carried by the protein ions as they migrate toward the appropriate electrode. Each molecular species of protein possesses its own characteristic ionic mobility, and different kinds of proteins move through the solution at different rates. This method may be used to separate individual proteins from one another. In the process of ultracentrifugation, the molecules of the protein are actually sedimented from solution by the application of very high gravitational fields, fields from 20,000 to 400,000 times gravity. Since heavier molecules sediment more rapidly then lighter molecules, it is possible to separate individual proteins on the basis of molecular weights. In all cases, the object is of course to obtain individual proteins free from other kinds of proteins, in order that the enzymatic properties of a single kind of protein may be studied.

Classification of Proteins

The plant proteins may be classified according to a number of different systems. They may be classified according to the organ or tissue in which they occur or according to their enzymatic functions or activities. From an experimental point of view, it has been more

Table 11-2. *A Classification of Some Common Plant Proteins According to Solubility Properties.*

Albumins, soluble in water and in dilute neutral salt solutions.

Globulins, insoluble in water, but soluble in dilute neutral salt solutions.

Glutelins, insoluble in water and in dilute neutral salt solutions, but are soluble in dilute alkali.

Prolamines, insoluble in water and in dilute neutral salt solutions but are soluble in 50–70 per cent alcohol and in dilute acid or alkali.

---

practical to classify plant proteins according to their solubility properties; such a classification is given in Table 11-2.

The albumins, which are soluble in water as well as in dilute neutral salt solution, include not only proteins of many cereal seeds but also many of the enzyme proteins of the leaf and other plant organs. The globulins are distinguished from the albumins by the fact that they are insoluble in water alone but are soluble in water in the presence of low concentrations of neutral salts such as NaCl or KCl. Globulins are of wide occurrence both in seeds and in the vegetative organs of plants. Prolamines and glutelins, which are typical proteins of the cereal seeds such as wheat, are distinguished by relative insolubility in water or dilute salt. They are soluble in more specialized solvents as dilute acid or alkali in the case of the glutelins and 50–70 per cent aqueous ethyl alcohol in the case of the prolamines. A general class of conjugated or complex proteins might also be recognized, a class including all proteins which have a protein portion combined with a nonprotein group. Examples are the dehydrogenases, flavoproteins, and other respiratory enzymes described in Chapter 10. Still other types of conjugated protein are the nucleoproteins, which will be described later in this chapter; lipoproteins, which contain bound fat; and glycoproteins, which contain bound sugars.

Proteins may be classified also on the basis of their function in the life of the plant. Much of the protein of the seed appears to serve only as a source of amino acids for the young seedling after germination of the seed. These nonenzymatic proteins are generally referred to as *reserve proteins*. On the other hand, the proteins of the vegetative portions of the plant, as well as certain proteins of the seed, possess enzymatic properties and appear to serve in metabolism as enzymes rather than as substrates for other enzymes. We might refer to these proteins as *enzymatic*, or *functional*, *proteins* of the plant.

The Seed Proteins

The proteins of the seeds of cereals, particularly of wheat, have attracted much study in relation to human nutrition and especially to the making of bread. The cohesive, elastic property of dough is due primarily to the content of proteins in wheat flour. In the wheat seed, protein is contained both in the embryo and in the endosperm, with a large concentration of protein in the aleurone layer of the latter. The endosperm proteins are primarily reserve proteins, including glutenin, a glutelin, and gliadin, a prolamine, which together make up some 8 per cent of the weight of the seed. Much smaller amounts of albumin and globulin also are present in the wheat seed, and these doubtlessly represent the actual functional, or enzymatic, proteins of the endosperm and embryo. Seeds of dicotyledonous plants, unlike those of the cereals, contain large amounts of globulin as reserve protein. These globulins may make up 40 per cent of the dry weight of the seed in some instances, and, since they are present in such concentrations, it has been possible to isolate several in pure crystalline form. This is true of edestin, the reserve protein of the hemp seed, as well as the globulins of seeds of tobacco, various cucurbits, and others.

The Leaf Proteins

The proteins of the leaf may be separated into three distinct classes according to their site of occurrence in the cells of the leaf tissue. The chloroplasts contain about one-third to one-half of the total leaf protein bound in a complex which may be termed *chloroplastic protein*. The bulk of the remainder of the leaf protein is present as the soluble *cytoplasmic protein* of the cell. An even smaller amount of protein is present in the nucleus, bound in the *nuclear protein* of the chromosomes and other nuclear constituents. The general distribution of proteins in a typical palisade cell of the leaf is shown in Figure 11-3.

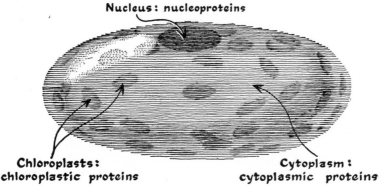

Figure 11-3. *The proteins of a leaf cell are located in cytoplasm, chloroplasts, and nucleus.*

To separate the proteins from the leaf tissue, it is necessary first to grind the material very finely, so that the cellular contents can escape through the ruptured cell walls. The ground leaf suspension is then run through a coarse filter or centrifuged at low speed to remove the cell wall fragments. The residual green solution now consists of chloroplasts or chloroplast fragments suspended in a solution of the cytoplasmic and vacuolar constituents. The chloroplasts may next be removed by higher speed centrifugation and obtained as a green sediment which may be resuspended in water or buffer solutions. These operations are summarized in Figure 11-4. The cytoplasmic proteins, which are contained in the residue after removal of the chloroplasts, may then be precipitated with ammonium sulfate or freed of other cellular components (sugars, organic acids, and so forth) by other means. The nuclear proteins make up such a small proportion of the total leaf protein that it is very difficult to isolate them from the major protein fractions.

It has been shown (Chap. 2) that the chloroplast consists of small, discrete, green bodies, the grana, which are imbedded in a colorless stroma, the whole being surrounded by a membrane, as shown in Figure 11-5. The proteins of the chloroplast are contained principally in the grana. (Although small amounts of protein may be contained in the stroma, there is no certain evidence on this point.) The chlorophyll

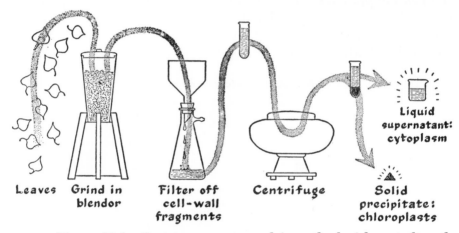

Leaves   Grind in   Filter off   Centrifuge   Solid

blendor   cell-wall   precipitate:

fragments   chloroplasts

Liquid supernatant: cytoplasm

Figure 11-4. *Proteins are extracted from the leaf by grinding the whole tissue and then separating out the solid cell wall fragments and chloroplasts by successive filtration and centrifugation.*

and the yellow carotenoid pigments of the leaf are bound to the granum protein very firmly, as are also fatty materials and small amounts of inorganic elements, including calcium, iron, copper, and zinc. The granum thus contains many materials; in fact the protein content accounts for only about one-half of the granum weight. All of these varied substances are, however, bound tightly together in the complex which makes up the laminar structure of the granum. It is this active complex that has the power to carry out the Hill reaction (Chap. 3). Many individual enzymatic activities, those of catalase, polyphenoloxidase, and others, have also been found in the granum, but few of the enzymes have yet been extracted in soluble form.

The cytoplasmic proteins of the leaf cell, unlike those of the grana, are soluble, and it has been shown that cytoplasmic protein is actually made of many different kinds of proteins, some of which are present in only very minute amounts. This is to be expected, since we have seen that each cell contains some one thousand different kinds of enzyme proteins, of which a great many are undoubtedly present in the

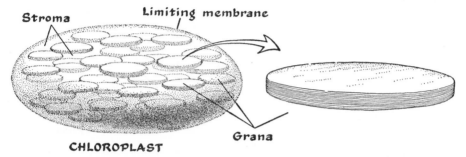

Figure 11-5. *The chloroplast is composed of chlorophyll-containing disc-shaped grana imbedded in a colorless matrix or stroma. Each granum is composed of a number of superimposed layers. The grana and stroma are surrounded by a limiting membrane.*

cytoplasm of the cell. A goodly array of enzymes has been found among the proteins of leaves, including various of the respiratory enzymes and enzymes for the phosphorylation and initial breakdown of sugars. On the basis of our present knowledge, it would seem, then, that the proteins of the leaf are principally functional enzymatic proteins, those involved in the manifold chemical reactions of metabolism.

Nucleoproteins

Nucleoproteins are of general importance in all living things as component materials of the chromosomes. In addition, however, nucleoproteins are found outside the nucleus in the cytoplasm of many, perhaps of all, cells. Nuclear and cytoplasmic nucleoproteins have in common a structure in which nucleic acid of high molecular weight is linked to protein. They differ, however, in the nature of the nucleic acid involved. To appreciate the nature of this difference, we must first understand that nucleic acids, like polysaccharides and proteins, are highly polymerized materials made up of relatively simple building blocks, the *nucleotides*. A single nucleotide consists fundamentally of a single pentose sugar molecule to which is attached at one end (the aldose, or reducing, end) a cyclic nitrogen material, while the other end is esterified with phosphoric acid. In the intact nucleic acid molecule, the phosphoric acid of one nucleotide serves as a link or bridge to the pentose molecule of the next nucleotide. In this way the nucleotides are attached together in long chains. Nuclear and cytoplasmic nucleic acids differ primarily in the nature of the pentose present

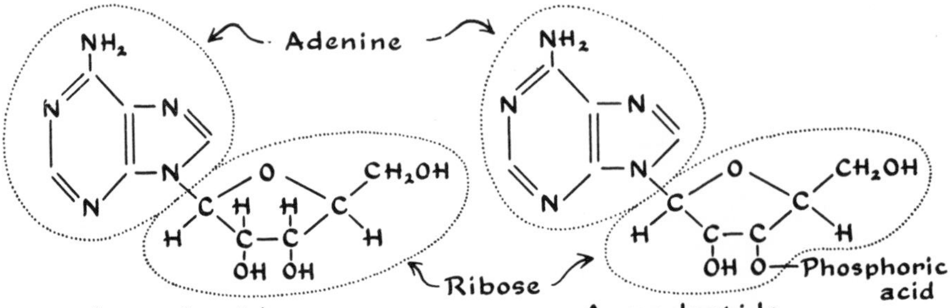

A nucleoside, adenosine

A nucleotide, adenylic acid

in the component nucleotides. Cytoplasmic nucleic acids contain the pentose D-ribose and are ordinarily referred to as ribonucleic acids. In the nuclear nucleic acids the sugar desoxyribose is present, and these nucleic acids are known as desoxyribonucleic acids.

The cyclic nitrogen compounds present in cytoplasmic nucleic acids are ordinarily the purines adenine and guanine and the pyrimidines cytosine and uracil, which participate in the formation of four

Adenine — Ribose — Phosphoric acid = Adenylic acid

Guanine — Ribose — Phosphoric acid = Guanylic acid

Cytosine — Ribose — Phosphoric acid = Cytidylic acid

Uracil — Ribose — Phosphoric acid = Uridylic acid

NUCLEOTIDES OF RIBONUCLEIC ACID.

different types of nucleotides, all of which are concerned in the formation of the nucleic acid molecule. In the desoxyribonucleic acids, adenine and guanine also participate, but the pyrimidines involved are cytosine and thymine. These chemical differences cannot yet be related to differences in their functions. Although we know now that chromosomes, and possibly genes, are composed of nucleic acid-containing proteins, we know very little about the way in which this nucleoprotein functions in exercising its control of developmental and hereditary processes.

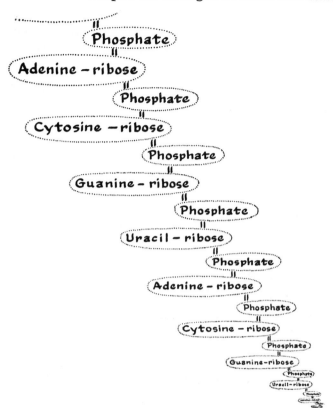

RIBONUCLEIC ACID.

Viruses

Among the many diseases of higher plants, one group in particular, the virus diseases, is related to proteins and protein metabolism. The infective agents which cause the virus diseases of higher plants are actually ribonucleoproteins, which may in some cases be extracted from infected tissues, purified, and even crystallized in presumably pure form. These crystals retain the capacity for producing disease. W. M. Stanley, in 1935, was the first to isolate and crystallize a virus in this way. The virus with which he worked was that which causes tobacco mosaic, a disease in which the tobacco plant is stunted in growth, and in which characteristic yellow, mottled areas appear in the tissues of the leaf. The disease is induced when a small amount of juice from a diseased plant or a small amount of solution of pure virus is rubbed on the surface of a leaf of a healthy tobacco plant, as shown in Figure 11-6. The virus multiplies in the tissues of the host, and it can be shown that a few weeks after infection the plant contains much more virus than was introduced in the original inoculum. The virus has, then, the property of multiplying in the tissues of the host. This vast amount of new virus nucleoprotein which is present in the cytoplasm of the cell of the host plant may readily be isolated from the normal plant proteins by centrifugation, since the virus has the enormously high molecular weight of 40 million, which is many times higher than that of any of the normal constituents.

Viruses other than tobacco mosaic have been obtained in pure form,

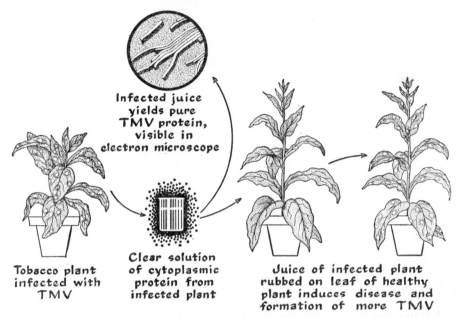

Infected juice
yields pure
TMV protein,
visible in
electron microscope

Clear solution
of cytoplasmic
protein from
infected plant

Tobacco plant
infected with
TMV

Juice of infected plant
rubbed on leaf of healthy
plant induces disease and
formation of more TMV

Figure 11-6. *Isolation and transmission of tobacco mosaic virus, TMV. The infected plant contains TMV as a cellular constituent. This constituent may be transmitted from one plant to another by direct contact of infected cellular material with an injured area of a healthy plant.*

and Table 11-3 gives a summary of some of their properties. These viruses differ not only in molecular weight and molecular shape, as shown in the table, but also in respect to the particular hosts they will attack. Viruses differ also in the manner in which they may be transmitted from plant to plant. Some, like tobacco mosaic virus, may be mechanically transmitted by rubbing the juice of an infected plant on a healthy leaf. Others are transmitted only by particular insects which feed on a diseased plant and subsequently feed on a healthy plant, to which they then transmit the virus.

The viruses constitute an important intermediate category of proteins lying between the world of living cells and the world of nonliving organic molecules. Like other kinds of proteins, viruses may be purified, crystallized, and identified as unique chemical substances. Like nonliving material, plant virus molecules have no recognizable metabolism apart from their host. Completely unlike other more conventional organic molecules, however, virus molecules have the power of carry-

Table 11-3. *The Properties of Some Plant Viruses.*

VIRUS	TYPICAL HOSTS	MEANS OF TRANSMIS- SION	GM VIRUS/ LITER OF PLANT JUICE	SHAPE OF VIRUS MOLECULE	MOLECULAR WEIGHT OF VIRUS
Tobacco mosaic	Tobacco	Mechanical	2.0	Rod, 600 $\times$ 15 mμ	40 $\times$ 10^6
Cucumber mosaic	Cucumber	Mechanical	0.3	Rod, 600 $\times$ 15 mμ	40 $\times$ 10^6
Alfalfa mosaic	Tobacco alfalfa	Mechanical, aphis	0.2	Sphere, diam. 16.5 mμ	2 $\times$ 10^6
Potato X	Tobacco potato	Mechanical, grafting	0.1	Rod, 420 $\times$ 9.8 mμ	26 $\times$ 10^6
Tobacco necrosis	Tobacco	Mechanical, air- and water- borne	0.04	Sphere, diam. 20 mμ	6 $\times$ 10^6
Tobacco ring spot	Tobacco	Mechanical	0.01	Sphere, diam. 19 mμ	3 $\times$ 10^6
Tomato bushy stunt	Tomato	Mechanical	0.05	Sphere, diam. 26 mμ	7 $\times$ 10^6

ing out or causing their own duplication. In this respect the virus molecule resembles the bacterial cell or even the higher plant as a whole. Perhaps an even closer comparison is that between the virus and the nuclear nucleoprotein of higher organisms, since nuclear nucleoprotein also is distinguished by its power of self-reproduction during nuclear divisions. For this reason, viruses have often been analogized with genes which have escaped from a nucleus into the cytoplasm.

Enzymes Attacking Proteins

Enzymes which attack and cleave the peptide bond are said to have *proteolytic activity.* The two general groups are: (1) the peptidases, which cleave the peptide bond only in the relatively small peptides containing one, two, or a few linkages; and (2) the proteases, which can attack the peptide bonds of intact protein molecules. In all cases the cleavage is a hydrolytic one, in which water is taken up with the formation of one free amino acid group and one free carboxyl group per peptide bond attacked. Curiously enough, the proteolytic enzymes are themselves proteins but are somehow immune to self-destruction.

Both peptidase and protease activity have been found in seeds and seedlings and in leaves. In the germinating seed, the proteolytic enzymes are doubtless responsible for the hydrolysis of the reserve protein, with the consequent liberation of the amino acids required for growth of the organs of the seedling. Extraordinarily high concentrations of proteases also are found in the latex of various plants, particularly in that of the papaya and milkweeds. The physiological significance of the latex proteases is, however, quite obscure.

Nitrogen Metabolism of the Germinating Seed

As the seed germinates, the stored reserve of the cotyledons or endosperm is drawn upon as a source of nutriment for the developing seedling. Among the materials thus mobilized, the proteins are of importance as a source of nitrogen and nitrogen-containing amino acids required for the synthesis of the protoplasm of the seedling. The germination of the seed is, therefore, accompanied by rapid hydrolysis of the reserve protein, with liberation of free amino acids. These amino acids are then translocated to the growing regions of the seedling, where they are utilized in cellular synthesis. The hydrolysis of reserve protein is, then, an important feature of germination and one which is, in part at least, due to the presence of proteolytic enzymes of the endosperm or cotyledons. The seedling exerts some measure of control over this proteolysis of reserve protein, however, since the rate and extent of the degradation of reserve depend on the demand of the growing seedling for nitrogen and on the amount of this material available from external sources in the form of nitrate or ammonia.

When seedlings are allowed to germinate and develop in darkness over an extended period of time, an abnormality of nitrogen metabolism results in the form of an accumulation of the amides asparagine and glutamine. When lupine seedlings are allowed to develop in darkness for twelve to fourteen days, asparagine may accumulate to the extent of 20–25 per cent of the total dry weight of the seedling. The formation of asparagine in etiolated lupine, or of glutamine in certain other species, is a result of the reactions which protect the plant against accumulation of ammonia. In the etiolated seedling, amino acids must serve as a substrate for respiration after depletion of other respiratory substrates. As the amino acid residues are oxidized, ammonia is released. This ammonia is then combined and accumulated by the seedling in the form of asparagine or glutamine. The accumulation of asparagine in seedlings can, in fact, be induced in some instances merely by supplying ammonia or ammonium ions to the nutrient solution in which seedlings are grown.

Nitrogen Metabolism and Nitrogen Supply

In a normal plant which is well supplied with nitrogen, the major portion of the leaf nitrogen is contained in the leaf proteins, and only a small part is contained in soluble amino acids or other soluble nitrogenous compounds. The individual leaves retain their same characteristic content of protein over prolonged periods of time. If, however, the plant is transferred to a nutrient regime deficient in nitrogen, the lower and older leaves will quickly yellow and wither, while the younger leaves will remain green. This is because under conditions of nitrogen deficiency, the proteins of the older leaves are hydrolyzed, and the soluble nitrogenous materials are mobilized and transported to the actively growing centers, just as reserve protein is hydrolyzed in the germinating seed. Yellowing of the leaf is due to the fact that the chloroplastic protein, as well as the cytoplasmic protein, is attacked and degraded, and with the loss of the chloroplasts the chlorophyll likewise disappears. The nitrogen status of the plant is, then, perhaps the most important single factor in regulating the protein content and the protein metabolism of the plant as a whole.

The Dynamic State of Plant Protein

An important feature of the nitrogen metabolism of the plant as a whole is the fact that the plant proteins appear to be in a state of continuous flux, wherein protein breakdown is balanced by resynthesis. Even though the total amount of protein in a leaf may remain constant over a long time, this does not mean that the same individual protein molecules remain in the leaf. On the contrary, it appears to mean only that the degradation of protein which is continuously taking place is nicely balanced by protein synthesis. We may imagine protein loss in the older leaves of nitrogen-starved plants, therefore, to be the result of the failure of resynthesis to balance degradation. The concept of the protein steady state as a balance between protein breakdown and resynthesis was first clearly enunciated by Schönheimer (1942) in his *The*

Dynamic State of Body Constituents. Although this book deals primarily with work on higher animals, Schönheimer, Vickery, and others later extended the observations to higher plants.

That a constant protein level is due to a balance between rates of degradation and resynthesis and that, even with constant protein level, the material is actually turning over, can be directly ascertained only by the use of isotopes. Suppose we supply a mature plant, in which the level of protein in the leaves is relatively constant, with a small amount of ammonium ions containing the isotope N^{15} rather than the ordinary N^{14}. It is found that this labelled nitrogen rapidly finds its way into the free amino acids, especially the free glutamic and aspartic acids of the plant. These amino acids containing the labelled nitrogen rapidly appear in the protein. This means, then, that new protein has been synthesized. Since the total protein content has remained constant, the new synthesis must have been balanced by an equal amount of protein breakdown.

Nitrogen Metabolism in Excised Leaves

When leaves are excised from the plant and placed with their petioles in water, rapid protein loss occurs, and the leaves yellow as a result of the loss of chloroplastic material. This protein loss is due to the removal of the leaf from the plant, and takes place even if the leaf is left in the light so that photosynthetic production of sugars may take place. The hydrolysis of protein is accompanied by a corresponding liberation in the excised leaf of free amino acids, which may be in part further oxidized with the liberation of ammonia and the production of asparagine or glutamine, just as in the case of dark-germinated seedlings. We have seen earlier in this chapter that in many species nitrate is reduced, and amino acids are produced in part or even wholly, in the roots, so that many of the amino acids used in the leaves may actually be manufactured in the roots. It seems probable that some factor, perhaps a particular amino acid or acids, produced in the roots is needed for the maintenance of protein level and normal protein turnover in the leaf. Thus in the excised leaf, in the absence of this root-produced factor, protein hydrolysis predominates over protein synthesis.

The Plant in Relation to Soil Nitrogen

We have seen that the plant contains on the average a total of from 1 to 5 per cent nitrogen on a dry weight basis. The soil from which the plant ordinarily derives its nitrogen only rarely contains as much as 1 per cent total nitrogen, and in general contains only from a few hundredths to perhaps 0.5 per cent. The struggle to obtain adequate nitrogen is hence one of the most general and continuing problems confronting the growing plant.

The nitrogen of the soil is contained in many different types of nitrogenous compounds. Of these, only a part, making up perhaps 2 to 10 per cent of the soil nitrogen, is ordinarily water-soluble and water-extractable from soil. The water-soluble or water-extractable nitrogen of the soil is made up in part of nitrate and ammonium ions and in part of amino acids, purines, and other organic compounds. The water-

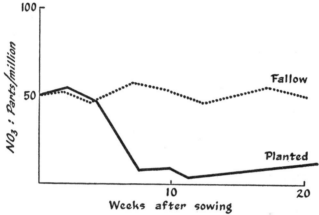

Figure 11-7. *During the growth of a crop, nitrate is rapidly depleted from the soil. If the soil remains fallow (without a crop), the nitrate level remains relatively constant. (Adapted from Burd, J. Agr. Research, 18, 1919, p. 66.)*

insoluble nitrogen of the soil is in part proteinlike, since it can be hydrolyzed with acid to yield soluble amino acids. In all probability, an appreciable proportion of this proteinlike nitrogen is present in the soil as a constituent of actual living microorganisms. A final fraction of the soil nitrogen is present as soil humin, a material which is insoluble in the common solvents and not hydrolyzed by acids.

Only the soluble forms of soil nitrogen appear to be immediately available to the growing plant. These forms include not only nitrate but also ammonium salts and organic substances, as mentioned above. There is a great deal of evidence, however, which indicates that ammonium salts as well as soluble organic nitrogen are rapidly converted to nitrate in the soil. The soil bacteria Nitrosomonas and Nitrobacter carry out, respectively, the oxidation of ammonia to nitrite and the oxidation of nitrite to nitrate. When pure amino acids are added to soil, ammonia is liberated by still other microorganisms, and nitrogen added to the soil in the form of pure amino acids can be recovered from the soil in the form of nitrate after periods as short as a few days. Protein nitrogen added to soil either as pure protein or as plant residues is also in part converted to nitrate through the successive actions of these several kinds of microorganisms.

Since both organic nitrogen and ammonium nitrogen are so rapidly converted to nitrate, and since nitrate is the principal source of nitrogen for plant growth, it is not surprising that the level of nitrate nitrogen in the soil varies according to intensity of plant growth. Figure 11-7 shows that with a particular soil the nitrate content dropped from about 50 ppm to less than 10 ppm during the first few weeks after planting of the soil to barley. When the soil was maintained fallow, the nitrate level remained more or less constant. It is typical of the nitrate level in soil, then, that it is decreased during periods of intensive plant growth but is slowly built up again during fallow periods or in the spring and fall, when microbial processes produce more nitrate from the reservoir of soil organic nitrogen than is used in plant growth.

Nitrogen Fixation

Nitrogen does not occur as a mineral in any of the parent rocks from which soils are derived, and the nitrogen which is found in soil may all be ultimately traced back to the atmosphere. Table 11-4 shows that the nitrogen contained in an acre of moderately fertile agricultural soil

Table 11-4. *Nitrogen Content in and above a Typical Fertile Midwestern Soil.*

	LB/ACRE
Soil Nitrogen	
Total N, first 40 inches in depth	10,000
Available N (NH$_4$, NO$_3$, etc.)	1,000
Atmospheric N$_2$ (Above acre)	300,000,000

is actually only a small fraction of the nitrogen present as molecular N$_2$ in the atmosphere above that acre of soil.

The conversion of the molecular nitrogen of the atmosphere to soil nitrogen available or potentially available to plants is accomplished in two principal ways: (1) Nitrogen may be oxidized to nitrous oxides by the action of lightning. These oxides are then carried to the ground by rain and deposited as nitrous or nitric acid. The contribution of this form of nitrogen fixation, although significant, is small in comparison with the amounts of molecular nitrogen which are converted to organic nitrogen by the process of (2) biological nitrogen fixation, a term which includes the various processes by which molecular nitrogen is converted into combined forms through the agency of living organisms. Certain free-living microorganisms have the power to utilize molecular nitrogen as a source of nitrogen and are able to reduce N_2 to the level of ammonia. Also, a large group of the higher plants, the legumes, are capable, with the aid of bacteria of the genus Rhizobium, of reducing and utilizing molecular N_2. These two agencies of biological nitrogen fixation are principally responsible for the maintenance of the nitrogen content of the soil.

The concept of biological nitrogen fixation arose from the discovery by Berthelot in 1882 that when soils are incubated under favorable conditions of water content and temperature, actual increases in total combined nitrogen may occur. Winogradsky, the French bacteriologist, a short time later isolated from soil a bacterium capable of reducing and utilizing molecular nitrogen. The organism which he isolated, an anaerobic spore-forming bacterium of the genus Clostridium, is still known as an important nitrogen-fixing soil microorganism. Perhaps the most important nitrogen-fixing microorganism of soil, the aerobic Azotobacter, was discovered still later by the Dutch microbiologist Beijerinck. Both Clostridium and Azotobacter utilize and oxidize organic matter and expend a portion of the energy derived from substrate oxidation in the energy-consuming process of nitrogen reduction. In both cases, moreover, the nitrogen removed from the atmosphere is converted to nitrogenous compounds which go to make up the actual structure of the microbial cells. Only secondarily, after death and decomposition of the microorganism, does the nitrogen ultimately become available, through microbial oxidation to nitrate, for the growth of higher plants. Although the bacteria are perhaps the most important of the nitrogen-fixing microorganisms, it is nevertheless of interest that the blue-green alga Nostoc is also able to carry out the process. Nostoc is a remarkably self-sufficient organism, since it carries out not only its own photosynthetic reduction of CO_2 but also its own reduction of molecular nitrogen.

The fixation of molecular nitrogen by leguminous plants is in actuality confined strictly to root nodules which are formed by the

Figure 11-8. *A leguminous root system with characteristic nodules formed as the result of infection with the bacterium Rhizobium.*

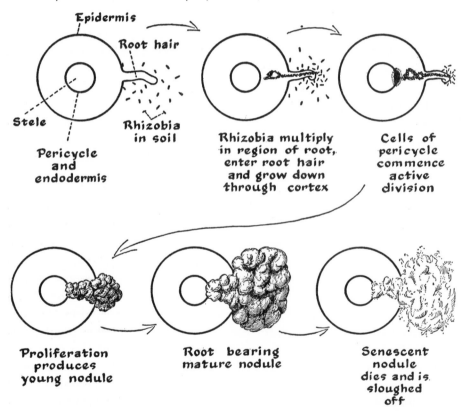

Epidermis

Root hair

Stele

Rhizobia in soil

Pericycle and endodermis

Rhizobia multiply in region of root, enter root hair and grow down through cortex

Cells of pericycle commence active division

Proliferation produces young nodule

Root bearing mature nodule

Senescent nodule dies and is sloughed off

Figure 11-9. *Formation of the legume root nodule as the result of infection with Rhizobium. (Modified after Wilson,* Biochemistry of Symbiotic Nitrogen Fixation, *University of Wisconsin Press, 1940, p. 47.)*

symbiotic union of legume and the appropriate bacterium (Fig. 11-8). These bacteria, various species of the genus Rhizobium, grow in soil as ordinary soil bacteria, incapable by themselves of any nitrogen fixation. In the presence of a root of a suitable legume, the Rhizobium invades a root hair and grows in through the tissues of the root, the invasion resulting in proliferation of the pericycle and the production of a warty lump or nodule on the root (Fig. 11-9). These nodules, containing not only the host tissue of the legume but also the cells of Rhizobium, carry out the process of leguminous or so-called "symbiotic" nitrogen fixation. Interestingly enough, although nodules had long been known as histological features of leguminous roots, it was not until the classical work of the German chemists Hellriegel and Wilfarth in 1887 that their relations to microbial infection and nitrogen fixation were clearly recognized.

In the root nodule, as in the cells of Clostridium or Azotobacter, nitrogen fixation is carried out at the expense of the energy supplied by respiratory oxidation. In both cases, molecular nitrogen is reduced to the level of ammonia and then rapidly appears in certain of the amino acids. We do not yet know, however, the mechanism by which energy production is linked to nitrogen reduction, nor do we have knowledge of the intermediates through which nitrogen passes on its way from molecular nitrogen to amino nitrogen.

Balance of Nitrogen in the Soil

We have seen that fixed nitrogen is contributed to the soil by both atmospheric and biological activities. On the other hand, fixed nitrogen is continuously being lost from the soil, particularly under agricultural conditions. When a crop is removed from the soil, the nitrogen contained in the produce is lost from that area. The soluble forms of nitrogen are also leached—washed out of the root zone by rains or irrigation. Erosion is also an effective agent of nitrogen removal, particularly since nitrogen is concentrated in the surface layers of the soil. Although both the leached and the eroded nitrogen may ultimately reach the ocean and contribute to the ocean's supply of fixed nitrogen, this nitrogen is lost as far as agriculture is concerned.

Let us now try to draw up a balance sheet of the income and outgo of nitrogen from an acre of typical agricultural land. The data in Table 11-5 shows that for the particular case considered, some sixty pounds of nitrogen are removed per acre per year in the average harvested crop. Another seven pounds or so are lost through leaching, and even more

Table 11-5. *Income and Outgo of Nitrogen in a Typical Fertile Midwestern Soil.*

NITROGEN LOST FROM SOIL		NITROGEN GAINED BY SOIL	
AGENCY	LB/ACRE/YEAR	AGENCY	LB/ACRE/YEAR
Average crop (nonlegumes)	60	Rain	5
Leaching	7	Nonsymbiotic biological fixation	25
Erosion	varies greatly		
TOTAL	67 or more	TOTAL	30
		Alfalfa cover crop	200–250
		Clover cover crop	100–150

may be lost through erosion and the biological process of denitrification, in which fixed nitrogen of the soil is converted to molecular nitrogen by microorganisms. Balanced against this annual loss of some sixty-seven pounds of nitrogen per acre, we may expect about five pounds of nitrogen per acre to be added from atmospheric nitrogen oxides brought down by rain. Another twenty-five pounds per acre may be contributed by nonsymbiotic nitrogen fixation during the crop year. It is clear, then, that in the typical crop practice there is a twofold or even greater disparity between the income and outgo of nitrogen. The various processes involved are shown diagrammatically in Figure 11-10.

Lightning	Free-living microorganisms	Legumes	Removal of agricultural produce	Leaching	Erosion	Dust storms

PROCESSES ADDING FIXED NITROGEN TO THE SOIL **PROCESSES REMOVING FIXED NITROGEN FROM THE SOIL**

Figure 11-10. *Fixed nitrogen is continually added to the soil by the varied nitrogen-fixing processes. At the same time, nitrogen is lost from the soil by other agencies.*

In the long run, this discrepancy must be made up by the addition of some form of fixed nitrogen to the soil. In some instances, the addition may take the form of ammonium sulfate, manure, or other nitrogen-containing materials. A more effective method of balancing the nitrogen economy, however, is the growing of leguminous crops. The data of Table 11-5 show that alfalfa, a legume, may contribute as much as two hundred and fifty pounds of nitrogen per acre per year, or several times the amount of nitrogen lost each year by the average nonleguminous crop. Other legumes, such as clover, contribute smaller but substantial amounts of nitrogen to the soil. For this reason, it is the practice in well-balanced and stable agricultural systems to alternate legume and nonlegume crops in a regular schedule of crop rotation. By such crop rotation, it is possible to hold soil nitrogen levels at relatively high values over many years even without the addition of any fixed nitrogenous fertilizer.

The Nitrogen Cycle in Nature

The nitrogen which is removed from soil in the form of plant products is in a great measure consumed by animals as food. Part of this nitrogen is returned to the same or different soil as animal excreta and as dead animal tissues. The same nitrogen, again converted to soil nitrogen by microbial activity, is once more available to plants, and the entire process may now be repeated.

Actually the nitrogen cycle is not as simple as that. As we have seen, there are leaks or losses in the system due to leaching, erosion, the modern practice of sewage disposal, and other factors, all of which either result in loss of nitrogen to the ocean or, in general, render fixed nitrogen unavailable to higher plants. These losses are compensated for by the processes of nitrogen fixation. The manifold interrelations of nitrogen are summed up in Figure 11-11.

Summary

Nitrogen, which is essential to the plant as a constituent of its amino acids, its proteins, and other varied components, is in general taken up by the roots in the form of ammonium or nitrate ions. Before nitrate can be metabolized further, it must first be reduced to the ammonium level, a reduction which may take place either exclusively in the roots or throughout the plant. The ammonia or ammonium ions thus produced are now available for incorporation into one of the twenty-two amino

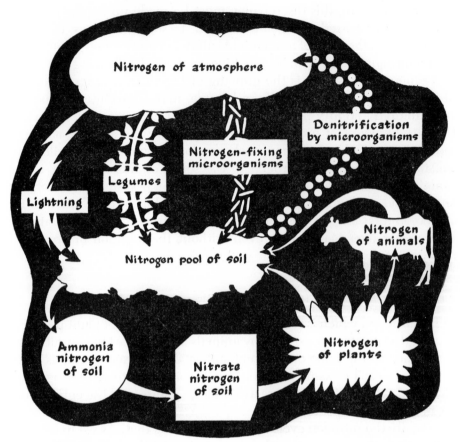

Figure 11-11. *The nitrogen cycle. The nitrogen of the soil, of liv-ing creatures, and of the atmosphere is in a state of continuous flux or turnover.*

acids which constitute the structure of the plant proteins. By precisely what mechanism amino acid molecules are coupled to form the proteins we do not know. We do know, however, that these same twenty-two amino acids, in varying ratios, numbers, and arrangements, make up all of the varied proteins of the plant, including the chloroplastic pro-teins, the various proteins of the cytoplasm, the reserve proteins of the seed, and the proteins of the nucleus.

The amino acids and proteins of the plant are labile materials, subject to continual degradation and resynthesis. Many environmental factors and especially the supply of nitrogen to the roots of the plant affect the amount of protein present in the plant and its distribution among the various organs. The nitrogen of proteins is capable of being mobilized.

that is, removed from older tissues and transported to the younger and more actively growing centers, where it is reutilized in protein synthesis.

The nitrogen of the soil, which is the source of supply for most kinds of higher plants, is deposited in the soil principally by the biological processes of nitrogen fixation. In this process, molecular nitrogen of the atmosphere is converted to nitrogen combined in organic materials. Fixation of atmospheric nitrogen is carried on by a variety of microorganisms, including free-living soil bacteria and blue-green algae, as well as the bacteria which live symbiotically in the root nodules of the leguminous plants. Nitrogen, once fixed in organic form through the processes of biological nitrogen fixation, is converted by still other microorganisms to the nitrate which serves as the source of nitrogen for most higher plants.

QUESTIONS

1. Warburg and Negelein found that in the green alga Chlorella the reduction of nitrate to ammonia is greatly accelerated by light. What is a possible mechanism for this effect?

2. How do virus proteins differ from the normal proteins of a green leaf cell?

3. How does the nitrogen metabolism of an etiolated seedling differ from that of a seedling grown in the light?

4. Most plants grow best with nitrate as a nitrogen source, but certain plants seem to prefer the ammonium ion. What can be suggested as a possible biochemical reason for this difference in behavior?

5. Cramer and Myers found that Chlorella can utilize either nitrate or ammonia as a nitrogen source, but that when a mixture of the two is fed, only nitrate is used. What does this imply about the regulation of nitrate reduction in this organism?

6. How can the fact that nitrate reduction occurs principally in the roots of certain species help to explain the paradoxes in nitrogen transport described in Chapter 7?

7. What are the structural features common to all amino acids? What special features distinguish (a) aspartic and glutamic acids; (b) lysine, arginine, and histidine; (c) glycine from all other amino acids?

8. Discuss several methods by which the plant synthesizes amino acids.

9. The parent rocks from which soils are derived are essentially devoid of nitrogen. How, then, has nitrogen appeared in soils?

10. Burström has found that over short periods of time, a low concentration of the substance n-diamyl-acetic acid interferes with nitrate reduction in wheat roots without disturbing growth or glucose utilization. How could this substance be used in tracing the pathway of nitrate reduction?

11. What evidence indicates: (a) that the proteins of the plant leaf are continuously being degraded and resynthesized, (b) that substances produced in other portions of the plant regulate the protein level of leaves?

12. When a cell dies, it usually undergoes a process of autolysis, or self-digestion, involving mainly a hydrolysis of proteins. Since proteolytic enzymes are present in the cell prior to death, why are the proteins not digested *in vivo*?

GENERAL READING

Burström, H., "The Nitrate Nutrition of Plants." *Ann. Roy. Agr. Coll. of Sweden*, 13: 1, 1945. An authoritative review of work on nitrate uptake and nitrate reduction.

Chapman, H. D., Liebig, G. F., and Rayner, D. S., "A Lysimeter Investigation of Nitrogen Gains and Losses under Various Systems of Cover-cropping and Fertilization, and a Discussion of Error Sources." *Hilgardia*, 19: 57, 1949. An excellent model for the study of nitrogen balance in agricultural soils.

McKee, H. S., "Review of Recent Work on Nitrogen Metabolism." *New Phytologist*, 48: 1, 1949. A thorough, modern review of the interconversion of nitrogenous compounds in higher plants.

Nightingale, G. T., "The Nitrogen Nutrition of Green Plants," Parts I and II. *Botan. Rev.*, 3: 85, 1937; *ibid.*, 14: 185, 1948. The general aspects of nitrogen in relation to the plant.

Schönheimer, R., *The Dynamic State of Body Constituents*. Cambridge: University Press, 1949. Endless biochemical flux in living systems described by a pioneer investigator.

Schreiner, O., and Brown, B. E., "Soil Nitrogen," in *Soils and Men*, U. S. Dept. of Agriculture Yearbook, 1938, p. 361. A detailed, yet semi-popular account.

Wilson, P. W., *The Biochemistry of Symbiotic Nitrogen Fixation*. Madison: University of Wisconsin Press, 1940. Full and readable treatment of the physiology and chemistry of the process. A classic.

CHAPTER 12

Lipids: Their Role in Structure and Function

The Lipids

We have seen that two major constituents of higher plants are the proteins and the carbohydrates, which serve not only as structural components of the protoplasm and of the cell wall, but also as reserve food materials in seeds and other organs. A third important class of plant constituents is the group known as the *lipids*. Lipids are fatty substances; the *true fats* are, in fact, one principal group of the larger category of the lipids. The fats, characterized by a particular kind of chemical structure which is discussed below, serve primarily as reserve food substances, just as does starch. The *waxes*, a second category of the lipids, serve, on the contrary, principally as cell wall materials and are found in the cuticle of many epidermal tissues. Still a third subdivision is constituted by the *phospholipids*, a group of compounds fatlike in their chemistry, of universal occurrence in protoplasm, and of only vaguely defined function. The composition of the three classes of lipids is shown in Table 12-1.

Table 12-1. *Classes of Lipids.*

TRUE FATS (RESERVE FOOD MATERIAL)	WAXES (CUTICULAR COMPONENTS)	PHOSPHOLIPIDS (STRUCTURAL MATERIALS)
Fatty acids esterified with glycerol to form triglycerides	1. Esters of fatty acids with long-chain alcohols	1. Glycerides containing two fatty acids and one phosphoric acid — phosphatidic acids
	2. Long-chain alcohols, ketones, hydrocarbons	2. Phosphatidic acids linked to choline — lecithin
		3. Phosphatidic acids linked to ethanolamine — cephalin

Role of Fats

Fat, like protein and carbohydrates, serves as reserve food in seeds. In almost 90 per cent of all seeds investigated, fat is found as the principal reserve material. It is deposited during the development of the seed and mobilized and reutilized as a source of energy during the germination and growth of the seedling. Fat may be stored either in the cotyledons of the embryo, as in the soybean and sunflower, or in the endosperm, as in the palms. In the cereals, on the other hand, the fatty materials are found primarily in the embryo and only in low or negligible concentration in the endosperm itself.

Fats occur also in leaves, stems, roots, fruits, flowers, and even in pollen grains. In general, however, fats are found in higher concentration in the seed or in the flesh of the fruit and in lower concentrations in the vegetative organs of the plant. In many seeds, fat makes up 35 to 50 per cent of the total dry material, while vegetative organs in general contain 5 per cent or less on a dry-weight basis. The edible fats used by mankind are, therefore, generally obtained from seeds or fruits, such as soybean, cottonseed, peanut, corn, and coconut palm. It is obvious that the yields of fat obtained per acre from fat-producing agricultural plants are very low as compared to the amount of carbohydrates available from the vegetative organs of such plants as sugar cane or sugar beet.

Fats are insoluble in water and are therefore found in the plant cell in the form of small droplets or globules dispersed in the cytoplasm. These globules are frequently large enough to be seen under the microscope, particularly if stained with dyes such as Sudan III, which are themselves fat soluble.

Structure of Fats

Fats are, chemically speaking, esters, or unions of organic acids with certain alcohols. In the ester linkage, one molecule of water is

GENERALIZED STRUCTURE OF A FAT MOLECULE.

eliminated between the carboxyl or acid group of the organic acid and the hydroxyl group of the alcohol. Hydrolysis or cleavage of the ester consists of the uptake of one molecule of water at the ester linkage with reconstitution of the free acid and free alcohol molecules. The characteristic alcohol of the fats is glycerol, a 3-carbon compound

HYDROLYSIS OF FATS.

in which each carbon atom bears a hydroxyl group. In the naturally occurring fats, each of these hydroxyl groups is esterified with an organic acid. The acids which are combined with glycerol in the naturally occurring fats are the so-called *fatty acids*, acids which contain even numbers of carbon atoms linked together in long chains which are, in general, unbranched. The carboxyl or acid group is at one end of this long-chain molecule, while the remainder of the chain consists of carbon and hydrogen atoms only. The principal fatty acids of higher plant fats are those containing from 12 to 26 carbon atoms. Of these acids, however, not all are equally important, and only the most widely distributed are shown in Table 12-2. The simplest is

Table 12-2. *Some of the Principal Fatty Acids of the Fats of Higher Plants.*

ACID	COMPOSITION	CHEMICAL STRUCTURE
Lauric	$C_{12}H_{24}O_2$	$CH_3 (CH_2)_{10} COOH$
Myristic	$C_{14}H_{28}O_2$	$CH_3 (CH_2)_{12} COOH$
Palmitic	$C_{16}H_{32}O_2$	$CH_3 (CH_2)_{14} COOH$
Stearic	$C_{18}H_{36}O_2$	$CH_3 (CH_2)_{16} COOH$
Oleic	$C_{18}H_{34}O_2$	$CH_3 (CH_2)_7 CH : CH (CH_2)_7 COOH$
Ricinoleic	$C_{18}H_{34}O_3$	$CH_3 (CH_2)_5 CHOHCH_2 CH : CH (CH_2)_7 COOH$
Erucic	$C_{22}H_{42}O_2$	$CH_3 (CH_2)_7 CH : CH (CH_2)_{11} COOH$
Linoleic	$C_{18}H_{32}O_2$	$CH_3 (CH_2)_4 CH : CHCH_2 CH : CH (CH_2)_7 COOH$
Linolenic	$C_{18}H_{30}O_2$	$CH_3 CH_2 CH : CHCH_2 CH : CHCH_2 CH : CH(CH_2)_7 COOH$
Chaulmoogric	$C_{18}H_{32}O_2$	$CH =CH$ $>CH (CH_2)_{12} COOH$ $CH_2—CH_2$

lauric acid, which contains 12 carbon atoms in a straight chain. Lauric acid is a so-called *saturated fatty acid,* in which all of the carbon atoms, aside from the terminal carboxyl group, are completely reduced to the CH_2 or CH_3 level. Myristic acid resembles lauric acid but contains 14 carbon atoms. Palmitic acid belongs to this same series, as does stearic acid; both are saturated acids and contain 16 and 18 carbon atoms, respectively.

In many of the fatty acids of the fats of higher plants, one or more double bonds occur between carbon atoms in the fatty acid chain. Thus, in oleic acid, which contains 18 carbon atoms, one double bond is found in the carbon atom chain. Linoleic acid, which also has 18 carbon atoms, contains two double bonds in the chain, while linolenic acid, another 18-carbon-atom acid, contains a total of three double bonds.

The fatty acids lauric, myristic, palmitic, stearic, oleic, linoleic, and linolenic are the most abundant fatty acids in the plant world, and many of the fats of numerous kinds of plants contain these seven fatty acids as their major components. For example, it has been estimated that oleic acid constitutes 34 per cent of the total fatty acids produced in all of the world's edible fats. There are, however, a great many other fatty acids which occur in larger or smaller amounts in particular species. The genus Hydnocarpus, for example, produces chaulmoogric acid, a component of the chaulmoogra oil which has been used in the treatment of leprosy. Erucic acid is a component of the fats of crucifer seeds, while ricinoleic acid is characteristic of the fat of the castor bean.

Plant fats are, then, made up of various fatty acids esterified with glycerol. As a general principle, each glycerol molecule tends to be associated in the fat molecule with different fatty acids, so that there are many different kinds of fats. Thus, in a particular instance, the fat molecule may be made up of glycerol esterified with one molecule each of lauric, oleic, and linoleic acids. Other fat molecules in the same fat may contain stearic, oleic, and linoleic acids or lauric, stearic, and oleic acids, and so on. In the fat of a single seed many of these differently constituted molecules are mixed and intermingled to form the characteristic fat of the particular species.

Plant fats may be either liquid or solid at ordinary temperatures. The liquid fats are ordinarily referred to as *oils,* while the solid fats are referred to as *fats* proper. The principal factor in the chemical constitution of a fat or oil which influences its physical nature is its proportion of unsaturated fatty acids, that is, fatty acids containing one, two, or more double bonds. For example, linseed oil, which is produced by flax seed, contains 60 to 75 per cent of unsaturated acids, whereas the solid fat of cocoa seeds, the so-called "cocoa butter," contains over 75 per cent of saturated acids, such as palmitic and stearic. Oils which contain a high concentration of unsaturated fatty acids may thicken and dry to a solid film when exposed to air. Because of their drying and thickening property, these oils are used in paint. The edible oils and fats are those which contain a lower proportion of unsaturated fatty acids and which are, therefore, not only less oily but also less unstable in air than the drying oils. Conversion of liquid plant oils to solid fats by hydrogenation, the direct addition of hydrogen to the double bonds of the unsaturated fatty acids, has become an important industrial procedure for the manufacturing of solid shortening and margarine from such seed oils as cotton, soybean, and peanut.

Accumulation and Mobilization of Fat

Even though fats are found especially in the mature seed or fruit, these organs initially contain very little fatty material. The accumulation of fat takes place during the development of the storage tissue. Figure 12-1 shows the course of fat accumulation during the growth

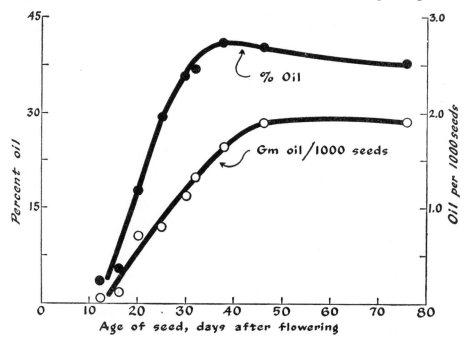

Figure 12-1. *The accumulation of fat in the flax seed. (Adapted from data of Eyre,* Biochem. J., *25, 1931, p. 1907.)*

of the flax seed. The fat content of this organ increases slowly at first but ultimately rises rapidly to the final high value. Fat increases both in quantity and in concentration during the development of the seed. This accumulation is probably due to the transformation of sugar to fat in the seed itself, and it is actually sugar rather than fat which is translocated into the seed from the leaves of the plant. That fat formation from sugar takes place in the ripening seed has been shown primarily by a consideration of respiratory quotients. We have seen in Chapter 10 that the respiratory quotient, the ratio of CO_2 evolution to oxygen consumption, is unity for the respiratory oxidation of hexose. If hexose were to be converted to fat, however, the respiratory quotient should be much higher than 1, as can be seen from the chemical reaction that would necessarily occur. In this reaction at least one molecule of hexose must be burned to CO_2 and water for each molecule

$$2C_6H_{12}O_6 + 3O_2 \longrightarrow 6CO_2 + 6H_2O + (-CH_2-)_6$$

APPROXIMATE OVER-ALL REACTION FOR THE CONVERSION OF SUGAR TO FAT.

of hexose reduced to the level of the —CH_2— group, the approximate reduction level found in fats. It is apparent, therefore, that to achieve this transformation six molecules of carbon dioxide would have to be given off for each three molecules of oxygen taken up. The R.Q. for the conversion of hexose to fat would, therefore, approach 2 as a maximum. If normal respiratory oxidation of hexose were to accompany the conversion of hexose to fat, the over-all R.Q. should then lie between 1 and 2. Actually, the R.Q. of ripening seeds of oil- or fat-producing plants is higher than 1, that is, is higher than the R.Q. for oxidation of hexose. Respiratory quotients of ripening seeds of flax and castor bean, among others, have been found experimentally to be as high as 1.5. It is clear, therefore, that in the ripening seed some hexose is being burned in respiration, and other molecules of sugar are being converted to fat, which is then stored away in the seed as a reserve material.

As the young seedling axis develops, fats disappear from the cotyledons or endosperm. They are not transported bodily to the growing seedling but are rather converted to sugars, which, along with other possible derivatives of the fat, are translocated to the growing tissues. In flax, which has been investigated particularly, fat disappears from the cotyledons during germination, but it does not reappear in the seedling. Instead, the carbon contained in the fat of the flax seed reappears in the form of carbohydrates, proteins, and the other components of the seedling. It would seem, therefore, that during germination, fat of the reserve tissue is reconverted to sugars and possibly other derivatives. This can also be shown by further considerations of the R.Q. of the reserve tissues and of the growing seedling tissues during germination. The R.Q. for the combustion of hexose, as seen above (p. 216) is approximately 1, that is, one mol of CO_2 is evolved for each mol of O_2 taken up. In the oxidation of fatty acids approximately 0.7 mol of CO_2 is given off for each mol of oxygen taken up, as can be seen from the equation shown below for the oxidation of a fatty acid to CO_2 and water. The conversion of fats to sugars, however, is a process which uses oxygen without the evolution of CO_2. In the germinating seed, for example the castor bean, the R.Q.

$$C_{18}H_{36}O_2 + 26 O_2 \longrightarrow 18 CO_2 + 18 H_2O \qquad R.Q. = 0.7$$

THE COMPLETE OXIDATION OF STEARIC ACID TO CO_2 AND H_2O.

of the endosperm is below 0.3. This means that, although some respiratory oxidation of fat may be taking place in the endosperm, the gas-exchange reactions are by and large those which have a very low R.Q., as does the conversion of fat to sugar. The R.Q. of the growing seedling tissue, on the other hand, is approximately 1. This means that these tissues are using sugar as the respiratory substrate.

In summary, fats are produced in the reserve tissues of the seed during seed development. These fats are produced from sugars translocated into the seed during ripening. During germination of the seed the reverse process takes place. Fats are reconverted to sugars, and the sugars are translocated to the developing tissues of the seedling.

Fat Breakdown and Synthesis

Fatty seeds and, in fact, nearly all plant tissues, contain an enzyme, lipase, which catalyzes the hydrolysis of fats to glycerol and their constituent fatty acids. Thus in the presence of lipase each molecule of fat takes up three molecules of water to hydrolyze the three ester linkages in the fatty acid molecule. Lipase can also, under appropriate conditions, carry out the reverse of this reaction, that is, in the presence of high concentrations of fatty acids and of alcohol, fats or synthetic esters can be produced. Lipase is therefore very probably the enzyme which first attacks the fat during the mobilization of the material. The

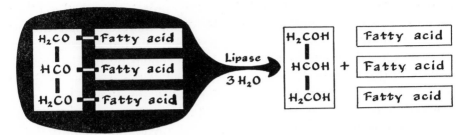

HYDROLYSIS OF FAT MOLECULE TO YIELD GLYCEROL AND FREE FATTY ACIDS.

fatty acids thus produced are next subjected to further oxidative attack.

The oxidation of fatty acids to carbon dioxide and water, that is, the respiratory oxidation of fatty acids, has been but little studied in plant tissues, and most of our knowledge of this process comes from studies on microorganisms and tissues of higher animals. The basic principle involved in the oxidation of fatty acids is that of *beta-oxidation,* a process by which a fatty acid is degraded through oxidative removal of successive 2-carbon fragments from the molecule. The

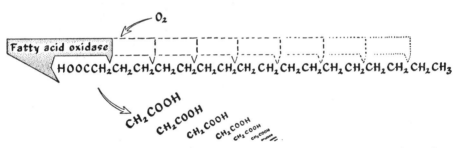

Figure 12-2. *In the oxidation of fatty acids, successive 2-carbon fragments are cleaved from the molecule.*

2-carbon fragments produced in the oxidation of fatty acids are similar to acetate, and are believed to be actually derivatives of acetate, possibly acetyl phosphate. This acetate derivative is then oxidized through the Krebs cycle (Chap. 10), just as is the 2-carbon fragment produced from pyruvate in the respiratory breakdown of hexose. In fact, the 2-carbon fragment from pyruvate cleavage may be identical with that derived from fatty acid breakdown.

The synthesis of sugar from fats is undoubtedly made possible by the fact that the pathways of fat and carbohydrate metabolism have a common point or junction. Fatty acid, once oxidized to the common

2-carbon fragment, may alternatively reascend through pyruvate to the level of hexose or undergo complete oxidation to CO_2 and water.

The synthesis of fatty acids in those organisms in which it has been studied proceeds in a manner just the reverse of fatty acid breakdown. In fatty acid synthesis, 2-carbon fragments similar to acetate are joined head to tail, until a fatty acid of the requisite length has been assembled, a process which is summarized in Figure 12-3. Fatty acid synthesis from the 2-carbon units similar to acetate is a process which requires energy-rich phosphate. This again, then, is a process in which the energy-rich phosphate produced in respiration is utilized in carry-

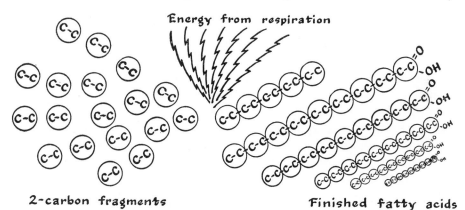

Figure 12-3. *In the synthesis of fatty acids, 2-carbon fragments are assembled to form the long carbon chain.*

ing out the synthetic processes of the living tissue. The condensation of acetate to fatty acid is accomplished by a series of steps in which the energy-rich phosphate of ATP is first transferred to acetate with the formation of acetyl phosphate. This material is now capable of reacting with acetate to form a 4-carbon compound which on reduction yields a simple 4-carbon acid, butyric acid. Butyric acid is now capable of phosphorylation, reacting with another molecule of acetate to form a 6-carbon acid, and so on. Since fatty acids are made up by union of these successive 2-carbon units, it is clear that the final fatty acid molecule must always contain an even number of carbon atoms, as was brought out earlier for the naturally occurring fatty acids of plants.

The Plant Waxes

Waxes resemble fats in chemical properties, particularly in their solubilities in typical fat solvents, such as carbon disulfide and chloroform. Unlike the fats, however, waxes consist chemically of fatty acids united, not with glycerol, but with long-chain alcohols containing from 24 to 36 carbon atoms. In the long-chain alcohols of the waxes, the carbon atoms are arranged in straight unbranched chains, just as in the fatty acids of the waxes. Waxes are therefore characteristically esters, as are fats, but they are esters of specific alcohols other than glycerol. Still other components may occur in waxes. Especially noteworthy are the long-chain hydrocarbons, substances similar to fatty acids or to the wax alcohols in structure, but with the difference that they contain no oxygen whatsoever and are completely reduced to carbon and hydrogen.

Waxes are found in the plant primarily as components of cell walls, such as those of cork, and of the cuticle of leaves and fruits. The bloom present on many species of leaves and fruits consists of waxes. The waxes of commerce, such as carnauba wax, are obtained from the cuticular waxes of leaves, in this case of a palm. The cuticle wax of the apple fruit, which is typical, has been studied intensively from a chemical standpoint and has supplied a considerable amount of our information on the chemistry of the waxes. In particular instances, waxes may occur dissolved in droplets in the cytoplasm, as do the fats. This is true, for example, of the seeds of *Simmondsia californica*, the goat nut. These seeds contain a wax rather than a fat as their reserve material. The wax is accumulated during growth of the seed and is utilized and remobilized during seed germination, just as are the fats of the fatty seeds.

Phospholipids

The fatlike phospholipids are found in small amounts in all plant tissues. Although phospholipids may occur to some extent dispersed in the cytoplasm in the form of droplets, as do the fats proper, the great majority of these materials appear to be involved in the structural framework of the protoplasm. Thus phospholipids occur as a part of the chloroplast structure. The protoplasmic membranes, as well as the limiting membrane of the chloroplasts, are also thought to include phospholipids as important components. In any case, phospholipids do not appear to function primarily as reserve materials, as do the fats proper.

The best-known phospholipids of higher plants are derivatives of glycerol in which one of the three fatty acid residues of the glyceride

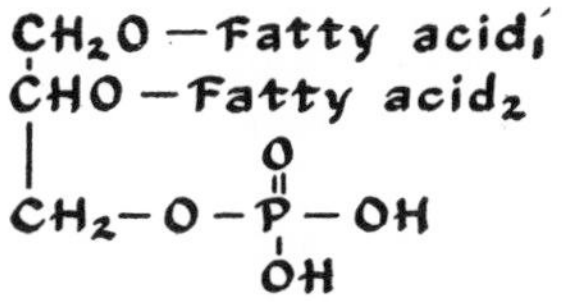

$$CH_2O-Fatty\ acid_1$$
$$CHO-Fatty\ acid_2$$
$$CH_2-O-\overset{O}{\underset{OH}{P}}-OH$$

Phosphatidic acid

is replaced by phosphoric acid. Such a glyceride, containing two fatty acids and one phosphate residue, is known as a phosphatidic acid. Phosphatidic acids constitute the principal phospholipids of leaves of various species. In the more complex phospholipids, the phosphoric acid is further bound, serving as a link between the glycerol and still other components. The phospholipid lecithin, for example, consists of a phosphatidic acid in which the phosphoric acid is esterified to an alcohol group of the nitrogenous base choline. Cephalin, which accom-

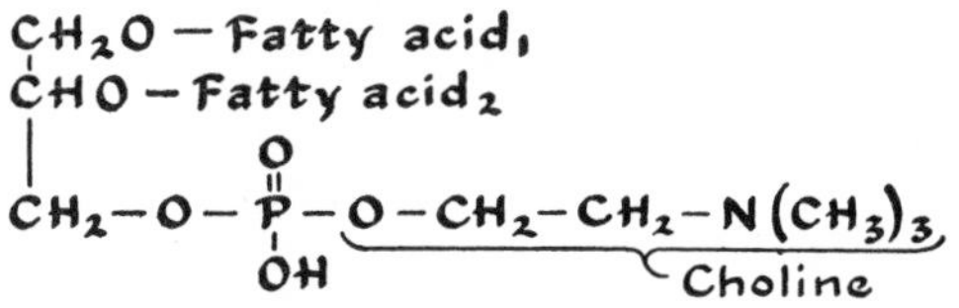

$$CH_2O-Fatty\ acid_1$$
$$CHO-Fatty\ acid_2$$
$$CH_2-O-\overset{O}{\underset{OH}{P}}-O-CH_2-CH_2-N(CH_3)_3,$$
$$\underbrace{\qquad\qquad}_{Choline}$$

Lecithin

panies lecithin in many plant tissues, resembles the latter in structure except for replacement of choline by the related ethanolamine. Leci-

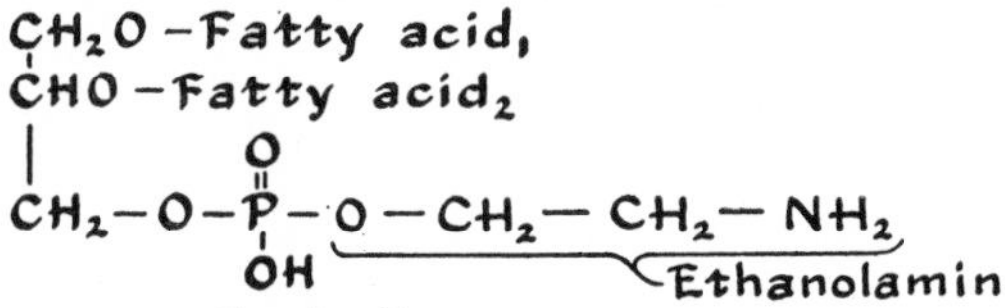

$$CH_2O-Fatty\ acid_1$$
$$CHO-Fatty\ acid_2$$
$$CH_2-O-\overset{O}{\underset{OH}{P}}-O-CH_2-CH_2-NH_2$$
$$\underbrace{\qquad\qquad}_{Ethanolamine}$$

Cephalin

thin and cephalin make up the great bulk of the phospholipids of seedling tissues and of many seeds.

Phospholipids combine the fatty hydrophobic properties of the true fats with the hydrophilic properties of the phosphate group, and the phospholipid molecule is for this reason outstandingly dipolar. Thus at a fat-water interface it is possible for a phospholipid molecule to orient itself with fatty acid residues projecting into fat and phosphate residue projecting into water. It is entirely possible that this ability to stabilize certain interfaces within the cell may hold the answer to the problem of the exact role of the phospholipids.

Summary

The lipids comprise an important group of plant constituents, including the fats, waxes, and phospholipids. Although the three different groups of lipids contain in common the long-chain fatty acids as building blocks, their structures differ in detail, and they serve quite different roles in the plant economy. Fats are accumulated as reserve materials and are found characteristically in seeds, where they are stored during seed maturation and mobilized during seed germination. Waxes are cell wall components and occur primarily in the waxy coating of leaves and fruits. The phospholipids, complex materials containing organically bound phosphate as well as fatty acid and other components, are cytoplasmic in their occurrence. Although their function is not yet firmly established, it is believed that they may have structural roles within the cytoplasm.

QUESTIONS

1. The alga Chlorella can produce up to 66 per cent of its dry weight in the form of fatty acids if kept in a low nitrogen medium. Addition of large quantities of nitrate may result in a tenfold reduction in the percentage of fat found. Present a possible explanation for this effect.

2. Plant fats are most abundant in seeds, and are often localized in the embryo. Of what advantage is this to the plant, from an energy point of view?

3. How are the physical properties of a fat related to the chemical nature of the fatty acids it contains?

4. The fat composition of organisms varies with the temperature to which they are exposed, being in general richer in unsaturated fatty acids the warmer their environment. Is this of any possible benefit to the organism? Through what kind of mechanism may temperature influence the kinds and amounts of fatty acids produced?

5. Fats are often found intimately associated with proteins, as in the lipoproteins of the chloroplast. What kind of chemical linkages may be supposed to exist between these classes of compounds?

6. Discuss the breakdown of fats from the point of view of (a) the enzymes involved, (b) the fate of the various fragments.

7. In what ways is the metabolism of lipids linked to that of carbohydrates?

8. Is fat *per se* translocated in plants?

GENERAL READING

Hilditch, T. P., *The Chemical Constitution of Natural Fats,* 2nd ed. New York: John Wiley & Sons, 1947. A chemical compendium.

Jamieson, G. S., *Vegetable Fats and Oils,* 2nd ed. New York: Reinhold Publ. Corp., 1943. A general discussion of the fats of different plants as well as the technology of fats.

McNair, J. B., "Plant Fats in Relation to Environment and Evolution." *Botan. Rev.,* **11**: 1, 1945. Ecological relationships of plant fats.

CHAPTER 13

Highways and Byways in Plant Metabolism

The Crossroads of Plant Metabolism

The substance of the plant is made up, as we have learned in earlier chapters, of an imposing variety of chemical materials. Sugars, cell wall components, organic acids, amino acids, proteins, nucleic acids, and fats, to mention but a few, are integral parts of the plant structure. The metabolism of the plant in an over-all sense is concerned with the production of these varied ingredients essential to plant growth. Photosynthesis, the transformation of the sugars; respiration, the synthesis of amino acids and proteins; and the synthesis and utilization of the fats are all principal highways along which a never-ending stream of metabolic traffic flows. These separate pathways are not to be likened to parallel highways; rather, they interact and interlock, linking the individual branches together into one cohesive, if complex, whole.

It is only in recent years that we have begun to perceive the unity of metabolic patterns. To this gradual clarification the Krebs cycle has contributed more than any other single concept. For the Krebs cycle is a sort of hub, a focus upon which many of the individual metabolic pathways converge and from which they diverge. Let us look upon the Krebs cycle in this light and see how, as portrayed in Figure 13-1, the synthesis and utilization of the most varied cellular materials are linked through common intermediate reactants. The hexose sugars, which are consumed in respiration, must be first converted through the glycolytic pathway to pyruvic acid, from which is derived the two-carbon fragment which directly enters the Krebs cycle for final degradation. This two-carbon fragment is metabolically equivalent to, and perhaps even identical with, acetyl phosphate, the building block from which the fatty acids may be constructed. This same two-carbon fragment is also produced as the resultant of the cleavage of the fatty acids by oxidation. Thus, final oxidation of the two-carbon fragment may be achieved by the Krebs cycle. Sugars and fats are, then, linked in their metabolism by a common intermediate, through which they may be interconverted in the living organism.

The organic acids, quantitatively important in the composition of the plant, are in the main synthesized and interconverted through the reactions of the Krebs cycle. The carbon atoms of organic acids may arise

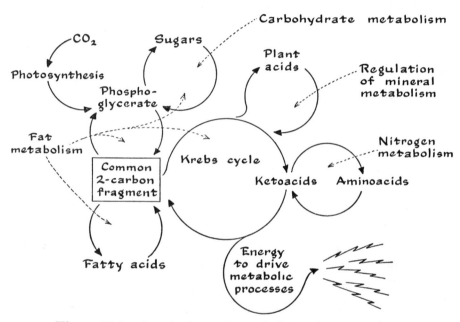

Figure 13-1. *Interlocking of metabolic pathways in the plant.*

from sugars, from fats, or from still other sources, since these same acids are both degradation products of and the raw materials for the synthesis of many amino acids. The keto acids α-ketoglutaric, oxaloacetic, and pyruvic may be withdrawn from the cycle for the synthesis of glutamic acid, aspartic acid, and alanine, respectively. Similarly, the degradation of these amino acids produces materials which may be further broken down through the Krebs cycle. The carbon skeletons of still other amino acids appear to be formed from acetyl phosphate through varied types of condensation of this intermediate. Through the Krebs cycle, then, the metabolism of the nitrogenous compounds is linked both to the metabolism of sugars and to the metabolism of fats.

So we see that the Krebs cycle is a junction point for many metabolic pathways. Other such points will doubtless be revealed as our knowledge of the plant increases. In addition, however, the metabolic pattern includes lesser junctions, intersections from which radiate the byways of plant metabolism.

Among the products of these metabolic side paths are many compounds which, although synthesized and utilized in relatively small amounts, are nonetheless essential to plant activity. Plants also possess the ability to form a great number of chemical compounds that have no apparent function in the plant. In some instances these substances make

Figure 13-2. *Plants synthesize many materials useful to mankind.*

up only a small proportion of the plant, while in other cases a particular material, even though it may appear to be quite unimportant to the plant's economy, may represent a major component of the plant. These substances, although of no obvious value to the plant, often have a great utilitarian interest to mankind, for the synthetic processes of plants provide us not only with food, clothing, and housing, but also with many of our other needs (Fig. 13-2). Oil, coal, rubber, vitamins, drugs, perfumes, tannins, and wood are part of an almost endless list of plant-produced material of daily importance in the life of man. It is with certain of these secondary products of plant metabolism that the remainder of the present chapter will be concerned.

The Alkaloids

The *alkaloids* are characterized chemically as nitrogenous bases; that is, they are organic compounds which contain nitrogen either in the form of amino groups or incorporated into heterocyclic rings containing both carbon and nitrogen atoms. The alkaloids of the plant include

many substances which are physiologically active in higher animals—
substances which we know as drugs, such as morphine and quinine,
and mildly active stimulants, such as nicotine and caffeine. Alkaloids
are not synthesized by, and are not contained in, all species of plants,
but they occur scattered through the plant kingdom in a rather random
way. However, some families, such as the Solanaceae, which include
potato, tomato, and tobacco, do tend to contain many alkaloid-produc-
ing species. As a general rule, alkaloids have no known function in the
plant.

One of the simplest and most studied of the plant alkaloids is
nicotine, produced particularly by species of the genus Nicotiana.

STRUCTURE OF NICOTINE.

Although nicotine is accumulated in the leaves, where it makes up
from a few tenths to 8 per cent of the leaf dry weight, it is actually
synthesized in the root of the plant. Thus, when a tobacco shoot is
grafted to a tomato root, the shoot produces no new nicotine. A
tomato shoot grafted to a tobacco root, on the contrary, accumulates
nicotine abundantly. Transport of nicotine from the root system to
the leaves appears to be through the xylem rather than through the
phloem, which is the path of transport for sugars and other elaborated
materials from the leaves to the roots. We do not yet know the
mechanism by which nicotine is made in the roots of Nicotiana. It is
known, however, that the related nicotinic acid is produced in the
plant from the amino acid tryptophan through a complex series of
reactions.

Nicotinic acid (niacin) is of importance to man as a vitamin of the
B complex. In the plant, as in other living things, nicotinic acid participates as an essential constituent of the coenzymes of the dehydrogenases (Chap. 10). Whether or not nicotine arises as a by-product
of nicotinic acid synthesis can only be surmised at present.

A second relatively simple alkaloid is caffeine, the principal alkaloid
of coffee and tea. Caffeine belongs to the group of purines, as does
adenine. Adenine has been mentioned in Chapter 10 as a constituent
of various kinds of coenzymes and of adenosine triphosphate, the

carrier of energy-rich phosphate. Adenine has also been mentioned in Chapter 11 as a constituent of the nucleic acid portion of the nucleo-proteins. Caffeine possesses the same carbon- and nitrogen-containing ring structure as adenine but differs from the latter in the nature of the groups attached to the ring. In the first place, caffeine is oxidized, as

Caffeine   Theobromine

TWO SIMPLE ALKALOIDS.

compared to adenine, and is in fact actually a derivative of xanthine. Xanthine is itself very widely distributed in plant tissues and can be produced from adenine through a series of enzymatic reactions carried out by the enzymes adenase and xanthine oxidase. Caffeine is derived from xanthine by methylation, CH_3-, or methyl, groups being present on three of the nitrogen atoms of caffeine. The reactions leading to methylation are unknown, but it is of interest that other methylated purines, heteroxanthine and theobromine, which contain one and two of the methyl groups of caffeine, respectively, are found in various plant tissues and may actually be intermediates in caffeine synthesis. Theobromine is of particular interest as the alkaloid which accumulates in the seeds of *Theobroma cacao*. Caffeine is not widely distributed in the plant world but is confined to the leaves and seeds of a few species, particularly of the genus Coffea of the Rubiaceae and the leaves of tea, *Thea sinensis*.

In all, some several hundred alkaloids are known, and they are found in a great variety of plants. The structures of some of the simple alkaloids have recognizable chemical relationships with some of the commonly occurring compounds, as has been shown for nicotine and caffeine. Others of the more complex alkaloids, such as quinine of Cinchona and morphine of Papaver, have no obvious relation in chemical structure to the more usual plant products. A great deal of work is still needed to clarify the way in which alkaloids are produced in plants.

Essential Oils

It has been estimated that less than 1 per cent of all the species of higher plants produces the aromatic and useful products known as *essential oils*. These essential oil-producing species are, in general, scattered in a random way throughout the plant kingdom, although certain families contain many oil-producing species. These families include the Pinaceae, Umbelliferae, and Myrtaceae, among others. In many cases, essential oils are produced and contained in glands,

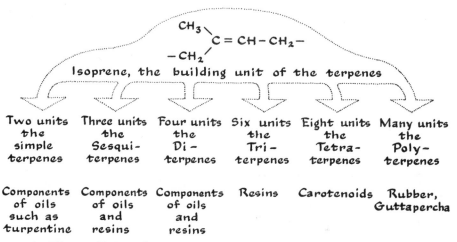

Figure 13-3. *The community of the terpenes. The same basic 5-carbon atom unit is the building block for terpenes of many different kinds.*

glandular hairs, or other specialized cells. Perhaps the best-known oil of this group is the turpentine produced by species of the genus Pinus and elaborated by glandular cells which line the resin canals present in the wood and bark of the tree.

Essential oils belong to the great group of isoprenoid compounds, materials which may be thought of as built up by fusion of units of the 5-carbon substance isoprene. In the essential oils, as in all of the isoprenoid substances, isoprenoid units are found condensed together to yield chain or ring compounds containing integral numbers of the isoprene building blocks. Some of the many plant products which may be thought of as being derived from isoprene are illustrated in Figure 13-3. Essential oils include 10-carbon, 15-carbon, 20-

carbon, and related substances. The 10-carbon isoprenoid compounds containing two isoprene units are known as *terpenes,* or *simple terpenes,* while the 15-carbon isoprenoid substances contain three isoprenoid units and are known as *sesquiterpenes.* Similarly, the 20-carbon *diterpenes,* the 30-carbon *triterpenes,* as well as a *polyterpene* group are known in nature. In the simplest case, that of the terpenes, two isoprenoid units are linked together into a straight chain, as in myrcene. In more complicated cases the two isoprene residues may be linked into a 6-membered carbon ring, as in limonene, a component of citrus and other oils. On this basic chain or ring structure, the plant superimposes many modifications and alterations. The terpene may be oxidized and contain an aldehydic or ketonic oxygen atom; double bonds may be shifted or reduced. There is, therefore, a vast variety of simple terpenes, and even the simplest essential oil contains many individual compounds.

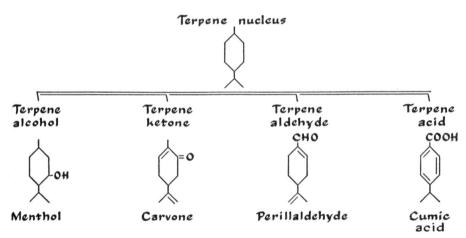

SOME OF THE SIMPLE TERPENES FORMED BY THE OXIDATION OF THE MONO-TERPENE NUCLEUS.

Sesquiterpenes, diterpenes, and triterpenes, like the simple terpenes, are made up of isoprene residues linked together in chains or cyclized into one or more rings. Like terpenes, these higher compounds may be oxidized or reduced in the plant to yield a variety of derivatives. Phytol, for example, is a diterpene which is not found in essential oils but is rather a component of chlorophyll. This compound contains four isoprenoid residues linked together in a chain which has been subsequently reduced so that it contains only one double bond. At one end of the chain of carbon atoms it contains a hydroxyl, or —OH, group. In the chlorophyll molecule this —OH group of phytol is esterified with a carboxyl group.

Essential oils are usually obtained from plants by steam distillation, in which the plant material is heated in water and steam blown through the entire mass (Fig. 13-4). Since the essential oils are volatile in steam, they pass over into the distillate. The distillate is collected

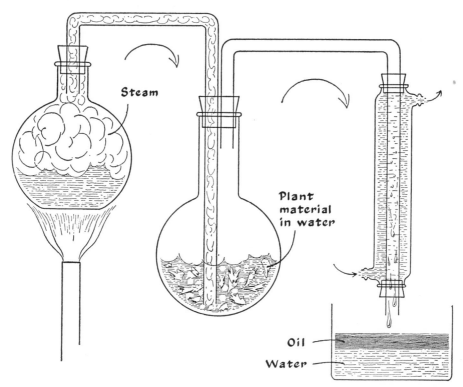

Figure 13-4. *Plant oils may be collected by suspending the plant material in water and passing steam through the suspension. The oils, which are volatile in steam, pass over and may be separated from the distillate.*

and the oil skimmed off the surface. This process is used, for example, in collecting such important oils as those of spearmint and peppermint, which are used widely for flavoring.

Essential oils have no known function in the plant but derive their name from the fact that they are used for the making of essences, perfumes, and flavorings. A considerable amount of any essential oil is lost from the plant by evaporation into the atmosphere, and the odor of such plants as the mints may frequently be detected at considerable distances. All green plants make and contain isoprenoid compounds, including phytol and the yellow carotenoid pigments.

Since isoprenoid compounds appear to be made in all cases from the same basic 5-carbon isoprenelike unit, it is possible that the essential oils may be made as a by-product in the synthesis of phytol and the other essential isoprenoids. We do not yet know the nature of the 5-carbon isoprenelike building block from which isoprenoid compounds are made in the plant. This building block is probably not isoprene itself, however, since this material has never been found in the plant. More probably the 5-carbon building block of the essential oils and other isoprenoids is a compound having the branched chain carbon skeleton found in isoprene, but containing also other and more reactive terminal groups than those of isoprene.

Carotenoid Pigments

The *carotenoids* are yellow, orange, or red pigments present in all green leaves as well as in the nongreen portions of most or of all plants. In the green leaf, carotenoids are masked by the presence of chlorophyll, particularly since chlorophyll is present in greater abundance in the tissues than are the yellow carotenoid pigments. In other instances, as in red fruit of the tomato or the yellow flowers of many species, the color of the tissue is due to the carotenoid itself.

Carotenoids typically are insoluble in water but soluble in organic solvents such as acetone or ether. Because they are insoluble in water, they are not found in solution in the cytoplasm but are present ordinarily in plastids. The carotenoids of the green leaf are found in the chloroplast. Here the carotenoid pigments are combined in the granum attached to the chlorophyll protein, just as is the chlorophyll itself. The universal appearance of the yellow carotenoid pigments in the chloroplasts suggests some role of the carotenoid in photosynthesis. Such a role has not yet been recognized with certainty, although in certain algae some of the light absorbed by carotenoids can apparently be used in some manner for the carrying out of photosynthesis.

Chemically speaking, carotenoids are tetraterpenes containing 40-carbon atoms arranged in eight isoprenelike residues. These eight isoprenelike residues are linked in a characteristic carotenoid structure in which 22 carbon atoms in the central portion of the molecule possess the same arrangement, an arrangement common to all carotenoids. The various carotenoids differ among themselves, however, in the arrangements of the nine carbon atoms situated at each end of this common 22-atom central portion. Thus, the terminal carbon atoms of the carotenoid chain may be closed in ring systems, as in β-carotene, the structure of which is shown below. β-Carotene is of importance as the principal carotene pigment of green leaves. On the other hand, the 9-carbon atom ends of the carotenoid molecule may be present in an open chain rather than in a ring structure, as is the case in lycopene, the red pigment of the tomato. The various carotenoids differ

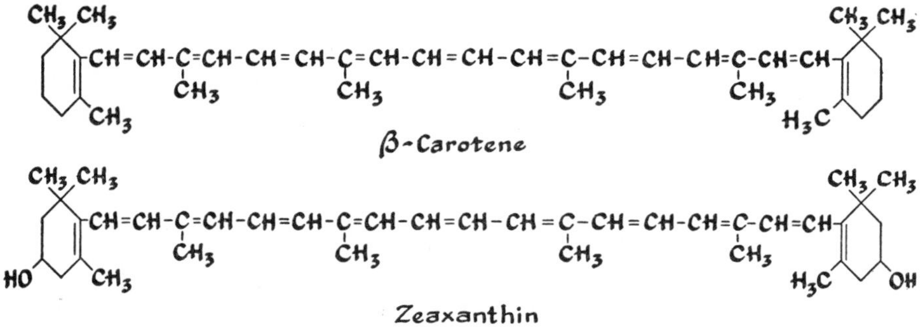

β-Carotene

Zeaxanthin

THE CHEMICAL STRUCTURE OF TWO TYPICAL CAROTENOIDS.

among themselves also in the number and arrangement of the double bonds present in the terminal portions of their molecules.

Carotenoids which consist exclusively of carbon and hydrogen are known as the carotenes proper. Plants also contain the related *xanthophylls,* compounds which possess oxygen atoms as hydroxyl or ketonic groups. In fact, xanthophylls are commonly more abundant in leaves, for example, than are carotene pigments themselves. The major component of the xanthophylls of many leaves is lutein, a carotene derivative containing a single —OH, or hydroxyl, group in each terminal ring. Zeaxanthin, the yellow pigment of yellow corn seeds, is, in fact, merely β-carotene containing an additional hydroxyl group in each terminal ring.

From a physiological standpoint, carotenoids are of interest in relation to the color changes which take place in fruits, flowers, and leaves. In the green tomato fruit, for example, there is much chlorophyll but relatively little carotene or other carotenoid pigment. During the ripening of the fruit, the chlorophyll decreases rapidly in amount, whereas carotenoid pigments are produced rapidly. Although the principal pigment produced in this process is the substance lycopene, mentioned above, small amounts of other pigments such as β-carotene are also produced. This disappearence of chlorophyll and the appearance of the yellow and red carotenoid pigments is, then, an integral part of the fruit-ripening process. In the development of color in many yellow flowers, carotenoid pigment formation is also involved. The coloring of leaves in the fall is often due primarily to the disappearance of chlorophyll and the unmasking of the yellow pigments normally contained in the leaves. These yellow pigments may, however, be subsequently converted to unknown red degradation products of the carotenoids proper.

Carotenoids possess importance from the standpoint of human nutrition. Vitamin A, for example, is a cleavage product of β-carotene. Vitamin A contains 20 carbon atoms and is produced in the animal by oxidative splitting of β-carotene at the center of the molecule.

Rubber

Rubber, like the essential oils and the alkaloids, is a material not universally produced by plants but by particular species and families scattered throughout the plant kingdom. There are over two thousand species of plants known to form rubber. Some of these produce rubber in only very minute amounts, others in concentrations of over 20 per cent of the weight of the plant. Of the families which produce rubber in high concentration, the Moraceae, Euphorbiaceae, and Compositae are perhaps particularly important. Most of the rubber-producing species are tropical plants, and there are relatively few plants of the temperate region which produce rubber in large enough concentrations to be considered potentially important. Most of the natural rubber of commerce is derived from one tropical species, *Hevea brasiliensis,* a member of the Euphorbiaceae. Of the temperate zone rubber-producing plants, the desert-dwelling guayule, *Parthenium argentatum,* and the various dandelion (Taraxacum) species are the most notable.

Rubber is generally produced in the plant in microscopic or submicroscopic particles suspended in a liquid serum, the whole forming a latex which is contained in specialized latex vessels or latex-containing cells. The milky latices of many of our temperate zone plants, such as Poinsettia, contain only small amounts of rubber, but contain suspended particles other than rubber which are responsible for the milky appearance of the latex.

Rubber is chemically a polyterpene or polyisoprenoid compound and is composed of 5-carbon isoprene residues linked together in very

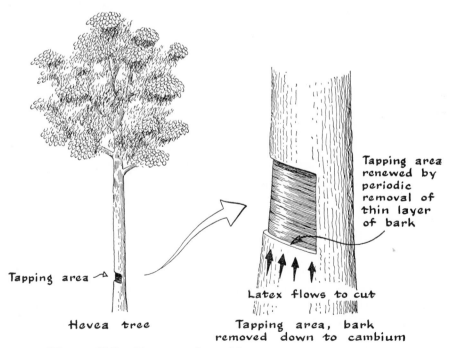

Structure of rubber

long chains. In natural rubber, on the order of 500 to 5000 isoprene residues are linked together in these long unbranched chains. The vulcanization process, by which rubber is hardened and caused to set in a definite form, consists of the introduction of sulfur cross-linkages between these long unbranched molecules.

The rubber-containing latex vessels of many trees, such as Hevea, are located in the bark. Since the latex in these vessels is under pressure, it tends to flow out of the plant through incisions in the bark, and use is made of this fact in the collection of latex. From the latex obtained in this way, the rubber may be separated. This process in-

Tapping area renewed by periodic removal of thin layer of bark

Tapping area

Latex flows to cut

Hevea tree

Tapping area, bark removed down to cambium

Figure 13-5. *Tapping the rubber tree (Hevea). The latex flows from the fresh incision and is collected as it drops from the plant.*

volves the denaturation of proteins, which surround each particle in a thin layer and make the rubber particle stable in suspension. When this surrounding protein film is denatured by heat or by action of acid or alkali, the rubber particles coagulate into a solid mass and may be removed from the latex.

Even though rubber is produced in very large quantities by some species of plants, it does not have any evident function in the plant. Rubber once deposited does not appear to be reutilized as a food material and is not, for example, mobilized during periods of starvation, as is starch. Plants are not known to contain enzymes for the breaking down of rubber, although certain microorganisms are capable of attacking the substance. It would appear that rubber, like the essential oils, may be a nonfunctional constituent of the plant, formed as a by-product of other essential metabolic activities.

The Anthocyanin Pigments

The great majority of the water-soluble red, blue, and yellow colors of higher plants, particularly flowers, are due to *anthocyanin* and related pigments. Unlike the carotenoids, the anthocyanins are water soluble and occur dissolved in the cytoplasmic or vacuolar contents of the plant. The anthocyanin pigments are typically *glycosides*; that is, they may be hydrolyzed enzymatically or by the action of acid into a sugar component or components and a nonsugar portion called an aglycon. These sugar-free aglycons of the anthocyanins are known as the anthocyanidins. The anthocyanidins have in common a basic ring structure which contains two aromatic or benzene nuclei linked together through a heterocyclic ring containing an oxygen atom as well as carbon atoms. The various anthocyanidin pigments vary among themselves in the number and nature of hydroxyl groups attached to these separate ring systems, as well as in the number of methyl groups attached to the hydroxyl groups. Anthocyanidins differ also in the nature and number of the sugar residues with which they are combined.

Anthocyanidins may be divided into three principal classes: the pelargonidins, cyanidins, and delphinidins. They contain, respectively, one, two, and three hydroxyl groups in addition to the three hydroxyl groups common to all anthocyanidins. These relations are shown below. Each of the structural variations entails its own specific effect on the color of the pigment.

Anthocyanidins are indicators; that is, they change color depending

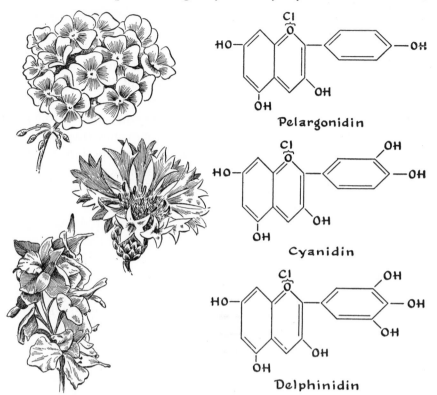

Pelargonidin

Cyanidin

Delphinidin

SOME ANTHOCYANIDIN PIGMENTS AND THE FLOWERS WITH WHICH THEY ARE CHARACTERISTICALLY ASSOCIATED. *Top,* RED GERANIUM; *middle,* VIOLET CORNFLOWER; *bottom,* BLUE LARKSPUR.

upon the acidity of the solution in which they are dissolved. Cyanidin is red in acid solution, violet in neutral solution, and blue in alkaline solution. It is clear, then, that the susceptibility of anthocyanidin color to alterations in chemical structure and acidity makes possible the great range of flower colors found in the higher plant.

The varying flower colors within a particular species have been shown to be due, in many instances, to genetic factors. Particular genes may affect either the nature of the anthocyanin produced by the plant or the acidity of the tissue containing the anthocyanin. In some species, specific genes are known to cause replacement of pelargonidin by cyanidin. This gene is associated with the introduction of an additional hydroxyl group into the anthocyanidin nucleus. Other genetic factors are responsible for methylation of the individual hydroxyl groups, while still others affect the number and kinds of sugar residues attached to the anthocyanidin nucleus. Particular genes affect also the vacuolar *p*H of anthocyanin-containing cells. Thus, in sweetpeas, a dominant gene is known to bring about a more acid *p*H, with a corresponding increase in redness of the flower color.

Environmental factors also influence production of anthocyanins. It is a common observation that plants deficient in nitrogen tend to produce red pigments in their stems or other vegetative organs. This pigmentation is due to an increase in anthocyanin, and nitrogen deficiency is a common cause of increased anthocyanin production. Another important factor regulating anthocyanin production is temperature. High temperatures may either increase or decrease the general anthocyanin content, depending upon the species involved. Light favors anthocyanin production in fruits such as peaches and apples. Other plants, such as etiolated seedlings of corn or red cabbage, are, however, capable of producing anthocyanin even in the dark.

Anthocyanins, like many of the other compounds discussed in this chapter, have no known physiological role in the plant. This does not mean, however, that the substances may not have an important part in the economy of the plant in connection, for example, with the attraction of insects necessary for fertilization, in seed dispersal, or in functions yet unknown.

Tannins

The term *tannin* covers a wide range of naturally occurring compounds of varying chemical structure scattered widely throughout the plant kingdom. Tannins are found in wood, bark, leaves, fruits, and roots of most plants and are particularly abundant, for example, in the galls of such species as oak, which may contain 80 per cent tannin. Tannins are aromatic compounds containing numerous phenolic hydroxyl groups. As a group they are astringent to the taste, possess the property of precipitating proteins, and yield deeply colored complexes with heavy metal ions, notably with iron. The simplest tannins are the gallotannins, typical of galls of oak, sumac, and other species. A typical gallotannin is m-digallic acid, which has two linked aromatic rings and five free hydroxyl groups in addition to a free carboxyl group. In the plant, however, m-digallic acid is present in the form of a glucoside, in which each hydroxyl group of the glucose molecule is combined with a gallic acid residue. Other and more complex gallotannins contain three or four aromatic nuclei bound in linkages similar to that of digallic acid.

The ellagitannins, like the gallotannins, are aromatic compounds but possess a more complex mode of linkage between the several rings. The phlobotannins are still more complex than the ellagitannins and are, in fact, not wholly understood from a structural standpoint. They do, however, resemble the anthocyanin pigments in general structure.

From the human standpoint, tannins are of importance in their role as protein-denaturing agents in the tanning of leather. Although synthetic tanning agents are used to some extent, the bulk of the leather tanning in the world is carried out with natural tannins. Many years ago in the United States, the tannin of commerce was derived from the bark of hemlock and oak, as well as from sumac leaves. With the exhaustion of these species, tannin extraction was shifted to the bark and wood of the chestnut. Today, however, a great deal of commercial tannin is obtained from the wood and bark of the quebracho tree native to South America. The wood of quebracho contains some 20 per cent or more of a highly effective tannin.

We have little or no knowledge of the pathways by which tannins are synthesized and an equally small amount of information concerning their role in the plant. Tannins may, however, be metabolized, as is evident from the fact that many immature fruits, such as persimmon and quince, contain much tannin which disappears during the final ripening of the fruit.

Sterols

The chemical group of the sterols is characterized by a tetracyclic ring structure which may be variously substituted. Sterol chemistry is complex not only in the establishment of the exact chemical nature of an individual sterol but also in the separation and isolation of sterols from one another. The sterols are, however, of the greatest interest in the physiology of the higher animal, since this group includes not only a great variety of male and female sex hormones but also the hormones of the adrenal cortex, as well as vitamin D. In the higher plant, also, sterols are of universal occurrence, although we have as yet no insight into their function in the economy of the plant. These plant sterols are of importance to man in that they may be used as starting materials for the chemical synthesis of the animal hormones for use in therapy. β-Sitosterol, a widespread sterol especially characteristic of seeds (wheat, corn, and soybean), has been used as the starting material in the synthesis of androsterone, a male sex hormone, while stigmasterol, principally obtained from soybean seed, has been used as the starting material for progesterone, the hormone of the corpus luteum. Ergosterol, a plant sterol commonly prepared from yeast, serves as the starting material in the production of vitamin D_2, a conversion which takes place as a result of the action of ultraviolet light. It is this conversion of ergosterol to vitamin D_2 which is the basis for the effectiveness of irradiation in the production of vitamin D in food products.

Perhaps the most spectacular developments in the human utilization of plant sterols concern the possibilities for the synthesis of the adrenocortical hormone, cortisone, from particular plant materials. Although cortisone, with its many spectacular applications to medicine, has in the past been prepared chemically mainly from related animal compounds, it appears possible that plant sterols or the related steroids may provide cheaper and more abundant starting materials.

Significance of Nonessential Compounds

As already stated, plants contain compounds which have no known function. This is true, for example, of one group of the yellow pigments, the xanthophylls. It is true also of the terpenes such as turpentine, of rubber, of the alkaloids, and of many other materials. It is typical of these nonessential compounds that they do not occur in all species of higher plants. In the case of rubber, for example, about two thousand of the four hundred thousand total species of higher plants actually produce rubber in larger or smaller amounts. Of the two thousand species producing rubber, only about five hundred produce rubber in quantities which are significant from an analytical standpoint; species which do not possess the ability to form rubber appear, however, to survive perfectly well, indicating that rubber can play no general and important part in plant metabolism.

A similar situation exists with the terpenes. Here, also, some two thousand species of the four hundred thousand total produce the terpenes. These species are scattered in a random manner through the families of higher plants.

The alkaloids, nitrogen-containing bases, many of which are useful to mankind, are also produced by individual species scattered throughout the plant kingdom. A particular alkaloid may be formed by only one species of higher plant and be entirely absent from all other known species. In general, then, the essential and nonessential metabolites can be distinguished from one another by the simple criterion of whether or not the compound in question is contained in all kinds of higher plants.

How does it come about that a particular plant can make an exotic and apparently useless material? The nonessential compounds formed by higher plants are frequently related chemically to other compounds which occur in all species and for which essential functions are recognized. This is true of both terpenes and rubber, which are believed to be built up from a common building block. This same building block is believed to be necessary for the manufacture of certain other compounds required by the living organism. In certain species, then, it would appear that this building block is produced in the plant and is then in part diverted from its normal function of making essential compounds to be used instead for the manufacture of nonessential materials.

In certain instances it can be shown that the accumulation of a particular nonessential material, such as a terpene or rubber, is conditioned by a single genetic factor in whose presence the nonessential material is made and in whose absence the nonessential material is not made.

Summary

The green plant, an organic chemist *par excellence*, is able to synthesize an enormous number of different compounds from the simplest of starting materials—carbon dioxide, water, and the mineral elements of the soil. The pathways by which the numerous plant constituents are formed, interconverted, and degraded constitute the complex of plant metabolism. The processes of synthesis, interconversion, and degradation of the sugars, the organic acids, the amino acids, and the fats are interrelated and integrated through a series of junctions or crossroads in their several metabolic paths. In particular the Krebs cycle serves as a center for the metabolism of sugars, organic acids, amino acids, and fats. Many of the principal components of the plant may be converted one to another or may be degraded through the respiratory oxidations of the cycle.

Individual species of higher plants are able to make not only the many chemical materials characteristic of, and essential to, the functioning of the plant, but also particular chemical substances which are not essential to the economy of the plant and which have no recognizable role in metabolism. It is characteristic of such compounds that they often occur only in scattered species distributed at random throughout the plant kingdom. Among these secondary products, products of metabolic byways, are the alkaloids, the terpenes, rubber, the sterols and steroids, the tannins, and many of the other plant materials which contribute to the welfare of mankind.

QUESTIONS

1. Are the "essential oils" essential to plants? Discuss the evidence bearing on this point.

2. Distinguish between nicotine and nicotinic acid with regard to: (a) chemical structure, (b) site of synthesis in the plant, (c) biochemical role in the plant, (d) effect on animals.

3. Discuss how the Krebs cycle may serve as a central mechanism linking the metabolism of carbohydrates, organic acids, fats, and proteins.

4. How are essential oils extracted from plant materials containing them? How can one essential oil be separated from another?

5. What structural features have essential oils, carotenoid pigments, and rubber in common? How do these compounds differ from one another?

6. What properties of tannins make them useful to man? What are the major sources of tannins? Once formed, may they be further metabolized by the plant?

7. What factors, both internal and environmental, govern the production of the anthocyanin pigments by plants?

GENERAL READING

Blank, E., "The Anthocyanin Pigments of Plants." *Botan. Rev.*, **13**: 241, 1947. A summary of the physiology of these compounds.

Bonner, J., and Galston, A. W., "The Physiology and Biochemistry of Rubber Formation in Plants." *Botan. Rev.*, **13**: 543, 1947. A summary of the physiology of the rubber-bearing plants.

Dawson, R. F., "Alkaloid Biogenesis." *Advances in Enzymol.*, **8**: 203, 1948. Includes the physiology of alkaloids as well as their chemistry.

Haagen-Smit, A. J., "The Chemistry, Origin and Function of Essential Oils in Plant Life," in E. Guenther, ed., *The Essential Oils*, Vol. I, Chap. 2. New York: D. Van Nostrand Co., 1948. The physiology and elementary chemistry of the essential oils.

Karrer, P., and Jucker, E., *Carotenoids*, trans. and rev. by E. A. Brande. New York: Elsevier Publishing Co., 1950. A modern treatment of the chemistry of the carotenoids.

Russell, A., "The Natural Tannins." *Chem. Revs.*, **17**: 155, 1935. Detailed chemical consideration of a physiologically obscure group of compounds.

Zechmeister, L., *Carotinoide*. Berlin: Springer-Verlag, 1934. This is the most extensive and useful summary of the plant physiology of carotenoids yet published. It is in German, and out of print, but a good reference for carotenoid problems.

PART THREE

Growth and Development

CHAPTER 14

The Dynamics of Growth and Development

Introduction

Growth in the plant, as in any organism, consists of an irreversible increase in size, which is commonly, but not necessarily, accompanied by an increase in solid or dry weight and in the amount of protoplasm. The changing shape, form, degree of differentiation, and state of complexity of the organism constitute the process of development. Thus, growth is, generally speaking, a quantitative matter, and is concerned with the increasing amount of the organism. Development, on the other hand, is a qualitative concept referring to changes in the nature of the growth made by the organism. It is difficult to draw a sharp line between growth and development; the two processes commonly go hand in hand and occur simultaneously in the same individual organ or organism. We may, however, better understand the distinction between the two concepts if we consider that growth is measurable with a ruler or balance, whereas development is most commonly assessed by qualitative observation.

The Cycle of Growth and Development

When a mature seed is placed under suitable conditions, it germinates with the production of a seedling. This is followed by the growth of the seedling into a plant. These processes are frequently referred to as the vegetative growth and development of the plant, as contrasted with the reproductive development and growth which follow. Initiation of the reproductive processes, with the formation of flowers and fruit, may take place in certain species, such as the tomato, when the plant has attained a certain size or number of leaves. In other species it may occur only as a result of particular external influences which are necessary to induce the onset of reproduction. These will be discussed in Chapter 17. In any case, the reproductive phase, of which flowering is the first stage, includes the formation of ovules and pollen, the sexual process of fertilization, the subsequent fruit growth, and,

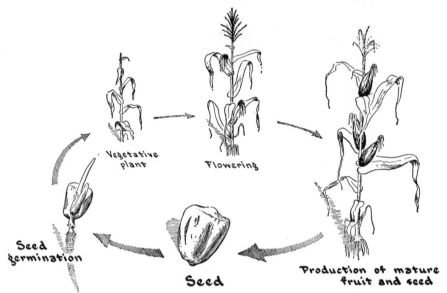

Figure 14-1. *The cycle of plant growth and development as illustrated by corn. Germination of the seed is followed by vegetative growth. This is in turn followed by flowering and the development of fruit. With the production of a mature seed the cycle is complete.*

finally, the development of the seed. With the production of the seed, the cycle of plant growth and development is complete and ready to commence anew (Fig. 14-1). In many plants, the successive steps of the cycle follow one another closely, merging into a continuous process. In our discussion of plant growth and development, however, we shall find it convenient to separate the vegetative phases on the one hand from the reproductive phases on the other.

The Kinetics of Growth

Suppose we follow the growth of an intact plant through its life cycle by means of measurements of height or of total dry weight. We shall find, in general, that the dry weight of the seedling plant first tends to decrease slightly following germination, as the reserves of the seed are depleted. This is followed as photosynthesis becomes established in the new leaves, by a rapidly increasing growth rate, which finally becomes constant at some relatively high level (Fig. 14-2). The growth rate during this period is often remarkably rapid. The bamboo stem may grow as much as 60 cm per day, and staminal filaments of certain grasses have been observed to elongate as much as 3 mm per minute over short periods of time. Growth continues at this rapid rate

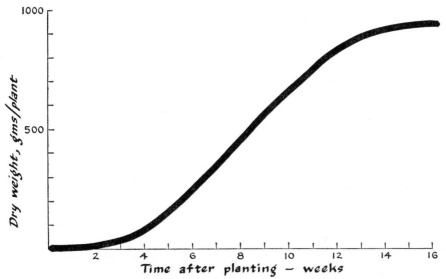

Figure 14-2. *A typical S-shaped growth curve. In this curve the dry weight of plant is plotted against time. The data apply to the growth of corn under field conditions. (Adapted from Stefanowska, from Backman, Ergeb. Physiol., 33, 1931, p. 924.)*

until the approach of maturity, at which time its rate slowly declines and approaches zero. The dry weight of the plant may even decrease in the final stages of senescence. The "S," or sigmoid, shape of the curve is typical of the growth of the plant as a whole and also of the growth of its individual organs, as well as of the growth of living organisms generally. The sigmoid growth curve of an entire organism is compounded of, and is the resultant of, the individual sigmoid curves of each of its component organs. For example, during the later phases of the growth of a plant, increase in dry weight may be largely manifested in the developing seeds and fruit, the vegetative organs contributing but little. In all of these instances we may distinguish three stages which together make up the so-called "grand period of growth": (1) an early period of slow growth, (2) a central period of rapid growth, and (3) a final period of slow growth. These relations are summarized in Figure 14-3.

The changing rate of growth of a plant or other organism during the grand period may be expressed mathematically in a variety of ways,

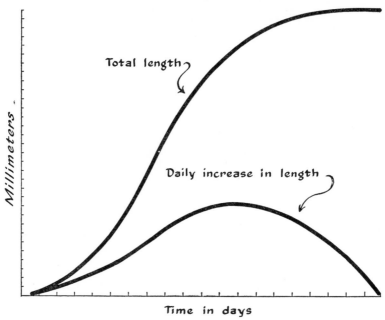

Figure 14-3. *Growth in length of a typical plant organ, such as the stem, over a period of days. The upper curve gives the total length of the organ on successive days. The lower curve gives the daily increment in growth. (After original data of Sachs, from Thompson,* On Growth and Form, *new ed., Cambridge University Press, 1942, p. 116.)*

one of which, perhaps the simplest to visualize, is the following: Let us suppose that the rate of growth—growth increment per unit time—is proportional (1) to the size which the organism has already attained and (2) to the differential between its present size and the final size it will attain. Consideration (1) says that organisms should grow faster as they get larger and at the same time have more with which to grow. Consideration (2) says that as organisms approach their final size their rate of growth should decrease. The final size may be determined by the exhaustion of some essential nutrient in the substrate in which the plant is grown or to the accumulation of toxic products of metabolism. It may, however, also be determined by purely internal structural features such as increasing resistance to transport of water or food. These considerations are all expressed in the differential equation:

$$\frac{\text{Growth per}}{\text{Unit Time}} = \text{Constant} \times \frac{\text{Present}}{\text{Size}} \times \left[\frac{\text{Final}}{\text{Size}} - \frac{\text{Present}}{\text{Size}}\right]$$

or:

$$\frac{dG}{dt} = K \times G \times \left[G_{final} - G\right]$$

This equation is one of the type used by chemists to describe the rate of chemical reactions in which rate is dependent upon the amount of product already produced, as well as upon the amount of residual or unused substrate.

Although equations aid us in visualizing some of the factors involved in determining growth rate, it should be realized that such equations do not, of themselves, give us any new information about the nature of the growth process. We should recognize, moreover, that factors other than those included in our first equation may also be of importance in determining the rate and extent of growth. Thus, growth of a plant consists of an integrated sum of the growth processes of individual organs and cells. Each of these organs and cells is affected in its growth by external factors such as temperature, light conditions, and the availability of water and nutrients, as well as by internal factors such as the genetic constitution of the plant. If we had enough information about all of these matters, we could presumably relate them in an equation which would express plant growth as the sum of the interactions of all the contributory factors and processes. We do not as yet have this information about any higher plant, however, and growth curves, as well as data on the final yield of plants and the like, must still be obtained by the classical method of experimentation.

Distribution of Growth

The growth of a plant is not ordinarily uniform throughout the entire organism but is concentrated in specific and characteristic growing zones or regions. This is demonstrated by an experiment originally performed by Julius Sachs in the middle 19th Century. A growing root, hypocotyl, or stem is marked off into zones of equal length with a nontoxic material, such as India ink. After the organ has grown for a period of time, it is found that the marks are no longer equidistant; from the distance between each pair of marks, the growth rate of that part of the organ may be determined. The results of such an experiment are shown in Figure 14-4. It is clear that the most rapidly growing

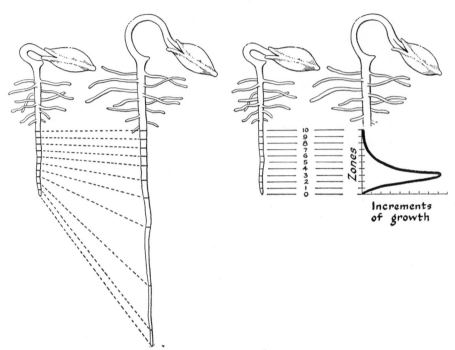

Figure 14-4. *Distribution of growth in a growing squash root. At the extreme left the growing root tip has been marked into ten equal zones. From the elongation of each zone, the distribution of elongation along the length of the root can be determined. This pattern is plotted in the curve at the extreme right. (Data from Sachs,* Text-book of Botany, *Clarendon Press, 1875, pp. 740 and 741. Figure by permission from* Botany, *4th ed., by Sinnott, copyright, 1946, McGraw-Hill Book Co., p. 235. Curve from Thompson,* On Growth and Form, *new ed., Cambridge University Press, 1942, p. 192.)*

portion of the organ, in this case a root, is located some distance behind the tip. If we express graphically the relation between the distance of a particular zone from the apex of the root and the rate of growth of this zone, we obtain a curve of the type shown in Figure 14-4. This relation, which is a general one for roots, stems, and many similar elongating organs, shows us that the rate of elongation is slow both at the extreme tip and at the base of the organ and reaches a maximum in the subapical regions.

Distributions of growth of the type shown in Figure 14-4, while they represent perhaps the simplest and best-known cases, are by no means the only type. In stems which possess well-marked nodes, it is common to find growth proceeding simultaneously in a number of internodes, so that the growth of the stem as a whole is made up

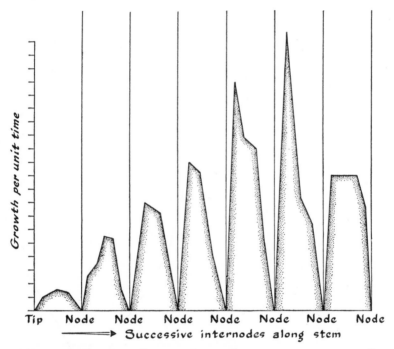

Figure 14-5. *Distribution of growth in successive internodes of the stem of Polygonum. The growth rate is rapid in the upper portion of each internode. No growth in length occurs at the nodes themselves. (After Van Burkom, from Kostychev and Went,* Pflanzenphysiologie, II, Julius Springer [Berlin], 1931, p. 271.)

of a series of growth curves of the type discussed above. In the stem of Polygonum, for example, each of the topmost six or seven internodes may grow simultaneously, as is shown in Figure 14-5. In each internode, growth is very slow at the apical end but rises to a maximum near the center, only to fall off again near the base—a lower node. Still other stems, such as those of Tradescantia, possess growth patterns in which an actively growing region is present at the base of each of a great many internodes. The expanding leaves of such broad-leaved plants as tobacco have their own pattern of growth. In this case, expansion proceeds in a relatively uniform manner throughout the entire leaf surface (Fig. 14-6). Elongating leaves of the grasses, on the other hand, grow primarily at the base, so that mature leaf tissue is being continuously expanded and pushed up by the growing region.

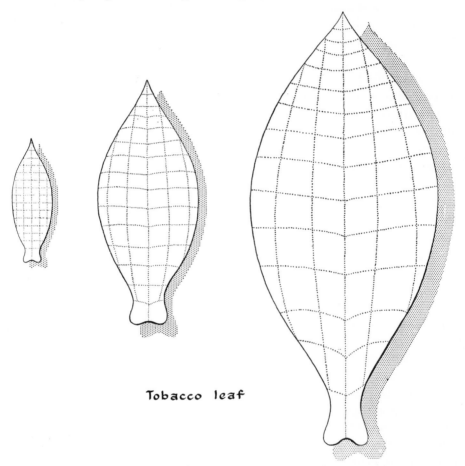

Tobacco leaf

Figure 14-6. *Pattern of growth of tobacco leaf. The young leaf to the left has been marked with India ink into regions of equal area. Each area has enlarged to approximately the same extent, showing that growth occurs all over the leaf blade. (After Avery, Am. J. Botany,* **20,** *1933, p. 576.)*

Meristems

Speaking very generally, the process of growth is initiated in regions of the plant in which cell division takes place—regions which are known as *meristems*. Apical meristems are present at the tips of roots and stems, and growth initiated by such apical meristems is known as *primary growth*, to distinguish it from *secondary growth*, initiated by the cambiums, which are essentially lateral meristems. Generally, the apical meristem is responsible for growth resulting in an increase in length and in the production of branches and other lateral parts, such as the leaves and flowers. The cambiums, on the other hand, since their cell divisions are typically in planes parallel to the long axis of the stem or root, are responsible for increases in diameter. Meristematic regions of a stem which are separated by mature tissues, as in the internodes of Polygonum or Tradescantia, are known as intercalary meristems.

The tip of the stem as seen in longitudinal section possesses at its apex a region of initial cells which, by repeated division, produce the tissues of the stem. Immediately below or lateral to the zone of the initial cells are more cells which are still actively engaged in division. In this region, the leaf primordia are produced as lateral protuberances which arise at regular intervals below the apex. At still greater distances below the apex, cell division becomes progressively less dominant, and cell enlargement becomes the dominant cellular activity. As cells enlarge to their full size, they differentiate; that is, they assume the special structural features which fit them for their particular physiological function.

The number and arrangement of the initial cells of the stem apex vary greatly between different species of plants. On the one extreme, a single cell at the apex may, by repeated division, produce the cells of the stem. At the other extreme are those species in which there is a sharp separation of the initial cells into a surface group which divides in essentially one plane to produce the outer layers of the stem, and an internal group of cells which, by division in all planes, produces the interior tissues of the stem. The single apical initial cell is characteristic only of certain lower forms, as for example among the bryophytes and some few pteridophytes. The angiosperms, on the contrary, tend toward the separation of the shoot initials into a single or multiple superficial layer, or tunica, and an internal initial region, or corpus. This is shown in Figure 14-7, depicting the shoot apex of a bamboo, in which the demarcation of the initial regions is particularly clear.

The apical meristems of roots are simpler than those of stems because they lack the complexity of leaf formation. The initial zone of the root meristem, like that of the stem, may consist of a single cell, or it may consist of two, three, or even four layers which tend to produce differing portions of the root. Thus, the most apical layer of initial cells may produce only root cap cells, or more commonly, root cap and epidermis of the root. The innermost layer of initials may similarly produce the central portion of the root, while the central layer of initials may principally form the root cortex. As in the shoot, the initial zone of the root is subtended by a region of continued meristematic activity. In this region, some specialization into the ultimate elements of root structure is evident.

The cells of the meristematic regions, and particularly the stem or root apex, are characteristically isodiametric or cuboidal. They possess only thin primary walls and are usually densely protoplasmic. In such cases, vacuoles are either relatively small or even altogether absent.

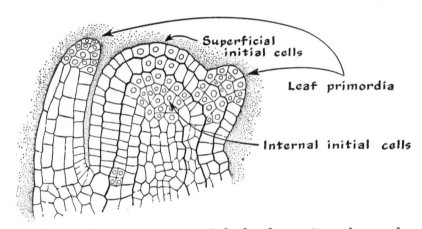

Figure 14-7. *A stem apex of the bamboo, a Sinocalamus, showing the regions of initial cells. (Adapted from Hsü, Am. J. Botany,* **31,** *1944, p. 405.)*

Immediately behind the meristematic region of the stem or root lies the region of elongation. Here, cell extension is the dominant process, and it is in this region that growth in length takes place most vigorously. Still farther back, behind the region of elongation, lies the region of differentiation, in which cells assume the structural patterns which fit them for the performance of specific tasks within the plant. Such differentiated cells are no longer engaged in either active cell division or elongation, although in some instances cell division activity can again be evoked in mature cells.

Cambial cells, unlike those of apical meristems, may not only be greatly elongated, but may also possess prominent vacuoles. The cambium is nonetheless a layer of actively dividing initial cells, and the cells produced by division of the cambium pass through stages of enlargement and maturation similar to those found in the apical growing regions.

Cell Division

The process of cell division, as it occurs in the meristematic regions, is one of the most intensively studied and best-described processes in all biology. Despite the effort put into its study, however, we have today little more than descriptive knowledge of the underlying physiology of cell division. The outstanding characteristic of cell division is the reduplication and division of the nucleus by mitosis. Through the mechanics of the mitotic process the distribution of identical complements of nuclear material to the daughter nuclei at each cell division is assured.

As a preliminary to nuclear division, the chromatic material of the nucleus contracts into threadlike chromosomes, which become progressively shorter and thicker. The short, thick chromosomes next move into one plane in the center of the cell. During the preliminary phases of the mitotic process, each chromosome has duplicated to form two daughter chromosomes. In the following stage, these identical daughter chromosomes are equally distributed, one to each half of the cell. In the final phase of nuclear division, the two groups of daughter chromosomes are again surrounded by new nuclear membranes, nucleoli are formed, and the chromosomes are slowly transformed into the chromatin reticulum of the nondividing nucleus.

We know from the study of genetics that each chromosome contains a series of genes, the factors which determine the growth, metabolism, and the form of the organism. The individual genes are fastened together in a fixed linear order, forming the chromosome as a whole. A key to the understanding of nuclear growth would consist in a comprehension of the manner in which each chromosome becomes exactly duplicated in the formation of two daughter chromosomes prior to nuclear division. In this duplication of the chromosomal nucleoprotein, not only are the general form and appearance of the whole chromosome preserved, but each constituent gene is said by geneticists to be copied exactly, even to the minutest chemical detail. The mechanism by which this duplication takes place is still one of the basic problems of biology.

Important as are the nuclear aspects of cell division, it should be remembered that other phenomena are also involved. The formation of a new cell wall, dividing the cell contents into two new cells, accompanies the final stages of the nuclear division. Particular bodies in the cytoplasm other than the nucleus also divide and are distributed to the daughter cells. This is especially true of the chloroplasts.

The chloroplasts of the plant cell develop by duplication and growth of pre-existing chloroplasts or chloroplast precursors, the proplastids. Chloroplasts or proplastids are thus transmitted from cell to cell, just as is the nucleus. More than one chloroplast or proplastid is ordinarily present in the cell, however, and several are then incorporated into each daughter cell at the time of cell division. Proplastids are frequently present in tissues which never develop chloroplasts; they are, for example, present in the ovule. Proplastids are handed down maternally from generation to generation, and the nature of the proplastids may in part be independent of the genotype of the pollen parent. In certain species, however, proplastids are also contained in the pollen tube and may be transmitted through the pollen parent.

During the development of the cell, the chloroplasts or proplastids divide. In algae and in bryophytes, division of the chloroplast to form two daughter chloroplasts may frequently be observed, either preceding or simultaneously with cell division. In the higher plant, however, the multiplication of chloroplasts takes place in the proplastid stage. The proplastids do not contain the typical pigments of the mature chloroplasts and are smaller in size. The proplastids of maize, for example, are about one micron in diameter. In the palisade cells of the leaf, the proplastid develops rapidly to a diameter of three to four microns before the development of extensive pigmentation. After this size has been attained, production of the chlorophyll and carotenoid pigments typical of the chloroplast takes place rapidly, the chloroplast at the same time continuing its expansion to a final diameter of six to eight microns in this species.

Cell Enlargement

Cell enlargement is the dominant and most obvious phase in the growth of the plant. This increase in size is caused primarily by an absorption of water. Through such water uptake, the plant cell expands, much as a balloon expands when it is filled with air under pressure. The measure of the driving force of cell elongation or expansion is, then, the diffusion pressure deficit of the cell. If the cell possesses a diffusion pressure deficit and if water is available, water will move in, and the cell will stretch. If the cell wall is sufficiently plastic so that this stretching is irreversible, then true cell elongation will occur.

Plastic stretching of the cell wall would, of course, lead to a gradual diminution in cell wall thickness, were it not for the fact, noted in Chapter 9, that elongation is generally accompanied by deposition of new cell wall materials. In tissues of the pea stem and the oat coleoptile, which have been studied relatively thoroughly, the deposition of the new cell wall keeps pace with cell elongation, so that the walls remain comparatively constant in thickness during growth.

During cell elongation, the vacuole of the elongating cell grows in size and becomes a prominent part of the cell, so that in the mature cell the protoplasm appears only as a narrow layer between cell wall and vacuole. Thus, there is a marked contrast between the small, richly protoplasmic cells of the meristem and the large vacuolate cells which result from cell enlargement. This difference in protoplasmic contents per unit length of cell would be the more marked were it not for the fact that usually synthesis of new protoplasm also occurs during the phase of cell enlargement. Cell enlargement is, therefore, not only a passive increase in cell volume due to water uptake, but it is also a process in which the synthetic processes of wall and protoplasm formation participate.

Differentiation

The differentiation of cells, which takes place following or accompanying cell enlargement, involves several different kinds of anatomical and physiological specialization. Cells may differentiate and become specialized with respect to size and shape, with respect to nature and extent of secondary cell wall development, or with respect to their protoplasmic contents. Frequently, differentiation in all of these characteristics is involved in the development of a particular kind of cell for a particular physiological function. Parenchymatous cells exhibit the least degree of specialized development and differ from cells of the meristematic region primarily in their greater size and degree of vacuolization. Secondary cell wall layers are not ordinarily formed by simple parenchymatous cells such as those of the pith or cortex of many species. The cells which are destined to become vascular elements, such as sieve tube elements, vessel elements, tracheids, and fibers, undergo much more drastic specialization. These cells enlarge greatly, generally maturing into greatly elongate elements. Secondary cell wall development is extensive in vessel elements, tracheids and fibers, and the specialized features of the cell wall—annular or spiral thickenings, bordered pits, and so forth—are developed. The characteristic lignification of the secondary cell wall is also a feature of this phase of differentiation in such cells.

Differentiation with respect to protoplasmic contents may involve complete disintegration and loss of protoplasm, as in the vessel elements, tracheids, and fibers. In other types of cells, such as the sieve tube elements, the nucleus disappears after some time, and the enucleate cytoplasm continues to function. In this case, it is believed that the nuclei of the adjacent companion cells, which are intimately connected with each sieve tube element, are in fact the functional nuclei of the sieve tube elements also. Finally, in parenchymatous cells, the entire protoplasm remains alive and functional over long periods of time.

Differentiation is, then, the transformation of apparently identical cells of the meristem into a variety of highly specialized cells. What factors control the process? What factors induce a particular cell to become, for example, a tracheid rather than a parenchymatous cell? Most plant physiologists assume that these questions are answerable ones and that the answers may become known through more detailed knowledge of the chemistry of plant growth. Our existing knowledge of the factors regulating the processes of differentiation will be further discussed in Chapter 19.

Summary

Growth is an irreversible increase in the size of the plant. It is due to the formation of new cells at localized regions called meristems, and to the increase in size and mass of the cells produced. The rate of growth of a plant or plant organ varies with age, being initially slow, later more rapid, and finally less rapid or zero. Thus, the increase in plant size or mass with time follows an "S"-shaped, or sigmoid, curve. Such sigmoid growth curves are typical not only of plants, but indeed of living creatures generally.

The genetic identity of all cells of an individual is guaranteed at mitosis by a duplication of the nuclear genes and their equal distribution into resulting daughter cells. Plastids and other cytoplasmic bodies may be perpetuated directly through the maternal cytoplasm, and may thus be relatively independent of nuclear genes.

Differentiation is the transformation of the apparently identical cells produced by the meristem into a variety of specialized cells. The manner in which differences arise in genetically identical material is still largely unknown.

QUESTIONS

1. In the "grand period of growth" of organs, organisms, and populations, a period of rapid growth is followed by a period of slower growth. Why should growth rate slacken in this manner?

2. The most rapidly elongating portion of a root is several millimeters behind the tip, although most of the cell divisions are occurring much closer to the tip. What is the reason for this?

3. How does the inheritance of chloroplast characteristics differ from that of most other cellular properties?

4. The rapidly dividing cells of an apical meristem are separated from differentiated vascular elements by a region of undifferentiated elongating cells. How do the meristematic cells obtain the water and nutrients essential for their great metabolic activity?

5. What is meant by differentiation? What kinds of influences could possibly operate in causing differences to appear in cells with identical genetic complements?

6. The process of cell division, although much studied and adequately described, is not at all understood in terms of the physiological or biochemical mechanisms involved. What difficulties have prevented more rapid advances in this field?

7. Discuss the various processes involved in the increase in size of a newly produced cell.

8. Embryonic cells are nonvacuolate, while most mature cells have large central vacuoles. How can a vacuole start developing in the cytoplasm? What causes it to increase in size?

GENERAL READING

Bünning, E., *Entwicklungs- und Bewegungsphysiologie der Pflanze*. Berlin: Springer-Verlag, 1948. In German. A most comprehensive summary of plant growth and development.

Eames, A. J., and MacDaniels, L. H., *Introduction to Plant Anatomy*, 2nd ed. New York: McGraw-Hill Book Co., 1947. Includes clear and readable discussions of the meristems, their organization, and their relation to growth.

Foster, A. S., *Practical Plant Anatomy*, 2nd ed. New York: D. Van Nostrand Co., 1949. A condensed account of our knowledge of plant structure.

Thompson, D'A. W., *On Growth and Form*, new ed. New York: Cambridge: University Press, 1942. A lengthy and scholarly discussion of the kinetics of growth and development. A classic.

CHAPTER 15

The Integration of Growth

Introduction

The growth of a plant is of course a composite of the growth of its individual cells, tissues, and organs. How do the growth rates of these different component parts keep in step with one another? By what  mechanisms is the growth of individual cells, tissues, and organs integrated to produce a whole plant? To discuss this integration, it is necessary to introduce a new concept—the concept of the plant growth hormone.

We now recognize that the growth of the plant is regulated not alone by the minerals taken up through the roots and by the carbohydrates synthesized in the leaves, but also by particular chemical substances which have specific roles as agents for the correlation of the growth of one part with the growth of others. These chemical agents—organic substances active even in very small amounts—are formed in one tissue or organ of the plant and then travel to other sites, where they produce special growth effects. Such agents are known as *plant hormones*.

Root Growth Hormones

Perhaps the simplest instance of hormonal regulation of plant growth is that relating to the interaction of leaves and roots. It can be shown that the growth of roots depends not only on the minerals taken up from the soil or nutrient solution and on the carbohydrates produced in the leaves and translocated to the roots, but also on three particular chemical substances manufactured in the leaves and translocated in small quantities to the roots. These chemical substances, which roots are not capable of synthesizing, but which are essential to their growth, function as root growth hormones. Their effectiveness is most simply demonstrated by the method of isolated root culture. The concept of isolated root culture as a tool for the study of plant growth was first introduced

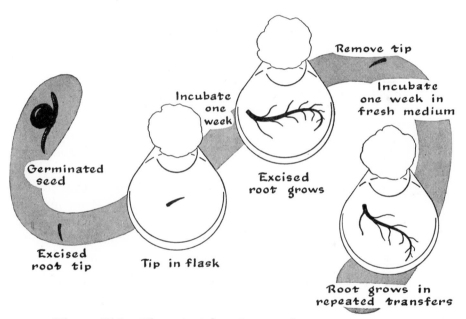

Figure 15-1. *The principles of root culture.*

by W. J. Robbins in 1922. For this purpose, seeds were allowed to germinate under aseptic conditions, and short pieces of excised root tip were transferred to an aseptic nutrient medium (Fig. 15-1). Provided that the aseptic nutrient medium contained all of the materials then known to be essential for growth, these isolated roots grew as normal or essentially normal roots. After a period of time, the growing tips were transferred to a fresh nutrient solution, where they continued to grow, although often at a considerably diminished rate. Robbins established then, that although excised roots of corn, pea, sunflower, and other plants could be cultured initially on media of known composition, growth in successive subcultures of the original excised root exhibited a progressively diminishing rate. The media used in this study did not, therefore, contain all the factors essential to continued root growth.

What, now, are the materials which must be present in the nutrient solution in order to support the indefinite growth of excised roots in a manner and at a rate similar to that which would have been attained had the root remained attached to the plant? If we culture excised roots of flax in a nutrient medium containing only the usual inorganic mineral salts, the roots fail to grow. This is in part because sucrose must be added to the nutrient solution to replace the carbohydrates which would otherwise have been transported to the roots from the photosynthetic organs of the leaf. If the flax root tip is cultured in a nutrient

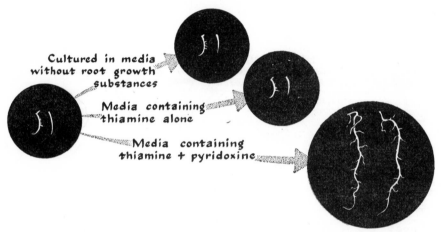

Figure 15-2. *Many strains of isolated tomato roots require addition of thiamine and pyridoxine to the media for normal growth.*

medium containing inorganic salts and sucrose, extensive growth will occur. After a week or more of growth, the tip of the cultured root may be transferred to a fresh medium. Growth in this transfer will be much less than in the original, and in succeeding transfers it will cease entirely. This is because one specific substance required for root growth and present in the original tip is slowly used up during growth and is not synthesized by the root. This substance, required in the very low concentration of 1 part in 10 million of nutrient solution, is thiamine. In a nutrient solution containing inorganic salts, sucrose, and thiamine, excised roots of flax will continue to grow through any number of transfers at a rate as great as or greater than would have been attained had the root remained attached to the living plant. Thiamine is required not only by excised roots of flax but by all excised roots which have thus far been successfully cultured apart from the plant.

Unlike flax, however, roots of many species grow in culture only when supplied with other substances in addition to mineral salts, sucrose, and thiamine. For example, excised roots of tomato require, in general, the presence of thiamine and pyridoxine (Fig. 15-2). The roots of certain varieties of tomato, as well as those of other species such as jimson weed, require thiamine, pyridoxine, and nicotinic acid in order to grow as isolated roots. Many of the leguminous species which have been in-

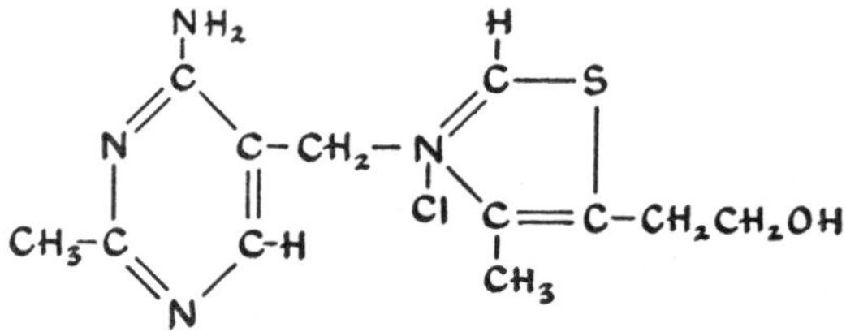

Thiamine

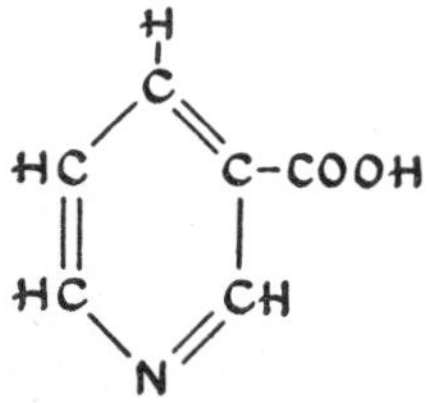

Nicotinic acid

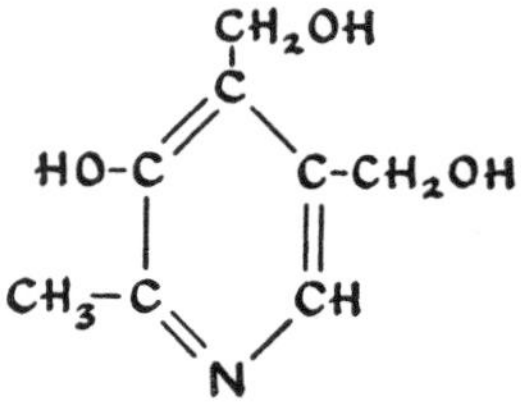

Pyridoxine

vestigated, such as pea, clover, and alfalfa, require thiamine and nicotinic acid. In general, it may be said that isolated roots of all species which have thus far been successfully cultivated *in vitro* require thiamine and one or both of the substances pyridoxine and nicotinic acid to attain a growth rate equivalent to that of the root which remains attached to the plant.

We may now ask ourselves the question: Where does the root of the intact plant normally obtain its supply of thiamine and other factors required for its growth? This may be answered simply by experiments designed to determine the site of formation and the direction of translocation of the thiamine. This can be done by girdling experiments similar to those described in Chapter 7. The application of this technique to the tomato plant, for example, shows that thiamine accumulates above a stem girdle located between the leaves and the roots (Fig. 15-3). Accumulation at the stem girdle does not take place if the plant is first

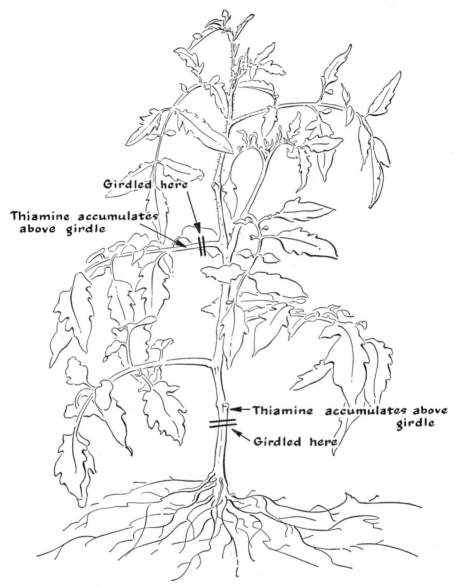

Girdled here

Thiamine accumulates above girdle

Thiamine accumulates above girdle

Girdled here

Figure 15-3. *The root growth hormone thiamine is synthesized in leaves and transported to the root system.*

defoliated. When a petiole is girdled, thiamine accumulates on the laminar side of the girdle (toward the leaf blade). The results of these experiments demonstrate unequivocally that thiamine is synthesized in green leaves and translocated from these green leaves down the stem to the roots. The same is true of pyridoxine. Since thiamine and pyridoxine are compounds required by and translocated to roots in minute quantities, and since they fulfill the other criterion of synthesis in one organ and transport to another where they are used, they are known as plant hormones—chemical regulators of plant growth.

We have seen in Chapter 8 that thiamine and pyridoxine, both known as vitamins of the B complex and required in the nutrition of animals, are substances which participate in the formation of the prosthetic groups of certain enzymes. Thus, thiamine in the form of thiamine pyrophosphate or cocarboxylase is the prosthetic group of the carboxylases, which have to do with carbon dioxide evolution in respiration. Carboxylases are required in the respiration of roots just as they are in the respiration of other organs and organisms. Pyridoxine in the form of its derivative, pyridoxal phosphate, is similarly the prosthetic group of the transaminase enzymes which participate in the synthesis of amino acids. Nicotinic acid, the third of the recognized root growth substances, is a component of the respiratory dehydrogenases. It is characteristic of hormones that they participate in the biochemical economy of the plant, and, where the roles of individual hormones have been worked out in detail, it has frequently been shown that these substances are required for the functioning of particular enzymatic reactions.

The absence of thiamine from the nutrient solution in which an excised root is allowed to grow results in certain typical and characteristic symptoms. Cell division becomes increasingly more sluggish in the root meristem as the thiamine deficiency becomes more acute, and in advanced thiamine deficiency, cell division may cease or essentially cease. From a histological point of view, thiamine might be referred to as a hormone for cell division in the root. We see, then, that there are different ways of viewing the activity of a plant growth hormone. From the point of view of the plant as a whole, thiamine is synthesized in sufficient quantities, and no external supply is ordinarily required. Considering the plant as an array of separate organs, thiamine is a substance made in the leaves and required by the roots. From a biochemical standpoint, thiamine is a component of essential enzymatic prosthetic groups. From a histological point of view, thiamine is a cell division factor.

We have known for many years that the higher animals, including man, require thiamine and the other vitamins of the B complex as essential components of the diet. These vitamins are made by plants. In fact, we have come to assume tacitly that vitamins are made by plants in order that animals, by eating the plants, may avoid deficiency diseases. It is now clear, however, that vitamins of the B complex have their own essential roles in the plant as well as in the animal. Plants and animals differ not in their requirement for thiamine, pyridoxine, and so forth, but in their ability to synthesize these compounds.

Knowledge of the fact that thiamine, pyridoxine, and nicotinic acid are required as factors for the growth of roots has resulted in individual, though minor, practical applications. It has been shown with certain species that the growth of roots on excised pieces of stem cuttings may be promoted by the application of thiamine or pyridoxine. In these instances it would appear that the cutting lacks the amount of thiamine or pyridoxine required for optimum root growth.

Leaf Growth Hormones

Just as it has been possible by tissue culture techniques to show that the plant possesses certain chemical substances or hormones for the regulation of root growth, so too has it been possible to establish by similar techniques that the growth of immature leaves to mature leaves involves particular factors which may be termed leaf growth hormones.

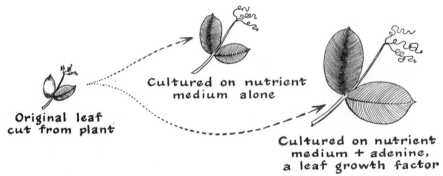

Original leaf cut from plant

Cultured on nutrient medium alone

Cultured on nutrient medium + adenine, a leaf growth factor

Figure 15-4. *The growth of excised pea leaves is stimulated by adenine.*

This has been shown most clearly with the leaves of pea seedlings. If immature, expanding leaves of pea seedlings are excised and placed in an aseptic nutrient solution containing inorganic salts and sucrose, they enlarge very little. If, however, such excised leaves are supplied not only with inorganic salts and sugar but with extracts of pea cotyledons or of mature leaves, the mesophyll of the excised immature leaves expands rapidly, and the leaves ultimately attain a size not greatly different from that which would have been attained had the leaf remained attached to the plant (Fig. 15-4). Extracts of pea seeds or of mature leaves would appear, therefore, to contain materials required for the growth of immature leaves. Chemical fractionation of pea seed extract has resulted in the identification of the active materials as purines, adenine and hypoxanthine, which, as we have seen in earlier chapters, are required as constituents of nucleic acid and of prosthetic groups of numerous enzymes. Adenine occurs and is synthesized in mature leaves, in roots, and possibly in other tissues also, but only to a small extent, if at all, in the developing pea leaf. Adenine may therefore function as a hormone of leaf growth in the pea plant. Adenine is ineffective, however, in promoting the growth of excised leaves of cereals, and it appears likely that in different species quite different chemical substances may have the role of leaf growth hormone.

Stem Growth Hormones

Just as there are substances or hormones for the control of root and leaf growth, so also the plant produces a specific substance which functions in the control of the growth of stem length. This growth substance is generally synthesized in the apical bud or young expanding leaves of the shoot and is translocated from these tissues to those of the elongation regions of the stem.

A simple demonstration of the role of growth hormones in the elongation of stem tissues may be carried out with the aid of excised sections from the growing regions of the stems of etiolated pea seedlings or of the hypocotyls of etiolated sunflower seedlings. If an excised section of the growing regions of the etiolated pea seedling is placed in nutrient solution containing mineral salts and sucrose, little elongation occurs. If, on the other hand, a small amount of indoleacetic acid is added to this nutrient solution, rapid stem elongation of the excised region will result (Fig. 15-5). The section may actually elongate as much as or more than corresponding sections growing in situ on the intact plant. Indoleacetic acid is, therefore, active in promoting the growth of stem tissues. It is, in fact, active in very low concentrations, since only 10 milligrams or less per liter (10 parts or less per million) are required to bring about this effect. It is possible by chemical means to show that indoleacetic acid is produced in the buds and apical leaves of the growing shoot, and that it is responsible for regulating the elongation of the subterminal portions of the stem.

Growth substances such as indoleacetic acid and related compounds,

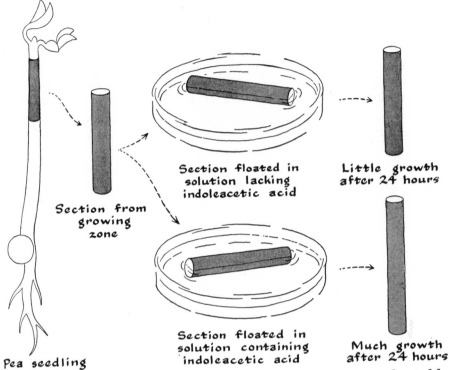

Figure 15-5. *The elongation of excised pea stems is accelerated by the addition of indoleacetic acid to the culture medium.*

known collectively as *auxins,* are responsible not only for stem elongation but for many other growth-coordinating effects within the plant. The manifold effects of the auxins will be discussed in more detail in the following chapter. The point to be stressed here is that in the growth of stems also, the plant makes use of the hormone principle to bring about a correlated growth pattern.

Other Instances of Hormonal Regulation

There are other instances in which the growth of a particular plant organ appears to be controlled by chemical substances produced in other organs of the plant. In many of these cases, demonstration of the role of growth substances or growth hormones can be effectively carried out by the use of the plant tissue culture technique. Thus for the study of the growth of fruits, it is possible to excise the fertilized ovary shortly after pollination and to culture the isolated organ (Fig. 15-6). If a suitable nutrient solution is used, the ovary will grow into a mature fruit. For excised tomato ovaries, for example, a suitable medium consists of a mineral nutrient solution containing the juice or extract of mature tomato fruits. The juice of mature tomato fruits contains materials, as yet unknown, which are beneficial to the growth of excised immature tomato fruits. In the intact plant these substances are presumably transported to the ovaries from other organs, but we do not yet have detailed information concerning either the site of synthesis or the chemical nature of these growth hormones.

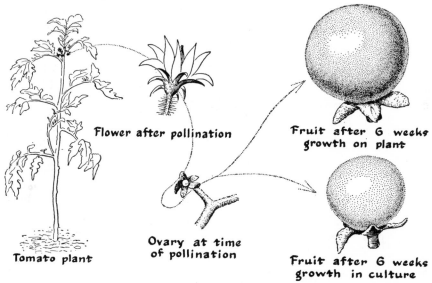

Flower after pollination

Fruit after 6 weeks growth on plant

Ovary at time of pollination

Tomato plant

Fruit after 6 weeks growth in culture

Figure 15-6. *Comparison of the growth of pollinated ovaries of the currant tomato in nutrient culture and on the plant. (After Jansen, 1950, unpublished.)*

Plant embryos also appear to require specific chemical substances other than the major nutrient materials for their growth and development. Excised immature embryos of many plants fail to develop further on a nutrient solution containing only mineral salts and sugar and require the presence of additional specific substances in minute concentrations. These substances include certain of the vitamins of the B complex, such as pantothenic acid, as well as root growth factors such as thiamine. Still other factors necessary for the growth of immature embryos are known to be contained in yeast extract, in malt extract, and in coconut milk, but the nature of these factors has not yet been determined. Even the growth rate of excised mature embryos may be increased by addition to the nutrient medium of thiamine, nicotinic acid, biotin, and other specific substances.

The healing of wounds in plants by the formation of new tissue appears to be initiated by particular chemical substances liberated from injured cells. Since the cells which are stimulated to activity are necessarily somewhat removed from the site of injury, the wound-produced substances which evoke the new cell activity must move within the plant, and may therefore be counted among the hormones. When a potato tuber is cut, the exposed surface will in time become covered by a newly formed layer of corky cells. If the injured surface is washed immediately after cutting, formation of this new layer does not occur. Application of an extract of crushed cells to the freshly washed surface will, however, evoke cell division activity. To the substances of injured tissue which are responsible for the initiation of growth in adjacent uninjured cells, the German physiologist Haberlandt gave the name *wound hormones.* Only one wound hormone has as yet been prepared in chemically pure form and characterized from a chemical viewpoint. This substance, traumatic acid, is produced during injury of the pods of green beans and is active in evoking growth in uninjured cells of similar pods. Since traumatic acid, which is chemically a dicarboxylic acid containing 12 carbon atoms and one double bond, is ineffective as a wound hormone on most plant tissues other than the bean pod itself, it is possible that the wound-healing reactions of different species may be mediated by chemically diverse substances.

In still other instances, the participation of certain hormones in the correlation of growth within the plant is suspected but cannot be proved by present experimental techniques. It is known that the growth of the stems in seedlings may be greatly inhibited by the removal of the roots. This has led to the suggestion that a particular hypothetical substance, caulocaline, which is required for the growth of stems, may be produced in roots. More definite evidence, which is to be given in a later chapter, has likewise indicated that substances responsible for the initiation of flower primordia and the production of flowers are synthesized in leaves and then travel from the leaves to the bud, where they bring about the transition from the vegetative to the flowering state.

Summary

We may picture the growth of the plant not only as dependent on environmental circumstances, on the mineral nutrients taken up from the soil, and on the carbohydrates produced from carbon dioxide through the process of photosynthesis, but also as controlled and integrated by the interaction of particular and specific organic substances within it (Fig. 15-7).

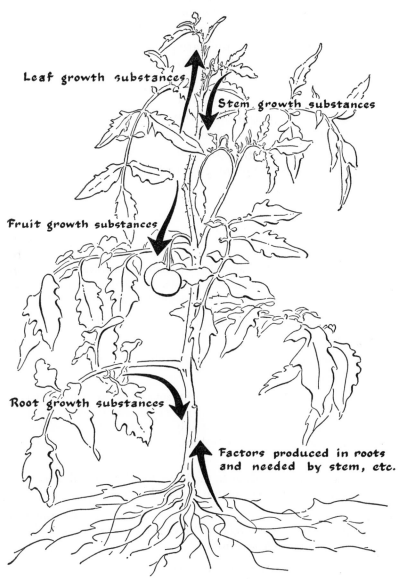

Figure 15-7. *The growth of a plant is controlled and integrated by many growth hormones, each produced in a particular organ and translocated to other regions.*

Specific substances required for the growth of roots are produced in leaves. Root growth is, therefore, in part regulated by the amount of root growth substances—thiamine, pyridoxine, and nicotinic acid—produced in the leaf and translocated to the root. The growth of young leaves, particularly the growth of the mesophyll, depends on certain leaf growth substances, such as adenine, which are produced in mature leaves. Similarly, growth of the stem depends, in part, on the growth hormones of the auxin group, which are produced in the apical bud and young expanding leaves and transported to the elongation regions of the stem.

In the plant, the principle of hormonal regulation has been developed to a high degree. The integration of the activities of one part with the activities of the other parts is achieved, in large measure, through the synthesis, transport, and utilization of specific, individual, chemical messenger substances—the plant growth hormones.

QUESTIONS

1. The development of any plant to maturity involves a synchronization and regulation of numerous events. In what ways is this regulation achieved? How may the normal regulational pattern be altered?

2. In what ways is the growth of a root dependent on other parts of the plant?

3. Explain how you would proceed to obtain an aseptic, growing culture of isolated tomato roots.

4. The excised roots of many herbaceous dicotyledonous species can be cultivated indefinitely *in vitro* on chemically defined media, but the roots of monocots and of woody species do not generally continue growth beyond several transfers. Discuss possible reasons for this difference in behavior.

5. What evidence leads us to the belief that leaf growth hormones exist? What is the probable nature of such hormones?

6. Most excised stem tips will produce adventitious roots spontaneously, but very few excised roots will give rise to adventitious buds. Can you propose a possible explanation?

7. What stem growth factors are known or supposed to exist? How could one demonstrate their effect?

8. The cells of a potato tuber are normally parenchymatous, thin walled, and contain abundant stored starch. However, if such a tuber is cut

open, the cells produced at the cut surface are typically corky, relatively thick walled, and devoid of stored starch. What factors might be responsible for the altered developmental pattern?

9. How can one demonstrate the existence of wound hormones?

GENERAL READING

Bonner, J., and Bonner, H., "The B Vitamins as Plant Hormones." *Vitamins and Hormones*, **6**: 225, 1948. A review of our knowledge of the B vitamins in relation to root growth and other aspects of plant growth.

Thimann, K. V., "Plant Growth Hormones," and "Other Plant Hormones," in Pincus, G., and Thimann, K. V., eds., *The Hormones*, Chaps. 1 and 2. New York: Academic Press, 1948. An extensive summary of all known plant growth hormones.

Went, F. W., and Thimann, K. V., *Phytohormones*. New York: Macmillan Co., 1937. Includes the development of modern concepts of the hormonal control of plant growth.

CHAPTER 16

Auxin and the Control of Growth

Introduction

We have seen that the growth of the plant is controlled and integrated by a great number of different and distinct hormones—that the growth of root, leaf, embryo, fruit, stem, and other organs is regulated by particular chemical messenger substances. Of these many different plant hormones, one group in particular, the *auxins,* is of special interest, for a variety of reasons. This hormone, or group of hormones, was not only the first plant growth hormone to be discovered, but it is also one which has a great number of different kinds of regulatory duties in the plant. Auxin is involved in the control of stem growth, root growth, lateral bud inhibition, abscission of leaves and fruits, fruit growth and, in all, some twenty different physiological activities of the plant. Auxin appears to be a master hormone, exercising regulatory action over many different sorts of plant processes and probably over many of the other plant hormones.

Special interest is attached to auxin also because our knowledge of this plant hormone has permitted the development of several important methods for the chemical control of plant development under practical agricultural conditions. Present-day practices for the rooting of cuttings, artificial setting of fruits, delay of fruit drop, and selective weed control are all based on our knowledge of this one group of plant hormones. Although we know that the auxins are involved in a great number of different kinds of plant growth activity, it was the relation of auxin to cell elongation which first brought about the discovery of, and the subsequent study of, plant hormones. Most of the detailed work concerning auxin physiology, such as concentrations at which it is active, factors affecting its activity, and the mechanism of its action, have therefore been related to studies on cell elongation.

350

Discovery of Auxin

The definitive discovery of auxin was realized in 1928 by F. W. Went, who built on the observations and experiments of numerous workers, including Charles Darwin. Darwin was actually interested in phototropism, a subject to which we shall turn later in this chapter. He happened to select for his work the coleoptile, or leaf sheath, of etiolated, or dark-grown, grass seedlings (Fig. 16-1). The coleoptile is a hollow cylinder enclosing the epicotyl and is attached to the axis of the seedling at

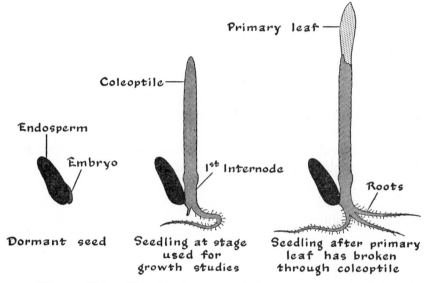

Figure 16-1. *The development of the oat seedling and its coleoptile.*

the first node. The coleoptile of the oat, for example, starts its development as a dome-shaped covering over the apical end of the seedling (Fig. 16-2). It enlarges principally by cell elongation for the first 70 to 100 hours of seedling growth. Eventually, the first leaf, as it expands, pierces the coleoptile at its apex, after which growth of this organ ceases.

During most of its growth period, elongation of the coleoptile takes place primarily in the center of the organ, almost to the exclusion of the extreme apical end and the basal portion, as is shown in Figure 16-3. If, however, the extreme apical tip (1 mm or less) of the growing coleoptile is excised, elongation of the more basal regions is suspended.

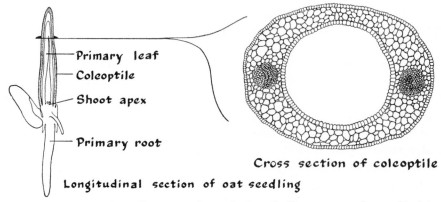

Cross section of coleoptile

Longitudinal section of oat seedling

Figure 16-2. *The oat coleoptile is a hollow, somewhat cylindrical sheath which envelopes the shoot apex and young leaves.* (*By permission after* Went *and* Thimann, Phytohormones, *Macmillan Co., 1937, p. 22.*)

This simple experiment, first done by the German plant physiologist Söding in 1923, indicates that the tip of the coleoptile produces something which is needed for the growth of the lower elongating regions. This view was greatly strengthened by the demonstration that when the excised tip is replaced on the decapitated coleoptile stump, growth of the stump is immediately resumed (Fig. 16-4). Söding's experiments, therefore, provided a solid basis for the supposition that a hormone needed for coleoptile growth might be formed in the tip of the coleoptile.

The growth-promoting substance of the oat coleoptile tip was first

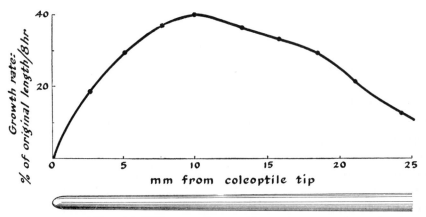

Figure 16-3. *Distribution of growth in the oat coleoptile.* (*After* Went, Rec. trav. botan. néerland., **25**, *1929, p. 73.*)

extracted by Went, who used the simple technique of allowing excised tips to stand for a few hours with their cut surfaces in contact with an agar block. The agar, as a result of the contact, acquires the growth-promoting quality previously possessed by the tip and is capable of restoring growth when placed on the stump of a decapitated coleoptile (Fig. 16-4). This shows that the growth-promoting property of the coleoptile tip is actually a substance capable of diffusing from tip to agar block and from agar block to coleoptile stump. This growth substance, now known to occur in a wide variety of plants, is called *auxin*. Various synthetic substances may also act as auxins in this test.

The growth-promoting property of coleoptile tips, or of agar blocks

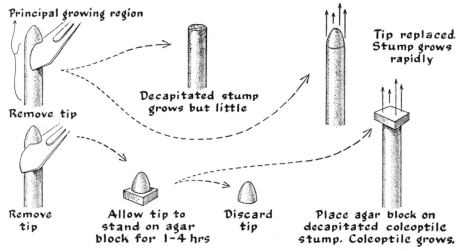

Figure 16-4. *Demonstration of the growth-promoting properties of the coleoptile tip.*

which have been in physical contact with them, may be demonstrated in a striking manner by applying the tip or agar block asymmetrically to the cut surface of a decapitated coleoptile stump. Under these conditions the growth-promoting principle passes unilaterally down the coleoptile, causing growth to occur on one side of the stump and not on the other, resulting in a curvature of the coleoptile. This curvature is, of course, away from the applied block or tip and hence is referred to as a *negative curvature*. The degree of curvature, which is proportional, over a wide range, to the concentration of the growth-promoting substance in the applied agar block, may be used for the quantitative determination of plant growth substances.

Physiological Determination of Auxin

The first step in the physiological determination of auxin by the cole-optile method is the removal of the tip. Since the tip supplies auxin to the lower portions of the coleoptile, its removal results in almost total depletion of auxin from the coleoptile stump. After a period of approximately three hours, however, the cut apical surface of the coleoptile stump reacquires the ability to produce auxin (a process known as *regeneration of the physiological tip;* see Fig. 16-5); so a second decapi-

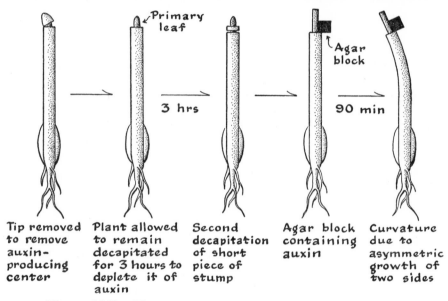

| Tip removed to remove auxin-producing center | Plant allowed to remain decapitated for 3 hours to deplete it of auxin | Second decapitation of short piece of stump | Agar block containing auxin | Curvature due to asymmetric growth of two sides |

Figure 16-5. *The oat curvature test for auxin.*

tation of the stump is made. At this time, the first leaf is pulled free of its attachment at the base of the coleoptile, so that its growth will not interfere with subsequent operations. After the second decapitation, agar blocks containing auxin are applied unilaterally to the cut surface of the stump. These blocks are placed on the shelf which is formed between the coleoptile and the remainder of the first leaf. After 90 minutes, the curvature resulting from the asymmetric growth of the co-leoptile under the influence of the unilaterally applied auxin is photographed and subsequently measured on the photograph. In the usual determination, twelve replicate plants are tested with replicate agar blocks for each solution or extract to be assayed for auxin content.

The average curvature from these test plants may then be compared with the average curvature caused by agar blocks containing a known concentration of a pure auxin. Such a standard demands, however, a knowledge of the chemical nature of the auxin growth substances of plants.

Chemical Nature of Auxin

Elucidation of the chemical nature of the growth substance of the coleoptile tip was a logical undertaking once its existence had been established. Although the problem has been studied by various groups of workers, isolation of the auxin of coleoptile tips has never been achieved. This is because it occurs in the tip in only the most minute quantities. We now know that each coleoptile tip contains about 10^{-10} gm of active growth substance, an amount so small that it has thus far proved impractical to collect sufficient material for chemical work.

It was early found that substances active in causing curvature in the oat coleoptile occur widely in nature, as for example in human urine as well as in culture media previously used for the growth of various fungi. The Dutch workers Kögl and Haagen-Smit therefore undertook the isolation of the active material of urine, and in 1934 announced the isolation of indoleacetic acid (IAA) from this source. IAA is highly active in the oat coleoptile curvature test. If, for example, 5×10^{-4} μgm (5×10^{-10} gm) of pure IAA in agar are applied to a coleoptile in the

Indoleacetic acid

manner prescribed above, a clearly visible curvature will result (roughly, $10°$). To state it another way, if a solution containing 50 μgm of IAA per liter were made into agar blocks of 10 mm³ volume, and a single block applied to each test plant, then each block will evoke an average curvature of $10°$. IAA is, therefore, tremendously effective physiologically, and is capable of bringing about growth responses similar to those evoked by the coleoptile tip itself. The curvature of oat test plants as a function of concentration of applied indoleacetic acid is shown in Figure 16-6.

Is IAA, in fact, the auxin of the oat coleoptile and other plant tissues? An increasing body of evidence supports the view that it is, although other chemical substances with similar physiological properties may occur in particular instances. IAA has been isolated in pure chemical form, both from higher plant tissues and from culture media in which Rhizopus or other microorganisms have grown. Developing corn seeds contain a particularly high concentration of IAA and have served as the raw material for isolation of the pure chemical. IAA has not been isolated from actively growing vegetative tissues of the plant. Somewhat

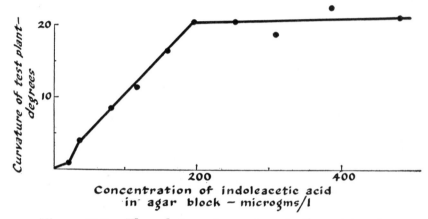

Figure 16-6. *The relation of curvature in the oat test to concentration of applied indoleacetic acid. (By permission after Went and Thimann,* Phytohormones, Macmillan Co., 1937, p. 41.)

more indirect methods indicate, however, that here, also, the auxin involved is probably IAA. Qualitative chemical tests have indicated that the bulk, or perhaps all, of the auxin of the oat coleoptile and various leaves and other tissues may be IAA. This, coupled with other evidence to be discussed later in this chapter, strongly suggests that IAA is a native auxin.

Before the discovery of IAA as an active auxin, two other chemical substances, auxin *a* and auxin *b*, were isolated from urine and shown to be highly active in the oat coleoptile curvature test. These substances are chemically quite unrelated to IAA. We have no critical evidence establishing these materials as native auxins of the growing plant or even as plant products of normal occurrence. It is difficult, therefore, to assess the role which auxins *a* and *b* may play in the plant. The possibility must be recognized, however, that auxins other than indoleacetic acid may occur in higher plants.

Auxin Distribution

We have seen that in the oat coleoptile, auxin is formed in the extreme tip but is translocated to, and is essential in, the growth of the elongating portions of the coleoptile, which do not ordinarily possess the ability to form the substance. Etiolated seedlings of other species synthesize auxin in the apical bud and occasionally in the cotyledons. The production of auxin in these cases may be demonstrated by means similar to that outlined above for the tip of the oat coleoptile. The

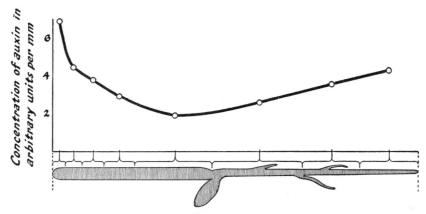

Figure 16-7. *The distribution of auxin in the oat seedling. (Data from Thimann, J. Gen. Physiol., 18, 1934, p. 32.)*

growing root tip also possesses the ability to produce auxin. In the normal green plant, auxin is produced in the apical bud or buds and translocated from these buds to the lower portions of the stems. The young expanding leaves may also produce auxin in large amounts, and in many species mature leaves serve as centers of auxin synthesis, although they in general export only small or negligible quantities of the material.

Auxin is, then, synthesized in large amounts in only a few localized centers, but it is transported through all of the tissues of the plant. This results in a quite characteristic pattern of auxin distribution—a pattern which is shown for the oat seedling in Figure 16-7. Auxin is concentrated in the tips of shoot and root of the seedling and decreases steadily in concentration as distance from the apices increases. In a typical green plant such as that shown in Figure 16-8, the highest concentrations of auxin are found in the apical bud, upper stem, and young leaves. In both the oat seedling and the green plant, it has been possible to show that if the auxin-producing center is removed, for example by excision of the coleoptile tip or apical bud, auxin concentration in the

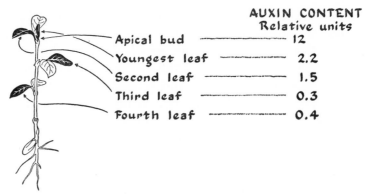

AUXIN CONTENT
Relative units

Apical bud	12
Youngest leaf	2.2
Second leaf	1.5
Third leaf	0.3
Fourth leaf	0.4

Figure 16-8. *The distribution of auxin in the apical bud and leaves of a green plant,* Vicia faba. (*By permission after Went and Thimann,* Phytohormones, *Macmillan Co., 1937, p. 62.*)

more basal portions of the plant drops rapidly to a low level. Auxin in these tissues is used up or destroyed during growth and must be continuously replenished by translocation from the auxin-synthesizing centers, if growth is to occur.

Synthesis and Destruction of Auxin

To understand the auxin economy of the plant it is necessary for us to know something about the processes which produce and those which remove auxin in living tissues. We now know a great deal about the generation of IAA in higher plants and something also of its destruction in living tissues. Certain plant tissues possess an enzyme system which catalyzes the transformation of the amino acid tryptophane to IAA. It is of particular importance that this system is found in highly active form in just those plant tissues or organs which serve as centers of growth hormone production. Thus, the apex of the oat coleoptile possesses a highly active tryptophane-IAA enzyme system, whereas lower portions of the coleoptile do not. The ability of a plant tissue to serve as an active center of hormone synthesis and export depends on the presence in that tissue of an active enzymatic machinery for synthesis of the hormone.

Although auxin is essential to many different growth processes, the welfare of plant tissues apparently requires the presence of a safeguard, a mechanism for the destruction of excess growth hormone. One such device is apparently represented by an enzyme system which destroys IAA, a system which is present in large quantities in tissues of etiolated plants, in roots, and to some extent in leaves, stems, and perhaps in other tissues as well. This enzyme, the IAA oxidase system, actually

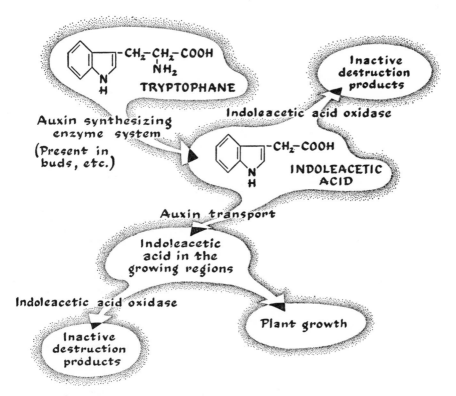

Figure 16-9. *Pathways of auxin production, auxin destruction, and auxin utilization.*

attacks IAA and converts it into a product which is inactive as a growth substance, a reaction involving oxygen uptake and carbon dioxide evolution. Enzymatic destruction is of great importance in experiments in which IAA is added to tissues such as those of etiolated pea seedlings, since in such cases a large portion of the added growth substance may be destroyed without causing any growth effect.

Regulation of auxin level in the living plant is, therefore, a complex matter, depending as it must upon a great many different and individual component processes, some of which are summarized in Figure 16-9. Auxin may be synthesized *in vivo* by the appropriate enzyme system; it may be translocated into or away from a given tissue; it may be destroyed by the IAA oxidase system. The net amount of auxin present in a tissue at any given moment and the net amount capable of being used in the growth process are dependent upon these and perhaps other unknown reactions.

Translocation of Auxin

The translocation of auxin in plant tissues possesses a feature which is unique and unlike the characteristics of the translocation of plant solutes in general. Auxin translocation is ordinarily polar; that is, auxin moves through a tissue from apex to base but not from base to apex.

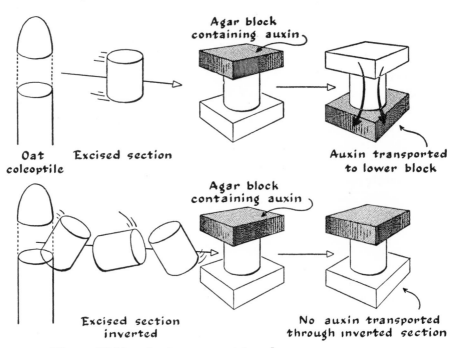

Figure 16-10. *Auxin transport is polar.*

Many of the growth responses and correlations achieved by auxin depend upon the polar nature of this transport. Thus the auxin produced by the apical bud of one branch of a plant can move down through and affect the growth of this same branch, but it cannot move up through and affect the growth of other branches on the same plant.

The polar nature of auxin transport was first appreciated by Went in his early work with the oat coleoptile, and his basic experiment is shown in Figure 16-10. A short cylindrical section is cut from the center of an oat coleoptile. This is now placed upright on an agar block. A second agar block containing auxin is placed on the opposite end of the cylinder. The rate of movement of auxin through the cylinder and into the basal agar block may now be followed by removing the lower block after a time and assaying it for auxin content by the oat coleoptile curvature test. If the agar block containing auxin is placed on the morphologically upper end of the coleoptile cylinder, auxin will move through it rapidly and may be collected in the lower block. If, however, the cylinder is inverted so that the agar block containing auxin is placed on the morphologically basal cut surface, transport of auxin does not occur.

Although many details of this process have been recorded, no insight into the basis of the polarity has as yet been achieved. We know that the rate of movement is 10 to 12 mm per hour and is independent of temperature. The amount of auxin transported per unit time does depend, however, on the temperature, increasing about threefold for each 10-degree rise in temperature. Transport from morphological apex to base takes place even against an auxin concentration gradient, that is, even if the bottom block already contains more auxin than the top block. It is clear, therefore, that this type of auxin transport is not a diffusion process but rather a process involving the expenditure of energy, presumably energy metabolically produced.

In the stem, auxin transport normally takes place only through living tissues and is abolished by girdling. Auxin therefore accumulates in the stem above the girdle and causes swelling and adventitious root formation, responses which will be discussed later in this chapter.

Although auxin transport is ordinarily polar, the application of large amounts of auxin to the plant by artificial means may result in the material leaking into the xylem, in which case it is transported upward in the transpiration stream. This type of auxin movement, while it may have significance for experimental work with auxin application to living plants, does not appear to have any place in the auxin economy of the normal plant.

Auxin and Cell Elongation

We have seen that auxin is essential to the process of cell elongation in the oat coleoptile. It similarly controls cell elongation in stems, flower peduncles, the petiole and midribs of leaves, and perhaps in other instances also. How does auxin, in the minute quantities which are produced in the plant, exert such disproportionate effects by which such striking growth responses are evoked?

Early in the study of auxin it was found by Heyn in Holland that the application of auxin to plant tissues such as those of the decapitated oat coleoptile causes an increase in the plasticity of the cell wall. This effect, which occurs only on the primary wall, is the basis of the relation of auxin to cell elongation. Heyn's basic experiment was as follows: When normal coleoptiles are decapitated, both the plastic (irreversible) and elastic (reversible) extensibilities of the cell wall are decreased. When auxin is applied, the plastic extensibility is increased. Elastic extensibility, on the contrary, is not affected by auxin directly but depends on the rate of tissue growth. Rapidly growing tissues have a greater elastic extensibility, while tissues which are supplied with auxin but which do not grow (for example, because of the lack of water) show low elastic extensibility. Although plastic and elastic extensibility may be determined by several methods, that used by Heyn and shown in Figure 16-11 is both simple and elegant. The coleoptiles, after auxin treatment, are excised at the base and fastened in a horizontal position on small pegs attached to a suitable holder. Weights are then hung on the end of each coleoptile section for a measured time period. The bending which takes place is made up of both plastic and elastic components. The weights are now removed. The permanent angle through which the coleoptile section remains bent immediately after removal of the weight is a measure of the plastic bending; the angle through which the section returns toward its original position is a measure of the elastic bending.

We have seen in our study of water relations that at osmotic equilibrium the osmotic pressure of the cell contents is just balanced by the pressure with which the cell wall restrains expansion of the cell. If the wall pressure is now decreased, as it is through the action of auxin, a diffusion pressure deficit will develop in the cell, water will move in, and the cell will be enlarged until the wall pressure again balances osmotic pressure. Thus, the driving force of cell elongation is the force exerted by the osmotic pressure of the cell contents. Control of cell elongation is, therefore, achieved by the regulation of cell wall plasticity through the mediation of auxin.

Although auxin clearly plays an important role in its effect on cell wall properties, this effect is by no means a direct one. Auxin exerts its influence only on the cell walls of living, metabolizing cells. The

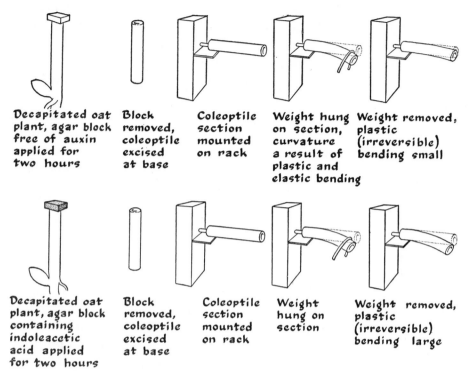

Decapitated oat plant, agar block free of auxin applied for two hours

Block removed, coleoptile excised at base

Coleoptile section mounted on rack

Weight hung on section, curvature a result of plastic and elastic bending

Weight removed, plastic (irreversible) bending small

Decapitated oat plant, agar block containing indoleacetic acid applied for two hours

Block removed, coleoptile excised at base

Coleoptile section mounted on rack

Weight hung on section

Weight removed, plastic (irreversible) bending large

Figure 16-11. *Auxin increases the plasticity of plant tissues.* (*Adapted from Heyn,* Rec. trav. botan. néerland., *28, 1931, p. 113.*)

effect on cell wall plasticity is but one of many manifestations of auxin activity in the plant cell, all of which probably have a common origin in a common, underlying and basic effect upon the cellular machinery. We will return to this more general aspect of auxin activity later in the present chapter.

Phototropism

Auxin not only regulates the everyday growth of the plant, but it also mediates certain plant responses to external stimuli. One of the best understood examples of this sort is that of the plant growth response to unilateral light, a response known as *phototropism*. Growing stems, hypocotyls, coleoptiles, and other organs tend to grow toward light or toward a region of higher light intensity, a response known as *positive phototropism*. Roots, on the contrary, tend to grow away from light, a response known as *negative phototropism*. In the positive phototropic response the rate of growth of the side of the organ toward the light is inhibited. The back, or dark side, of the organ, on the other hand, increases in growth rate. As a result of this differential growth, the plant organ, stem, or hypocotyl bends toward the source of the light. Phototropism is therefore a growth response. Actually, work on phototropism laid the basis for our modern knowledge of auxin.

Charles Darwin initiated the modern study of phototropism in 1880 with experiments in which he showed that with the coleoptiles of grasses the extreme tip of the organ is the phototropic receptor, that is, the part of the organ which is sensitive to light. This is remarkable when it is remembered that the growing region of the coleoptile is not at the tip but lower down in the coleoptile. Darwin shielded the extreme tip of grass coleoptiles with opaque material and showed that, even though light was allowed to shine on the growing region itself, no growth response took place, or at most that responses were obtained only toward very high light intensities. On the contrary, when only a small portion of the tip was exposed, normal phototropic responses were obtained with small quantities of light. This discovery was a basic one in that it showed for the first time the existence of a correlational growth response, a reaction in which stimulation of one part of a plant brought about a response in a different part.

In the early years of the 20th Century, the Danish plant physiologist Boysen-Jensen, following Darwin's general line of investigation, showed not only that the tip is the receptor for the phototropic stimulus, but also that the phototropic stimulus is capable of crossing a gap made by excising the tip and then replacing it on the stump. This occurs even if the gap is filled by a thin layer of gelatin. Boysen-Jensen's experiment indicated, therefore, that the phototropic stimulus is transported from the tip of the coleoptile to the basal growing regions by some diffusible chemical substance.

The results of these observations of Darwin and Boysen-Jensen, as well as those of other early workers, may now all be interpreted in the light of our knowledge of the control of growth by auxin. This correlation was first made by Went, who showed by the use of the diffusion technique that exposure of the coleoptile tip to unilateral light results in an unequal distribution of auxin on the two sides of the tip. If the auxin from each half of a unilaterally illuminated coleoptile tip is collected by diffusion into separate agar blocks, as is shown in Figure 16-12, the dark side always produces more auxin than the side which was previously illuminated. Went interpreted this as a combination of auxin destruction on the lighted side of the coleoptile tip and a light-induced transverse migration of auxin from the light side to the dark side. Later experiments have indicated that a light-induced, decreased sensitivity of the tissue to auxin may also be involved in the phototropic growth reaction. The relative importance of these three different phenomena has not as yet been adequately assessed, but in general it may be concluded that phototropic curvature is the result of differential growth rates on the two sides of the coleoptile brought about by differential auxin concentration induced by light.

The phototropic response of a plant depends upon many factors,

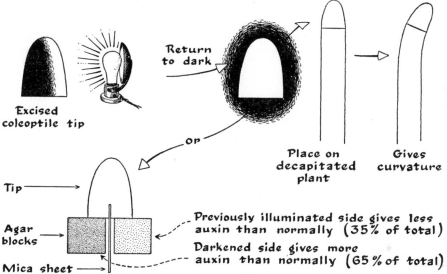

Figure 16-12. *The exposure of coleoptile tips to unilateral light results in auxin redistribution. Such tips can cause curvatures of coleoptile stumps which have not been illuminated.* (*By permission after Went and Thimann,* Phytohormones, Macmillan Co., *1937, p. 156.*)

among which is the amount of light energy allowed to fall unilaterally upon the plant. The amount of energy depends, in turn, on two factors, intensity and duration of illumination. If a completely etiolated plant is subjected to varying quantities of light, it may be shown that over a very great range of time and intensity values, a given amount of energy produces a given amount of phototropic curvature. Thus, approximately the same curvature can be effected by exposure of an oat coleoptile for 25 seconds to a light of 1 meter-candle intensity as by exposure for one thousandth of a second to a light of 25,000 meter-candles intensity. That the product of the light intensity and the period of illumination needed to bring about a given phototropic response is constant (Table 16-1) shows that a definite amount of light energy is needed to bring about the response and that it is similar to other photochemical responses which have been studied in purely physico-chemical systems.

For light to be photochemically effective in any system it must first be absorbed by a pigment. Since all of the auxins known at the present time are colorless compounds, it is clear that the auxins themselves cannot be the absorbers of the visible light which is effective in producing phototropic curvature. Some idea of the nature of the pigments involved in light absorption may, however, be gained from investiga-

Table 16-1. *Relation Between Duration and Intensity of Unilateral Illumination Needed to Cause a Detectable Phototropic Curvature in the Oat Coleoptile. (Data after Blaauw, Rec. trav. botan. néerland., 5, 1909, pp. 288, 229.)*

INTENSITY OF ILLUMINATION, METER-CANDLES	DURATION OF ILLUMINATION	INTENSITY × DURATION, METER-CANDLE SECONDS
0.00061	10 hours	22
0.090	4 minutes	22
5.46	4 seconds	22
511	0.04 seconds	20
7,900	0.0025 seconds	20
26,500	0.001 seconds	26

tions of the effectiveness of different colors of light in producing such curvatures.

The investigations of many workers have established the fact that blue light is phototropically the most effective portion of the spectrum. Thus, the curve of relative phototropic effectiveness plotted against wave length—the action spectrum of phototropism—exhibits a maximum at 4500 Ångstroms. Of the pigments which are present in the oat coleoptile only two are so far known to be similar in absorption spectrum to the action spectrum of phototropism. These two pigments are, respectively, the carotenoids and the flavoproteins, whose absorption spectra are shown in Figure 16-13. Both of these groups of pigments have high absorptions in the blue region of the spectrum and much lower or even negligible absorptions in the red portion. This coincides well with the phototropic sensitivity, since we know that red light is ineffective in producing the phototropic response. The carotenoids, however, can hardly be the pigments responsible for light absorption in phototropism, since it is known that certain strains of seedlings which are free of carotenoids as a result of genetic mutation are, nevertheless, able to carry out the phototropic response in a normal fashion. The pigment which absorbs light for the phototropic response may more probably be a flavoprotein. The flavoprotein pigments are known to occur in higher plants and, in particular, in the oat coleoptile.

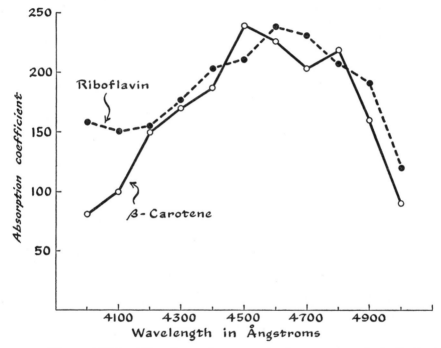

Figure 16-13. *The absorption spectra of carotene and of riboflavin. Both absorb strongly the blue light which is active in phototropism. (After Galston and Baker, Am. J. Botany, 36, 1949, p. 778.)*

Earlier in this chapter the enzyme associated with the destruction of indoleacetic acid was discussed. It has been shown that the rate of destruction of auxin by this enzyme system is greatly increased in the presence of blue light such as is absorbed by the flavoprotein. It would appear possible, therefore, that the mechanism of the phototropic response involves absorption of light by a flavoprotein, which results in an increase of auxin destruction on the lighted side.

In summary, there is now abundant evidence that the bending of plants toward light—phototropic curvature—is due to a differential auxin distribution in the tip or bud of the growing organ. This results in differential growth rates in the regions below the illuminated side and darkened side of the tip. Differential auxin distribution may, in turn, be brought about by differential auxin destruction through a light-activated system.

Geotropism

Geotropism, like phototropism, is a plant growth response, a bending toward or away from the gravitational field of the earth. When a plant stem, for example, is placed in a horizontal position, the growth rate of the lower side of its growing region tends to increase, and that of the upper side to decrease, as compared to the rates attained by similar stems in an upright position. The growing region therefore curves upward. With a root, on the contrary, the geotropic response to the horizontal position is a downward movement. Thus, stems, as is shown

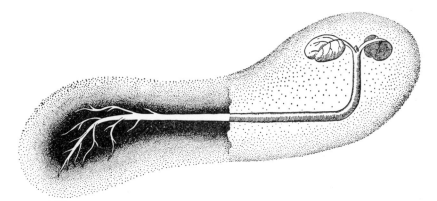

Figure 16-14. *Roots are positively geotropic. Stems are negatively geotropic.*

in Figure 16-14, are *negatively geotropic*, while roots are *positively geotropic*.

That geotropism, like phototropism, is a response due to an asymmetric redistribution of auxin has been clearly demonstrated, particularly in the early experiments of Herman Dolk. In these experiments the amount of auxin diffusing from oat coleoptile tips was determined both for tips maintained in a vertical position and for those maintained in a horizontal position. Although the total amount of diffusible auxin was the same in the two cases, its distribution was remarkably different, as is shown in Figure 16-15. The vertical tips pro-

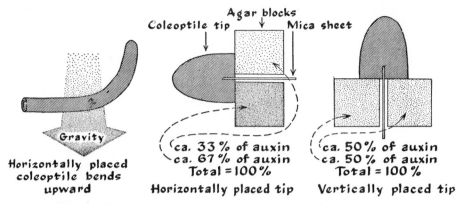

Figure 16-15. *Geotropic responses are due to redistribution of auxin in the plant, under the influence of gravity.*

duced equal quantities of auxin from the two longitudinal halves. Tips placed in a horizontal position, on the other hand, invariably yielded more auxin from the lower half. This redistribution was such that approximately two-thirds of the total auxin appeared in the lower half and only one-third in the upper half. As in phototropism, this unequal distribution of auxin results in unequal growth of the two sides of the

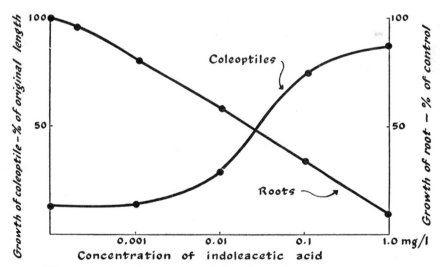

Figure 16-16. *Roots are inhibited in their growth by concentrations of auxin which enhance growth of stems or coleoptiles. (Adapted from Bonner and Koepfli, Am. J. Botany, 26, 1939, p. 558; and Bonner, Am. J. Botany, 36, 1949, p. 326.)*

coleoptile. The geotropic curvature is a result of this unequal growth response.

The geotropic response of roots is less well understood than that of coleoptiles, stems, and hypocotyls, but it seems, nevertheless, to fall into the same general scheme. Roots, unlike stems and hypocotyls, are inhibited in their growth by applied auxin over a wide range of concentrations. The concentrations of auxin which increase the growth of hypocotyls and stems are inhibitory to the growth of roots. These relations are shown in Figure 16-16. When roots are placed in a horizontal position, auxin is transported from the upper to the lower side, just as in stems and hypocotyls. Since root growth is inhibited by the higher concentration of auxin, the upper side containing the lower concentration grows faster than does the lower side, and the result is, hence, a positive geotropic curvature.

The Manifold Roles of Auxin

Although the discovery and early work on auxin were concerned only with the effect of this material on cell elongation, it has become evident in more recent years that auxin is involved in a great variety of responses in the plant. So numerous are these physiological activities with which auxin is concerned that it has become almost axiomatic in a discussion of plant responses to consider the possibility that auxin may in some way or another be involved. This was first appreciated by Thimann and Skoog in 1933, and in the following years the roles of auxin in growth responses other than cell elongation were discovered in quick succession. Among the more important of these are the inhibition of lateral bud growth, the inhibition of abscission, the stimulation of cambial growth and other meristematic activity, the inhibition or promotion of flower bud initiation, and the promotion of nonosmotic water uptake. Still later investigations on the physiology of the auxins have resulted in practical agricultural applications in which auxins or synthetic chemical substances related to them have been used for the inhibition of fruit and leaf drop, control of weed growth, and other important purposes. We will now survey the present state of our knowledge concerning the role of auxin in the more important of these growth responses.

Initiation of Root Primordia

It is a fact well known to horticulturists that when pieces of stem are excised from any of a great number of plant species, new roots may be formed at the base of the excised stem fragments or cuttings. These roots may arise either from root primordia present in the stem section before its removal from the plant or from adventitious root primorida which develop after, and as a result of, excision. Many early investigations indicated the possibility of the existence of specific root-forming substances concerned with the initiation of such adventitious root primordia. These substances were thought to be formed in buds or young leaves and translocated to the base of the cutting.

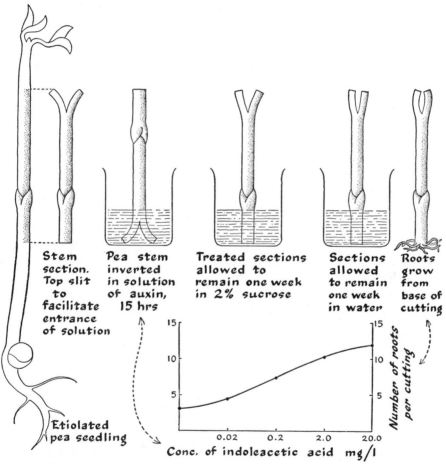

Stem section. Top slit to facilitate entrance of solution

Pea stem inverted in solution of auxin, 15 hrs

Treated sections allowed to remain one week in 2% sucrose

Sections allowed to remain one week in water

Roots grow from base of cutting

Etiolated pea seedling

Number of roots per cutting

0.02   0.2   2.0   20.0
Conc. of indoleacetic acid mg/l

Figure 16-17. *A brief treatment with indoleacetic acid results in the subsequent appearance of root primordia on stem cuttings of many plants, including peas. (Adapted from Went,* Proc. Koninkl. Nederland. Akad. Wetenschap., *37, 1934, p. 448; and Went and Thimann,* Phytohormones, *Macmillan Co., 1937, p. 197.)*

In the early 1930's, Thimann and Went embarked upon a program aimed at the chemical isolation of such a specific root-forming substance, using as a biological test cuttings made from etiolated pea epicotyls. For this test, pea epicotyls are inverted for 15–24 hours in a test solution containing an active root-forming substance. They are then reinverted and maintained in the dark for a period of seven days in a solution containing sugar. After a further period of one week the roots grow out of the base of the cutting (Fig. 16-17). The number of roots produced can be taken, within wide limits, as the measure of the activity of the root-forming substance present in the original solution. It was found that the activity of root-forming substances paralleled very closely the auxin activity of the source material. It was, in fact, established that the root-forming substance active in inducing adventitious root primordia in the pea-rooting test was identical with indoleacetic acid. The concentrations of indoleacetic acid required for root initiation are higher than those used in cell elongation but are nevertheless still quite low. For example, 20 mgm of indoleacetic acid per liter causes near maximal root formation in the pea epicotyl.

It is now known that indoleacetic acid can be used to cause the initiation of adventitious root primordia on a great variety of species. Other compounds chemically related to indoleacetic acid, but not necessarily natural plant products, may be used to replace indoleacetic acid for this purpose. Auxins, both natural and synthetic, and made up in the form of powders, pastes, or solutions, are therefore widely used in the treatment of cuttings for the production of roots in commercial horticultural practice. Although many difficult-to-root species respond well to externally applied auxins, still other species do not respond at all. In these latter plants, some factor other than auxin must limit root initiation.

Although auxin is an important and even a primary factor in the initiation of adventitious root primordia, other factors are also involved. In certain instances it is known that root primordia may be formed at the base of the cutting through the action of applied auxin, but these may fail to grow out because of a deficiency in the cutting of one of the root growth factors, such as thiamine or pyridoxine (Chap. 15). Application of the suitable root growth factor will cause the root primordia induced by the action of auxin to grow out into visible roots. Still other, and as yet unknown, substances produced in mature leaves are also necessary for the rooting of cuttings of many species. The elucidation of these additional factors which cooperate to bring about the initiation of adventitious roots is still an important aspect of the study of root initiation.

Bud Inhibition

In most species of plants the buds formed in the axil of each leaf do not immediately grow out but remain inactive as long as the terminal bud of the shoot is present and actively growing. If, as is shown in Figure 16-18, the terminal bud is removed, one or several of these

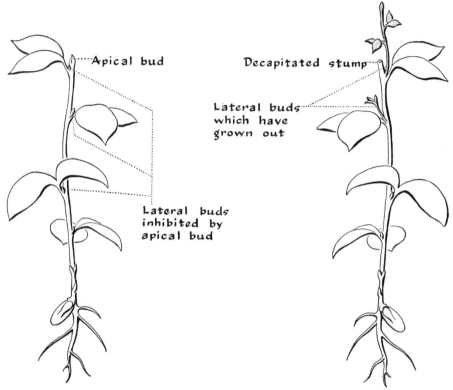

Figure 16-18. *Removal of the apical bud permits the inactive lateral buds to grow out.*

lateral or axillary buds will commence to grow. In general, one such bud will ultimately predominate and will take over the function of the former apical bud in suppressing the growth of axillary buds below it. This phenomenon, the suppression of lateral bud growth by the terminal bud, is known as *apical dominance*. The completeness of the apical dominance of a plant bears an intimate relation to the branching habit and hence to the shape of the plant. In tall, unbranched species, apical dominance is strict, while in shrubby or other much-branched forms, apical dominance is less closely observed.

The relation of apical bud to lateral buds in apical dominance resembles in many ways the relation of the apical bud to the auxin-mediated elongation in the growing region of the stem. Thus, the inhibition of lateral buds by the apical bud is, in general, a polar phenomenon; the inhibiting influence moves downward from the apical buds readily enough but cannot move upward through a stem. The very fact that

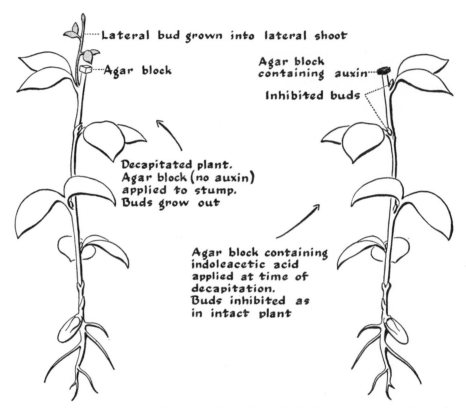

Figure 16-19. *The growth of lateral buds after removal of the apical bud is inhibited by the application of auxin to the cut surface of the stem.*

apical dominance is dependent on the bud itself also suggests some relation to auxin, which is, as we have seen, synthesized in the apical bud. These considerations led Thimann and Skoog in the early 1930's to conduct experiments to find out whether or not the inhibitory influence exerted by the apical bud on growth of the axillary buds might not be identical with auxin. In these experiments, plants of *Vicia faba*, the broad bean, were used. If the terminal buds of the broad bean were removed, the axillary buds developed rapidly. If, however, the terminal buds were removed and agar blocks containing auxin were placed on the cut-stem surfaces, as shown in Figure 16-19, the axillary buds remained dormant, just as though the apical bud were itself in place. This type of experiment has now been done with many species of plants. In certain instances the young developing leaves are major sources of auxin and exert an inhibitory influence on the growth of axillary buds below them. In a few particular species such as Parthenium, the guayule, the mature leaves themselves exert inhibitory influence on the axillary buds.

Interesting, and as yet unresolved, problems of plant physiology are raised by this phenomenon of axillary bud inhibition. We have seen, for example, that the apex of the plant produces abundant quantities of auxin. Why does not this auxin inhibit the growth of the apical bud itself? Why, since the concentration of auxin decreases as we proceed down the stem from the apical bud, should the axillary buds be inhibited by these concentrations of auxin which are lower than those found in the uninhibited apical bud? Although many hypotheses have been advanced, none is at present satisfactory for the complete explanation of this paradox. Comprehension of the mechanisms of axillary bud inhibition will have to await a more complete understanding of both the exact factors necessary for bud growth and the biochemical mechanisms by which auxin exerts its effect on growth.

Auxin and Meristematic Activity

If a cut stem surface of a plant such as sunflower or bean is treated with a high concentration of indoleacetic acid applied in the form of a paste, large swellings or calluses may appear at or near the site of application. Since histological examination such as that depicted in Figure 16-20 reveals the presence of one or more centers of cell division in the tissue mass, these swellings are the result not only of the elongation of pre-existing cells but also of the formation of many new cells. It is characteristic of these swellings that the normal patterns of differentiation are somewhat disturbed. The vascular elements may occur in irregular whorls rather than in direct connection with the organized vascular elements of the stem or other tissue on which the auxin-induced swelling occurs.

If a portion of such a callus is excised, freed of contaminating microorganisms, and transferred aseptically to a sterile nutrient medium containing appropriate mineral salts, sugar, and in some instances or-

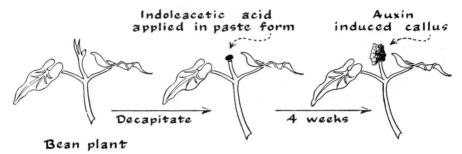

Indoleacetic acid
applied in paste form

Auxin
induced callus

Decapitate

4 weeks

Bean plant

Figure 16-20. *Formation of callus tissue as the result of the application of auxin to the decapitated stem of a bean plant.*

ganic growth factors, the excised callus will continue to grow, provided that it is also supplied with auxin. The rate and nature of the growth produced are dependent on the concentration of auxin supplied. Figure 16-21 shows that such a callus grows vigorously if supplied with 0.1 mgm of indoleacetic acid per liter of nutrient medium. A concentration of 10 mgm of indoleacetic acid per liter of nutrient medium, on the other hand, suppresses meristematic activity, and only cell enlargement takes place, so that growth of these cultures ultimately ceases. In the absence of added auxin neither meristematic activity nor cell elongation occurs.

There are in nature several instances of swellings or calluses which

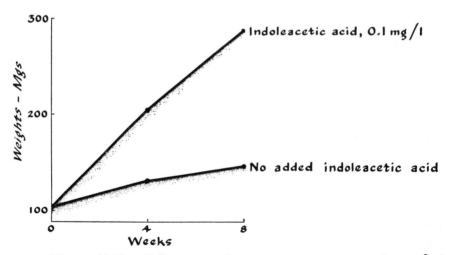

Figure 16-21. *Callus tissue from carrot roots grows vigorously in vitro when supplied with indoleacetic acid.* (After de Ropp, Am. J. Botany, 37, 1950, p. 358.)

are similar in appearance to the auxin-induced calluses. One example is the tumor produced on many species of plants by the crown-gall organism *Agrobacterium tumefaciens*. This organism, when introduced into plant tissues, produces a condition known as crown-gall, the symptoms of which are the production on the stem and roots of many tumor-like outgrowths. Crown-gall tumors are malignant, grow in an extensive and disorderly manner, and when grafted onto disease-free plants

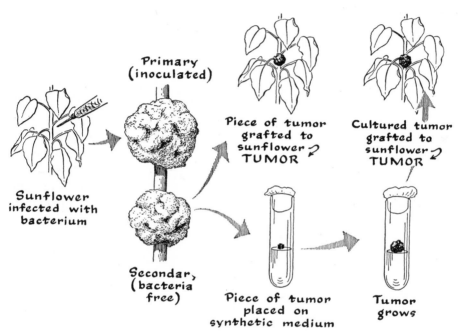

Figure 16-22. *Tumors induced in normal tissues by the action of the crown-gall bacterium are capable of synthesizing auxin and grow vigorously on the plant or in culture without addition of auxin.*

stimulate the formation of new, bacteria-free secondary tumors upon the new host plant. These relations are shown in Figure 16-22.

Because of the tumorlike quality of these crown-gall outgrowths, much interest has centered on their study, and many comparisons of the metabolism of crown-gall tissue with that of normal stem tissue have been made. Perhaps the most interesting one is that concerned with the auxin metabolism of crown-gall tumor and callus tissue. If a bacterium-free fragment of crown-gall tumor is transferred to a culture medium containing sugar and mineral salts, it will continue to grow even in the absence of the orginal bacteria and in the complete absence of any added auxin. Callus tissue, as we have seen, requires the presence of added auxin in order to continue growth. It may be shown by auxin analyses that the crown-gall tissue possesses the ability to produce its own auxin, even after transfer to *in vitro* culture. It would appear, then, that one difference between malignant tumor cells and nonmalignant callus cells resides in their respective abilities to produce auxin.

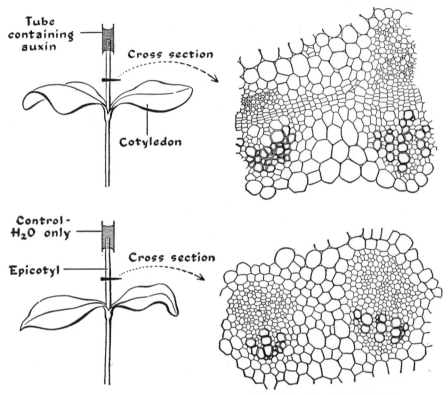

Figure 16-23. *Auxin controls cambial growth. The first demonstration of this relation was carried out with sunflower seedling as shown above. (After Snow,* New Phytologist, *34, 1935, pp. 349, 353, 354.)*

Auxin affects the meristematic activity of cells other than those involved in tumor and callus production. Auxin produced in the apical bud stimulates and regulates the activity of the cambium in woody plants. It seems probable that the resumption of cambial growth in the spring is due to auxin produced by the buds at this season. Cambial growth may also be induced by the artificial application of auxin. The experiment of Figure 16-23 shows how the production and activation of cambial activity in decapitated sunflower seedlings may be brought about by auxin application.

Auxins and Abscission

The fall of leaves and fruit from the plant is preceded in many species by the formation of a special group of cells, the abscission layer, at the base of the petiole or fruit stalk. The cells of the abscission layer possess particularly weak walls, so that the separation of leaf or fruit from the plant occurs by rupture of the cell walls in this region. The Germans

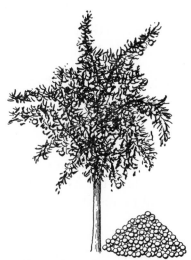 

Oranges dropped from unsprayed tree | Oranges dropped from tree sprayed with 25 p.p.m. of 2,4-D

Figure 16-24. *The use of an auxin (2,4-D) spray on citrus trees prevents premature fruit abscission, thus increasing yield. (From experiment of Stewart and Klotz, Botan. Gaz., 109, 1949, p. 160.)*

Laibach and Mai first showed in 1933 that the application of auxin to leaves delays or prevents formation of the abscission layer, and this finding was later extended to the abscission layer of fruits. The premature drop of fruits such as apple, pear, and citrus can be greatly decreased by application to the plant of auxin-containing sprays, a method which has found widespread horticultural use (Fig. 16-24).

Auxin and Flower Initiation

The production of flowers is regulated by environmental factors such as temperature and day length, and the exact manner in which these factors interact to determine flower development will be discussed in Chapter 17. It is of importance to note here, however, that the artificial application to plants of auxins such as IAA influences the flowering process, and it seems quite probable that the influence of environmental factors on flowering may be exerted, in part, through effects on the auxin economy of the plant.

In the great majority of species which have been investigated the application of IAA or other active auxins to the leaves of a plant delays the appearance of flower buds, and, in certain instances, repeated or daily application may inhibit flowering for long periods of time. One species, the pineapple, constitutes an exception to this rule in that the application of low concentrations of certain synthetic plant growth substances causes initiation of flowering in plants which otherwise would remain vegetative. Even with the pineapple, however, the application of high concentrations of auxin causes inhibition of the flowering process.

Auxin and Fruit Development

The growth of the fruit depends intimately on auxin, the source of this auxin being, in general, the developing seeds of the fruit. The role of seeds and of auxin in fruit development will be reserved for discussion in Chapter 17.

We may note here, however, that the auxin relations of the fruit were first studied in connection with investigations on the role of pollination in fruit development. The immature ovary ordinarily develops over some period of time before it is ready for pollination. If pollination does not occur, growth ultimately ceases, and the ovary abscisses from the plant. If pollination does occur, development of the ovary into a mature fruit continues. Thus, pollination bears an intimate relation to, and is essential for, continued normal growth in the vast majority of fruits.

The auxin relations of pollination were elucidated by Gustafson in 1936. He found that unpollinated ovaries of tomato, petunia, and other species would develop into fruits if an active auxin preparation were applied to the style in the manner shown in Figure 16-25. That artificial application of auxin can replace the need for pollination in fruit development has since been shown for a great many species, and, in fact, the auxin treatment of crops such as those of tomato, holly, and others is frequently carried out in order to insure a full fruit set even in the absence of complete pollination.

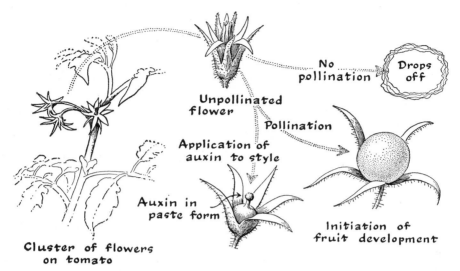

Figure 16-25. *The requirement of pollination for fruit develop-ment can be replaced in part by application of auxin to the unpolli-nated flower.* (*Adapted from Avery and Johnson,* Hormones and Horticulture, *McGraw-Hill Book Co., 1947, pp. 160, 161.*)

Auxin Activity of Related Synthetic Compounds

We have seen that indoleacetic acid, IAA, is a common constituent of higher plants and that this compound is responsible in the normal plant for many different growth-regulatory activities. The artificial application of IAA to a plant or plant tissue likewise brings about characteristic growth responses. IAA is therefore a naturally occurring auxin, a compound which is active in all the complex of functions de-scribed above, including the ability to regulate cell elongation and meristematic activity, induce adventitious root primordia, inhibit growth of roots and axillary buds, and so forth. The term "auxin" refers to a physiological concept rather than to any particular chemical com-pound. Strictly speaking, any compound active in all of these varied ways would be an auxin, although not necessarily a plant growth hor-mone. The concept of a hormone includes the provision that the sub-stance in question be one actually made in the plant and used by the plant in the regulation of some vital activity. IAA is, as we have seen, the principal and perhaps the only auxin which has been demonstrated with certainty to be native to the plant.

There are, however, a great many different chemical compounds related to IAA which, while not of natural occurrence in the plant, are nevertheless highly effective as substitutes for IAA in the artificial regulation of plant growth. In fact, certain of these synthetic substitutes are more effective than IAA itself. The first two important materials discovered to be effective replacements for IAA were indolebutyric acid and naphthaleneacetic acid. Indolebutyric acid possesses the indole nucleus characteristic of IAA but has a 4-carbon, rather than a

Indoleacetic acid   Indolebutyric acid   α-Naphthaleneacetic acid

2-carbon, side chain. Naphthaleneacetic acid, on the other hand, possesses a side chain similar to that of IAA but contains a different nucleus. Both indolebutyric acid and naphthaleneacetic acid are active over the entire range of auxin functions. Naphthaleneacetic acid, in particular, is a much sturdier compound than IAA, is not attacked by IAA oxidase in the plant, and is readily and cheaply synthesized. It is not surprising, therefore, that naphthaleneacetic acid, rather than IAA, is the principal material used for rooting of cuttings and inhibition of fruit drop in pears and apples.

Still other related compounds have particular utility for one or another practical application. β-Naphthoxyacetic acid has been found especially effective in the induction of parthenocarpic fruiting in many

β-Naphthoxyacetic acid   2,4-Dichlorophenoxyacetic acid

species, while 2,4-dichlorophenoxyacetic acid is particularly effective in the reduction of fruit drop in citrus. In all, several thousand different chemical compounds have been studied for auxin activity by a great number of investigators, and no doubt additional compounds of specific applicability will be uncovered from time to time.

Auxins as Herbicides

A large-scale application of auxin lore has developed in the field of weed control. This application is based upon the fact that certain synthetic chemical substances which possess auxinlike activity at very low concentration are, nevertheless, highly toxic to many plants at higher concentrations. The best known and most widely used of such materials is 2,4-dichlorophenoxyacetic acid (2,4-D), whose structure

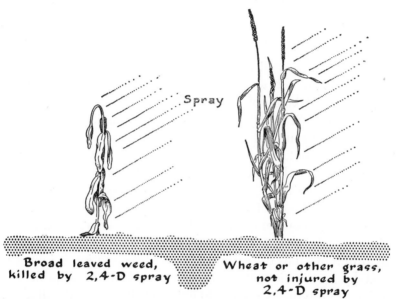

Figure 16-26. *Broad-leaved plants are often killed or severely injured by 2,4-D, whereas grasses are not.*

has been noted above. It is as effective as, or more effective than, IAA in the regulation of cell elongation and in other typical auxin responses. At slightly higher concentrations it is, however, highly toxic to many broad-leaved plants, its effect being especially great on meristems and other rapidly growing regions. Since 2,4-D is readily and rapidly taken up by leaves and translocated within the plant, it may be applied as a dust or spray. Because it is much less effective against narrow-leaved plants, such as cereals, than against broad-leaved plants, it finds particular application in the control of weeds growing in such cereal crops as wheat (Fig. 16-26). Therefore 2,4-D is a *selective herbicide*, a weed-killing agent which can be used to attack one class of plants while leaving another class unaffected. The use of selective herbicides has so simplified weed control in certain types of agriculture that widespread search for further agents of this kind is continuously being carried on, and we may hope in the future to have available an entire gamut of selective herbicides for use in different kinds of crops. Since, unfortunately, neither the mechanism of the herbicidal action of 2,4-D nor the basis of its selectivity is known, this search must at present be conducted on quite an empirical basis.

Biochemistry of Auxin and Growth

A basic question concerning auxin is that of the mechanism by which it exerts its manifold effects on plant growth. We have seen that the influence of auxin on cell elongation is exerted through an effect on the plasticity of the cell wall. Cell elongation is, however, only one of the many different kinds of responses elicited by auxin, and most investigators now hold that the effect on wall plasticity is only one of the possible end results of a much more general and basic effect of auxin on cellular metabolism. To put it another way, it seems reasonable to adopt as a working hypothesis that auxin is involved in a master or key reaction, and that once this master process has been set in motion, the end result—the final growth manifestation—may depend on the nature of the tissue employed. That the master reaction controlled by auxin is somehow related to respiration is indicated by the fact that in many different kinds of tissues the rate of respiration is immediately increased by application of auxin in concentrations suitable for the stimulation of growth. As yet we do not have, however, detailed knowledge of the way in which respiration and auxin-induced increase of respiration are linked to the varied growth responses evoked by auxin. Since only very minute amounts of auxin are involved in these responses within the living plant, it seems probable that auxin may function as a prosthetic group or as a portion of a prosthetic group of an enzyme. To reveal the exact nature of this enzyme will be an important task of plant physiology.

Summary

The auxins are characterized by their chemical nature and by their particular regulatory activities within the plant. The principal auxin known to be synthesized by and used in the plant is the compound indoleacetic acid. This material is primarily formed in apical buds and young leaves. The auxin produced by the apical bud is responsible for the promotion and control of stem elongation, the inhibition of the growth of lateral buds, and the initiation and maintenance of cambial activity. Auxin is also involved in the inhibition of leaf and fruit abscission, the production of adventitious root primordia and the initiation of the flowering condition in certain species of plants. Many of these plant activities can be controlled and directed by the artificial application of auxins. Auxin is, then, a master hormone, regulating and directing many different aspects of growth and development.

The mechanism whereby auxin causes these many, varied growth responses is unknown. We may presume, however, that they all have in common one basic reaction—a master reaction which results in increased plant activity. The particular manifestation of the resultant activity would appear to vary with the species, organ, tissue, and past history of the plant to which the auxin is applied.

Many different chemical compounds more or less related to indoleacetic acid in structure are able to substitute for this material in eliciting plant growth responses. Based on this fact, a whole science of auxin pharmacology has developed, and there is known and available a wide range of compounds which possess auxin activity to a greater or lesser degree. Certain of these compounds have proved particularly valuable in the control of plant growth responses under agricultural conditions. Indolebutyric acid and α-naphthaleneacetic acid are especially suitable for the rooting of cuttings of many species, while 2,4-dichlorophenoxyacetic acid and α-naphthaleneacetic acid are particularly suited to the control of fruit drop. At higher concentrations, 2,4-dichlorophenoxyacetic acid has also found widespread application as a weed killer.

QUESTIONS

1. How did work on the physiology of phototropism lead to the discovery of the auxins? How has our knowledge of auxin in turn helped to elucidate the nature of the phototropic response?

2. How do you account for the fact that auxin produces so many different effects in the plant?

3. Describe one native auxin. Where in the plant is it made? From what probable precursor? How is it translocated to other parts of the plant?

4. Discuss various ways by which the auxin level of tissues is regulated. Why is such regulation so important?

5. How do roots differ from stems in their response to auxin? How is such knowledge helpful in interpreting the opposite geotropic responses of stems and roots?

6. Can you propose an explanation for the fact that auxin inhibits the growth of lateral buds but does not apparently inhibit the growth of the terminal bud which produces it?

7. How do crown-gall cells differ in their behavior from normal cells? To what may this difference be due?

8. How can one explain the fact that 2,4-D will kill certain plants while leaving others relatively unharmed?

9. It has been calculated that 1 molecule of auxin can affect the deposition of 1.5×10^5 glucose molecules in the form of cellulose of the cell wall. What does this signify concerning the mode of action of auxin?

10. It is characteristic of the auxins that as one increases their concentration above a certain critical point, growth is sharply inhibited. How can one explain this growth inhibition by a substance which is also a growth promoter at lower concentrations?

11. Several hours after excision of a coleoptile tip, the new apical region acquires the ability to produce auxin, an ability which it lacked in the intact coleoptile. How can one explain this?

12. How can the earth's gravitational field possibly lead to the vertical displacement of auxin which results in geotropic curvature?

GENERAL READING

Avery, G. S., Jr., and Johnson, E. B., *Hormones and Horticulture.* New York: McGraw-Hill Book Co., 1947. The applications of auxin lore to problems of crop production.

Boysen-Jensen, P., *Growth Hormones in Plants.* New York: McGraw-Hill Book Co., 1936. Another early summary of auxin matters by one of the first workers in the field.

Heyn, A. N. J., "The Physiology of Cell Elongation." *Botan. Rev.,* **6:** 515, 1940. Concerns particularly the relations between auxin, cell wall plasticity, and cell growth, written by the person who discovered these relations.

Mitchell, J. W., and Marth, P. C., *Growth Regulators.* Chicago: University of Chicago Press, 1947. Practical applications of auxins.

Skoog, F., ed., *Plant Growth Substances*. Madison: University of Wisconsin Press, 1951. Modern views on all relations of auxin to plant growth by a group of distinguished workers.

Went, F. W., and Thimann, K. V., *Phytohormones*. New York: Macmillan Co., 1937. The early basic work on auxins clearly and logically presented. A classic.

CHAPTER 17

The Physiology of Reproduction

Introduction

Having considered the growth of plants from the standpoint of increase in size of the individual, let us now turn our attention to plant growth as it concerns increase in the number of individuals, that is, in the population of a given species. It is characteristic of all living things, of course, that they possess the ability to leave descendants of their own kind—the ability to reproduce. The ways in which this is carried out may be divided, broadly, into two general categories: *vegetative propagation* and *sexual reproduction*. In vegetative propagation the stems, roots, or leaves of the individual are subdivided to form new individuals. In sexual reproduction, on the other hand, the gametes—eggs and sperm—are formed by the plant, just as in the sexual reproduction of other organisms. Through the union of egg and sperm a fertilized egg or zygote is formed, and from this zygote a new individual arises. Initiation of the processes of sexual reproduction marks a qualitative alteration in the growth of the plant, an alteration which may be thought of as development from the vegetative to the reproductive state.

Vegetative Propagation

Vegetative propagation is encountered in many familiar instances among the horticulturally important plants. With ornamental species, such as the chrysanthemum or carnation, it is customary to remove shoots from the parent plant and to place these excised shoots under conditions suitable for the formation of new roots, perhaps with the aid of root-inducing substances as described in Chapter 16. The rooted cuttings constitute new individuals, plants which are identical with the parent in genetic constitution and character. Similarly, many kinds

388

of fruit trees, including apples, peaches, and various citrus species, are propagated by budding or grafting. In these practices, one of which is shown in Figure 17-1, a bud, or short piece of stem containing a bud, is removed from the parent plant and its tissues brought in contact with the exposed cambium of a seedling of the same or related species.

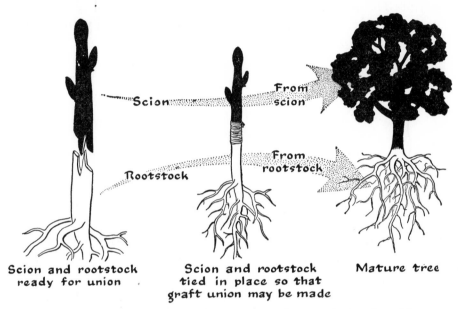

Scion and rootstock   Scion and rootstock   Mature tree
ready for union   tied in place so that
                          graft union may be made

Figure 17-1. *Vegetative propagation by one form of grafting.*

When a graft union is established between the cambium of the bud, or scion, and the cambium of the root stock, a new individual plant is produced whose upper and lower portions both retain the genetic constitution of the parent tree from which they were derived. In this way it is possible to accumulate and to maintain large stocks, or clones, of individual trees derived solely from a single original parent plant.

Flowering as a Reproductive Process

The process of sexual reproduction in higher plants, which is summarized in Figure 17-2, is initiated at the time of flower formation. With the growth of the flower, there develop the floral parts of critical importance for reproduction. These are the ovary, containing its ovule or ovules, and the stamens, which ultimately bear the pollen. Following the process of pollination, a sperm nucleus from the pollen unites with an egg within the ovule to form the zygote. The zygote develops into an embryo contained within the seed, which in the angiosperms is enclosed by the tissues of the ovary of the female parent. Accompanying the development of the seed or seeds within the ovary may be a conspicuous enlargement of the ovarian or other maternal tissues. The enlarged tissue and seeds which it contains together constitute the fruit. The fully developed seeds removed from the mature fruit may then be germinated with the production of new individual plants.

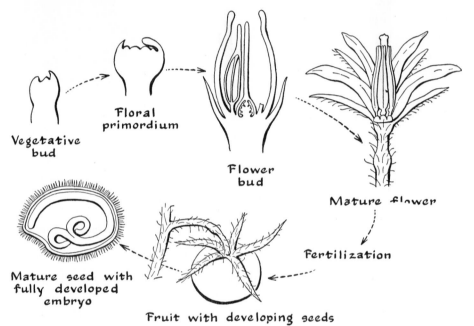

Figure 17-2. *The reproductive cycle, illustrated with the tomato.* (*By permission after Hayward,* The Structure of Economic Plants, *Macmillan Co., 1938, pp. 554, 558, 569.*)

Sexual reproduction in the higher plants is therefore a process which has its orgin in the initiation of flower primordia. After differentiation, these primordia grow into mature flowers capable of producing pollen and ovules. Pollination of the pistil and fertilization of the egg by the sperm initiates still a third phase in sexual reproduction, namely, the development of the fruit. Finally, with maturation of the fruit and production of mature seeds, the sexual cycle reaches completion. The cycle may begin anew immediately, with germination of the seed, but more usually, a period of relative inactivity intervenes before new growth commences.

The Histology of Floral Initiation

Although the term "flowering" is often used loosely to refer to the entire process of reproductive development from initiation of flower primordia to final production of ripe fruits, we will use the term in a somewhat more limited sense. The critical aspect of the flowering process as a whole lies in the very first stage, the differentiation of vegetative buds to form floral buds. The vegetative growing point in many species of plants is rather flat, saucer-shaped, and inconspicuous. Leaf primordia are continuously being differentiated from this vegetative growing point. During differentiation of the vegetative apex to

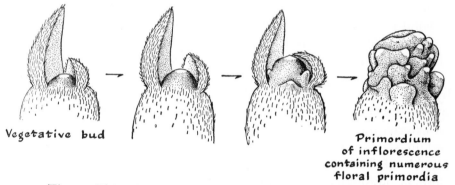

Vegetative bud

Primordium
of inflorescence
containing numerous
floral primordia

Figure 17-3. *Successive stages in differentiation of floral primordia from the vegetative shoot apex in Xanthium, the cocklebur. (After Bonner and Thurlow, Botan. Gaz., 110, 1949, p. 616.)*

a floral apex the growing point becomes larger in diameter, swelling to form a conspicuous dome-shaped bud. As the floral primordium becomes expanded into a visible flower bud, the characteristic floral parts appear. Still later, after pollination and fertilization of the ovary, the ovary wall and other tissues such as the receptacle grow vigorously to form the fruit.

Our discussion of the flowering process will be concerned first of all with the conditions required for the very first process, the initiation of floral primordia. In an experimental study of the conditions required for the initiation of such primordia, it is ordinarily not sufficient to determine whether the plants have formed visible flowers, but it is necessary to dissect the unexpanded buds and examine the apices under the microscope. The course of floral differentiation in the cocklebur, Xanthium, may be followed by microscopic dissection, as shown in

Figure 17-3. In many species, once floral differentiation has occurred, floral primordia will grow to mature flowers, regardless of whether or not the plant is maintained under conditions necessary for floral initiation. It should be emphasized, then, that the conditions required for floral initiation are not necessarily identical with the conditions required by the same species for further development of floral primordia to mature flowers.

The Onset of Flowering

We have seen in the preceding chapters—and we know also by experience—that upon germination of the seed, a seedling plant is produced which grows vegetatively for some time. This vegetative stage of the plant's growth is ordinarily terminated by the production of floral primordia and the onset of the chain of processes leading to the production of mature fruits and seeds. With certain species, control of flowering appears to be purely internal, the individual plant flowering in response to age or size. In other species, flowering is determined by a particular climatic factor, or by a set of external influences. In all species, including those in which flowering is conditioned by a particular external factor, it is commonly found that the plant must attain a certain size—a certain amount of vegetative growth—before it is capable of flowering, a fact that was first clearly recognized by the German physiologist Klebs in 1918. The stage of development which must be attained before the plant is capable of flowering is commonly known as the condition of *ripeness-to-flower*.

We may say that all plants must pass through a vegetative stage of growth in order to attain the stage of ripeness-to-flower. Once the ripeness-to-flower condition has been attained some plants flower without further environmental stimulation. This is true of the tomato, for example, certain varieties of which flower after the production of thirteen nodes, regardless of environmental conditions. With many other species, however, the ripeness-to-flower condition is followed by actual flowering only under proper environmental conditions. Among the external factors which have been found to be relevant in the control of flowering, two are now recognized to be of primary importance—length of day and temperature.

Photoperiodism

The response of plants to length of day, or more correctly, to the relative length of day and night, is referred to as *photoperiodism*.

The principles of photoperiodism were first appreciated and clearly enunciated in 1920 by two workers in the U. S. Department of Agriculture, Garner and Allard. They had observed that a particular variety of tobacco, Maryland Mammoth, in contrast to many other varieties, failed to flower in Washington, D. C., during the summer growing season. Similar plants grown in the greenhouse during the winter season flowered profusely. Garner and Allard suspected that some seasonal factor might be at play in regulating the development of these plants. This seasonal factor was shown to be the relative length of day and night.

During the summer season the duration of the daily period of solar illumination is greater than 12 hours, whereas during the winter it is shorter than 12 hours. By the simple technique of growing plants in different artificially controlled day lengths, Garner and Allard subjected

Figure 17-4. *The Maryland Mammoth tobacco flowers only when grown under short days* (left). *On longer days it remains vegetative* (right). *It is therefore a short-day plant.* (*Adapted from Garner and Allard,* Yearbook of Agriculture, *1920, p. 399.*)

to direct test the hypothesis that the seasonal increase and decrease of day length might be the factor involved in the control of flowering. Long days were achieved in the greenhouse in the winter by the use of supplementary light from electric lamps, and short days were achieved during the summer months by darkening the plants during a portion of the day. With these techniques, Garner and Allard showed conclusively that flowering of Maryland Mammoth tobacco does depend upon day length. Flowering occurs in this plant only under conditions of short days (Fig. 17-4).

We recognize today that plants fall into three broad photoperiodic classes with respect to their flowering behavior:

Short-day plants flower only when the daily period of illumination

Table 17-1. *Examples of Well-Known Plant Species Which Are Short-Day, Long-Day, or Day-Neutral with Regard to Their Flowering Behavior.*

SPECIES	COMMON NAME	CRITICAL DAY LENGTH, HOURS
Short-Day Plants		
Xanthium pennsylvanicum	Cocklebur	15.0 to 15.5
Glycine soja, var. Biloxi	Soybean	14 to 16
Cosmos sulphureus var. Klondike	Cosmos	12 to 13
Nicotiana tabacum var. Maryland Mammoth	Tobacco	13 to 14
Chrysanthemum indicum var. Queen Mary	Chrysanthemum	14 to 14.5
Euphorbia pulcherrima	Poinsettia	12 to 12.5
Long-Day Plants		
Anethum graveolens	Dill	11 to 14
Hyoscyamus niger (annual variety)	Henbane	10 to 11 (22°C)
Spinacea oleracea	Spinach	13 to 14
Hibiscus syriacus	Rose Mallow	12 to 13
Day-Neutral Plants		
Lycopersicon esculentum	Tomato	
Zea mays	Corn	
Fagopyrum esculentum	Buckwheat	
Antirrhinum majus	Snapdragon	
Nicotiana tabacum var. Java, etc.	Tobacco (most varieties)	
Capsicum annuum	Chili pepper	
Cucumis sativus	Cucumber	

is shorter than a particular critical length. Biloxi soybeans, for example, flower only if the daily period of illumination is less than 16.5 hours; the plants remain vegetative if grown on a 17-hour day. Such short-day plants form the great group of our fall flowering annuals, including the chrysanthemum, ragweed, cocklebur, and other species of which further examples are listed in Table 17-1.

Long-day plants flower only when the daily period of illumination exceeds some critical duration. Spinach, for example, flowers only when the daily period of illumination is greater than about 13 hours. Many of our summer flowering annuals and biennials are long-day plants.

Day-neutral plants flower under any of a wide range of day lengths. The tomato, for example, is a day-neutral plant in which the production of flower buds is controlled primarily by the number of nodes differentiated, rather than by photoperiodism. Plants whose flowering is controlled by factors other than day length are thus day-neutral plants.

It is to be stressed that the concept of photoperiodism refers not to the absolute length of day but rather to whether flowering occurs at day lengths longer or shorter than critical day length. Xanthium, the cocklebur, for example, will not flower if the daily period of illumination exceeds 15.5 hours. Dill (Anethum), a long-day plant, on the other hand, will not flower unless it receives more than about 11 to 14 hours of light per 24 hours. Cocklebur, a short-day plant, is thus able to flower on day lengths which are actually longer than those needed to initiate flowering in dill, a long-day plant. In fact, short-day plants might more properly be referred to as "long-night plants." Cocklebur produces flower buds only when it is kept on regimes which provide uninterrupted dark periods of longer than approximately 8.5 hours. The intervening light periods may be either longer or shorter than the 15.5 hours. Our world is based, however, on a daily rhythm of 24 hours, in which an 8.5-hour night must necessarily be combined with a 15.5-hour day. Long-day plants, in contrast to short-day plants, require no periodic intervals of darkness. Flowering in the long-day plants is limited by the duration of the daily exposure to light and may even be inhibited by the intervening dark periods.

Photoperiodic Induction

We have seen that floral initiation in many species requires an appropriate alternation of day and night. We may now ask ourselves how long a plant need be maintained under the appropriate photoperiodic circumstances for flowering to result. Can, for example, a brief treatment induce subsequent flowering even after the plant has been returned to a day length otherwise unfavorable to flowering?

Of the great number of plants studied, it has been found that all (both of the short-day and long-day groups) respond to exposure to a relatively small number of 24-hour cycles favorable to flowering by the development of floral primordia and flowers, even after the plant has been returned to a previously unfavorable day-length regime. Soybeans, for example, require two to four successive cycles of short days and long nights if they are to develop floral primordia after they have been returned to long days. The cocklebur is even more sensitive

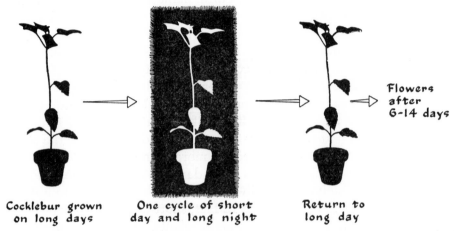

Cocklebur grown   One cycle of short   Return to
on long days   day and long night   long day

Figure 17-5. *Photoperiodic induction. The cocklebur, if induced by a single short-day cycle, will subsequently initiate floral development even in long days.*

and, as Figure 17-5 shows, will produce floral primordia on long-day cycles if it has been subjected to even one short-day, long-night cycle. Chrysanthemum, on the other hand, is more sluggish, and requires 8 to 30 cycles of short day in order to flower when returned to long days. Similarly, certain long-day plants may be converted from the vegetative to the flowering condition by treatment with a few long-day cycles followed by return to short days. Thus, the henbane (Hyoscyamus) forms flowers even on short-day cycles after exposure to about 72 hours of continuous light. Flower buds do not usually form during this short exposure to a favorable photoperiod, but rather as a result of the treatment, and after return to the photoperiod previously unfavorable to flowering. This persistence of a photoperiodic after-effect is referred to as *photoperiodic induction*. It is apparent that physiological changes must have occurred in the plant during the photoinductive treatment which are perpetuated during the subsequent unfavorable photoperiods and which ultimately result in floral initiation.

Amount of Light Required to Effect Photoperiodic Responses

The amount of light energy required for the suppression of flowering in short-day plants or the initiation of flowering in long-day plants is very small—in fact, very much smaller than the amount of light required by the same plant for vigorous photosynthesis and vegetative growth. It is common in photoperiodic experiments to grow plants under a regime in which they are subjected to natural sunlight for 8 hours of each 24. During this period the plants may carry out vigorous photosynthesis and produce the materials required for growth.

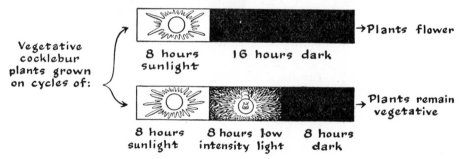

Figure 17-6. *Very low intensities of light are sufficient to inhibit the flowering response of short-day plants.*

The plants are then removed to a separate room in which they are illuminated by artificial light, the duration and intensity of which may be varied at will. At the end of 16 hours the plants are returned to the greenhouse for the commencement of another daily cycle. When a short-day plant, cocklebur, for example, is grown under 8 hours of natural daylight and then subjected to 16 hours of dark, the plant will initiate flower primordia. If, however, it is illuminated with a low intensity of artificial light for 8 or more hours of the 16-hour period, flowering is suppressed (Fig. 17-6). The light intensity required to suppress flowering in cocklebur is as little as 0.3 foot-candles, an intensity not greatly above the intensity of bright moonlight. Similarly, with long-day plants, flowering is induced by supplementary illumination of low intensity. The amounts of energy which must be given as supplementary illumination in order to cause photoperiodic responses are thus very small in comparison to the amounts of light energy which the plant requires for its maintenance by photosynthesis. In the example given above, the supplementary light provides less than one ten-thousandth the energy of the high intensity natural light period.

It has been indicated above that the flowering of short-day plants depends on the length of the dark period. This dark period must be an uninterrupted one longer than a certain critical minimum length. If cocklebur is exposed to a regime in which it receives 10 hours of

Figure 17-7. *Even a single flash of light during the long dark period will suppress floral initiation in the cocklebur.*

natural light followed by 14 hours of continuous dark, floral primordia are produced. The 14-hour dark period is longer than the critical dark period length of 8.5 hours. If, however, the 14-hour dark period is interrupted midway by a single flash of light—a flash as short as one minute in length—the plant remains vegetative (Fig. 17-7). The dark period is ineffective in bringing about the processes which result in floral initiation if it is interrupted by even minute amounts of light. The system involved in bringing about floral initation in the cocklebur is, therefore, very sensitive to photochemical alteration.

The long-day plants, like the short-day plants, are influenced in their flowering behavior by interruption of the dark period with flashing light. A particular variety of barley, for example, a long-day plant, remains vegetative if grown on a regime of 12-hour light periods combined with 12-hour dark periods. If the 12-hour dark period is interrupted near the middle by a single light flash, flowering promptly follows.

The interruption of the dark period for the suppression of flowering has found practical application in the sugar cane industry. In the culture of sugar cane the vegetative portion of the plant, particularly the stem, is economically important, and the flowers and seeds are at best troublesome by-products. The fact that sugar cane is a typical short-day plant permits us to control its growth habit. By the use of flashing light at night during the short-day period of the year, it is possible to maintain sugar cane plants in a vegetative state, with a resultant increased yield of cane and sucrose.

Light Quality and Photoperiodic Response

We have discussed in earlier chapters how a knowledge of the action spectrum has aided in identification of the pigments involved as the photoreceptors in photosynthesis and in phototropism. The action spectrum of the photoperiodic process also gives us a clue to the nature of the compound which is acted on by light. For such experiments a large spectrograph is necessary, and an instrument specifically adapted to photoperiodic work has been constructed by workers in the U. S. Department of Agriculture. This spectrograph produces a spectrum approximately three meters wide at the focal plane. Individual plants are mounted at specific wave-length stations along this spectrum, and the effect of supplementary illumination on photoperiodic induction is determined. For the short-day plants, such as the cocklebur and Biloxi soybean, the light is administered in the middle of the long dark period, and the amount of light energy needed for suppression of the effectiveness of the dark period is measured. With long-day plants, such as henbane or barley, irradiation near the middle of the dark period brings about flowering, and the effectiveness of light of different wave lengths on floral initiation may thus be measured.

Long-day plants and short-day plants have both been found to respond primarily to wave lengths in the red region of the spectrum, light of wave lengths from 5800 to 6800 Å being particularly effective. The flowering response is also affected, although much less efficiently, by wave lengths in the blue region. This action spectrum, reproduced in Figure 17-8, resembles that of photosynthesis in a qualitative way. However, red light is relatively far more effective than blue light in eliciting photoperiodic responses than in photosynthesis. The action

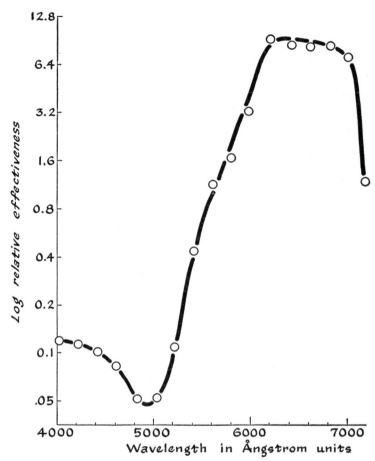

Figure 17-8. *A generalized action spectrum for photoperiodism. (Calculated from data of Parker, Borthwick, Hendricks, and Went, Am. J. Botany, 36, 1949, p. 202.)*

spectrum of the photoperiodic response does not coincide with the absorption spectrum of any presently known pigment of higher plants, and such a pigment must be discovered before the nature of the photoreceptor can be known.

Hormonal Nature of the Flowering Process

The effect of length of day or length of dark period on the flowering process occurs in the leaves of the plants. Thus, with cocklebur, if a single leaf of a plant is exposed to short days and long nights while the remaining leaves are exposed to long days and short nights, as shown in Figure 17-9, flowering occurs systemically through the entire plant. Plants from which all leaves are removed are insensitive to photoperiodic stimulation. Since the photoperiodic stimulus is directly upon the leaves, and since the response of flower initiation occurs in the meristematic tissue of the bud, it is clear that the floral stimulus must be capable of movement from leaf to bud.

That this floral stimulus moves both up and down the plant may be readily shown. If, for example, one branch of a two-branched cocklebur

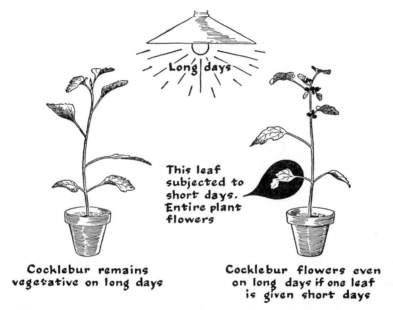

This leaf subjected to short days. Entire plant flowers

Cocklebur remains vegetative on long days

Cocklebur flowers even on long days if one leaf is given short days

Figure 17-9. *In many species, as in the cocklebur, short-day treatment of a single leaf results in flowering of the plant. (Adapted from Hamner and Bonner,* Botan. Gaz., **100**, *1938, pp. 390, 398.)*

plant is subjected to short days and the other branch to long days, the floral stimulus moves down from the short-day branch and up through the long-day branch, inducing flowers through the entire plant.

Mature leaves kept on an unfavorable photoperiod oppose the action of photoinduced leaves in many species, with the result that in such species flowering resulting from photoperiodic treatment may be to some extent confined to the treated portion. Such an inhibition is also clearly shown in experiments with two-branched cocklebur plants. Defoliation of the long-day or receptor branch leads to more rapid and profuse flowering of this branch. This may be largely due to effects on the transport of the flowering stimulus from the short-day or donor branch.

The pathway of translocation of the flowering stimulus is through the living vascular elements. Thus, girdling of the stem completely inhibits translocation of the flowering stimulus from leaf to buds. Localized low-temperature treatment of the stem likewise inhibits transport of the flowering stimulus, just as it inhibits translocation of other organic materials. Generally speaking, then, the flowering stimulus travels through the plant in the same tissues, in the same directions,

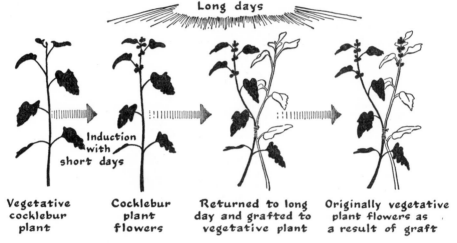

Figure 17-10. *The flowering stimulus may be transmitted from plant to plant across a graft union. (Adapted from Hamner and Bonner, Botan. Gaz., 100, 1938, p. 390.)*

and according to the same principles as the flow of photosynthetic products manufactured in the leaf.

The flowering stimulus moves readily not only through the plant but also from plant to plant across a graft union between a flowering plant and a nonflowering or vegetative plant. This is apparent in cocklebur or soybean plants which have been subjected to photoperiodic induction and then allowed to flower under long-day conditions. If such an induced plant is grafted as a donor to a vegetative receptor plant, flowering is brought about in the receptor. The sequence of events in such an experiment is shown in Figure 17-10.

Although we know that the flowering stimulus produced by photoperiodic treatment moves readily about the plant and from plant to plant through graft unions, it has not thus far been possible, despite many attempts, to extract this flower-inducing material for transmission to vegetative plants. Thus, we have no way of discovering what materials are active in bringing about flowering in treated vegetative plants, and the nature of the flowering hormone remains obscure.

Long-Day Plants

The photoperiodic behavior of long-day plants is characterized, as noted above, by the ability to flower even in continuous light. Thus long-day plants fail to flower when they are grown in photoperiodic regimes in which light periods shorter than the critical are combined with long dark periods. Most evidence indicates that this failure to flower is due to excessive length of the dark period rather than to

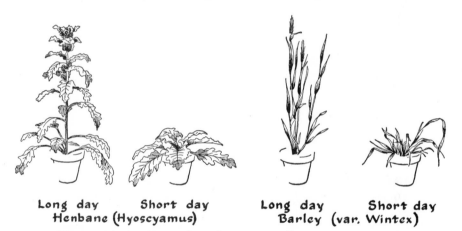

Long day   Short day
Henbane (Hyoscyamus)

Long day   Short day
Barley (var. Wintex)

Figure 17-11. *Long-day plants typically form rosettes under short days. Longer day lengths result not only in the initiation of flowers but also in elongation of the stem.* (*After Melchers and Lang*, Biol. Zentr., **67**, *1948*, *p. 148.*)

excessive shortness of the light period. Thus, in early experiments of Garner and Allard it was shown that typical long-day plants would flower when grown on a regime of short light periods, provided that these were combined with short dark periods to make alternating cycles of light and dark shorter than the usual 24-hour cycle.

Among our common long-day species are such familiar examples as the annual beet, radish, coneflower (Rudbeckia), henbane (Hyoscyamus), and certain cereal grains. When these plants are grown under short-day conditions, the internodes of the stem fail to elongate, and the leaves remain closely compressed at the crown, the whole forming a rosette. If a plant in the rosette state is transferred to long-day conditions, the internodes rapidly elongate to form a flower stalk bearing the buds which differentiate to floral primordia. The flowering response of a typical rosette plant involves not only the formation of floral primordia but also the characteristic elongation or bolting of the stem or axis which is to bear these primordia (Fig. 17-11).

We have seen that in the short-day plants flowering results from a stimulus produced in the leaves as a result of treatment with long dark periods. Long-day plants fail to flower on a regime of short days and

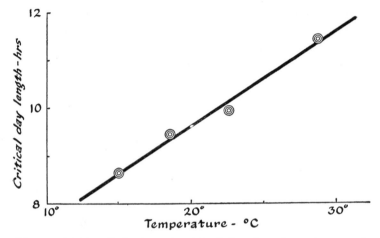

Figure 17-12. *Relation of critical day length to temperature with Hyoscyamus (henbane), a long-day plant. (After Lang and Melchers,* Planta, 33, 1943, p. 680.)

long dark periods, and it has been shown that this failure may, in one case at least, be due to production in the leaves during the long night periods of a factor which inhibits stalk elongation and flowering. If all leaves are removed from the crown of a henbane plant which is in the rosette form, it will flower even under conditions of short day. Similarly, the inhibitory effects of long nights are lessened if the leaves are cooled. Thus, the critical night length for flowering depends on the temperature at which the plant is grown. In the henbane, for which data are given in Figure 17-12, the day length must be more than 12 hours for flowering to occur at 30° C, while 9 hours suffices at 15° C.

The inhibitory effect of leaves on the flowering process which is exerted during long dark periods is related in some manner to the respiratory metabolism of the leaf. Not only is the inhibitory effect lessened by cooling of the leaf, but it is also diminished by placing the leaves in an atmosphere lacking oxygen, so that respiration is suspended. The inhibitory effect can also be overcome by supplying the leaves with sugar during the dark period.

Sequence of Processes in Photoperiodism

The response of a short-day plant to the interplay of light and dark may be summed up somewhat as follows: During long, uninterrupted dark periods the leaves of the plant become altered in their biochemical characteristics so that they are capable of producing a stimulus to flowering. This biochemical alteration, which is known as photoperiodic induction, occurs only during dark periods which have been preceded by appropriate light periods. The dark process is itself inhibited by

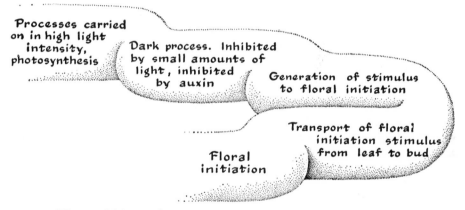

Figure 17-13. *The sequence of processes in the response of short-day plants to photoperiods below the critical.*

even minute amounts of light and by applied growth substances, as we have seen in Chapter 16. The biochemical alterations of the leaf which constitute photoperiodic induction render the leaf capable of producing and exporting a flower-forming stimulus. This stimulus, which may be a chemical substance or hormone, travels readily through living tissues, is transported in the phloem, and is the agent finally responsible for the differentiation of the vegetative to the floral bud. This sequence of events is portrayed in Figure 17-13.

Elucidation of the nature of the photoperiodic response in long-day plants would appear to revolve around identification of the factor which is produced in long nights and which, when exported to the growing point, is responsible for inhibition of stem growth and of flower bud initiation.

Photoperiodic Effects on Vegetative Growth

Although the effects of photoperiodism are most marked and spectacular in relation to the initiation or suppression of the flowering response, many other kinds of photoperiodic responses have been noted in plants, and animals also are subject to effects of day length. Most plants, of both long- and short-day floral behavior, tend to grow more luxuriantly under long days. It has already been mentioned that many of the long-day plants form only a compact rosette of leaves when grown on short days. Short-day plants grow luxuriantly on long days, but when such plants are transferred to short days, growth is abruptly decreased or ceases altogether. Even plants which are indeterminate, or day-neutral, may show marked differences in vegetative growth as between conditions of long and short days.

The onset of winter dormancy and the autumnal shedding of leaves in deciduous trees are, in part, responses to length of day. Both effects can be delayed or abolished by using artificial illumination to arrest the normal process of day-shortening. It is reported that in some instances evergreen trees have been brought from dormancy to growth by the artificial application of long days.

Finally, many morphological characters of the plant are affected by length of day. In general, root growth is less, often strikingly so, on plants grown under short-day conditions than on those grown under long-day conditions. Formation of tubers and other storage organs is influenced by length of day. Leaf size and shape may differ widely, and succulence, the relation of thickness to the area of the leaf, may be affected.

We may conclude that numerous plant responses are influenced by the relative length of day and night. It would seem probable that many different physiological processes within the plant are affected by photoperiodism. Whether all of these various physiological processes have their basis in a common mechanism by which the plant is able to respond to relative length of day and night will be a subject for future investigations.

Relation of Temperature to Flowering

The relation of temperature to flowering may be broadly subdivided into two categories—the direct effects of the temperature under which a plant is grown, and the aftereffects of temperature treatment.

The direct effects of temperature are related to, and intermeshed with, the effect of photoperiodism, as we have seen above in the case of long-day plants. In short-day plants, also, the flowering response of the plant to long dark periods is conditioned by the temperature of these dark periods. At low temperatures, effectiveness of the dark period in bringing about photoperiodic induction is decreased in the sense that more such dark periods are required to achieve a given degree of induction.

The aftereffects of temperature treatment on flowering behavior are best observed in biennial plants. The biennials produce only vegetative growth during the first year, frequently merely a rosette of leaves. Production of flowers and fruits occurs during the second growing season, after the plant has experienced a cold winter period. Characteristic of the biennial type of growth is the plant's requirement for low-temperature treatment before the formation of flower primordia becomes possible. Many biennials are photoperiodically sensitive and require long days in order to complete the flowering process, even after the necessary temperature treatment has been supplied. This is true of the biennial henbane. The interdependence of cold requirement and long-day requirement for this plant is shown in Figure 17-14.

A low-temperature requirement for flowering is often a genetically controlled characteristic. Thus in the henbane there are both annual and biennial types. Annual henbane flowers in the same season in which it is sown, in contrast to the biennial henbane, which flowers only after exposure to a cold winter. The annual form differs from the biennial in having a particular dominant gene which substitutes for the effect of cold in bringing about the chemical changes which lead to flower formation. The annual henbane is therefore limited in its flowering only by length of day. The genetic basis of the annual-biennial habit of the henbane is of historic interest, since its study and elucidation by Correns in 1904 constituted the first demonstration of a gene-controlled physiological characteristic.

Similar genetic relations have been found in the sugar beet, which has an annual in addition to the generally known biennial form. Both annual and biennial forms occur also in several of the cereal grains. The annual, or so-called "spring," forms produce flowers and fruits during the same growing season in which they are planted. The biennial, or "winter," types do not normally produce flowers or fruits until they have overwintered in the field. Experiments with such cereals have shown that it is the low temperatures of the winter period which are effective in causing subsequent flowering. It is clear, therefore, that

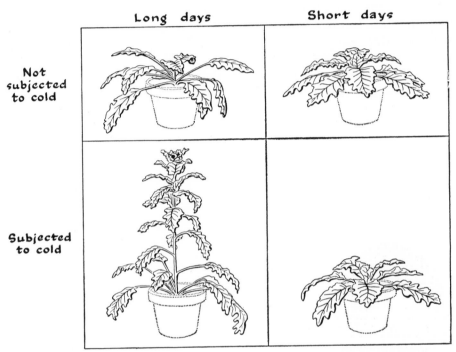

Figure 17-14. *Henbane, a typical biennial plant, requires low-temperature treatment before it will respond to long-day treatment by flowering. (After Melchers and Lang, Biol. Zentr., 67, 1948, p. 148.)*

these winter cereal varieties are capable of flowering only after certain biochemical changes have been brought about by exposure to low temperature.

The spring varieties, on the other hand, possess genetic constitutions which bring about, even at high temperature, biochemical changes within the plant which are equivalent to those brought about in winter varieties by low temperature. In some instances, as in Petkus rye, the spring vs. winter habit is inherited in a straightforward manner. Crosses between winter and spring varieties of this plant yield an F_1 generation composed entirely of plants having the spring habit. When the F_1 generation is selfed, the F_2 generation shows the typical three-to-one segregation of spring-to-winter forms, indicating a simple one-gene inheritance, the cold requirement being recessive.

In agricultural practice the winter cereal varieties, which require cold treatment, are planted in the fall, allowed to overwinter in the field, and harvested early the next summer. The spring varieties, which do not require cold treatment, are planted in the spring and harvested the same fall. Generally speaking, winter cereals are grown in regions with hot, dry summers and relatively mild winters, spring varieties in regions of very cold winters. In the case of wheat, winter varieties dominate in the southern United States, including Texas, Kansas, and Oklahoma, whereas in the northern wheat belt, spring forms are used.

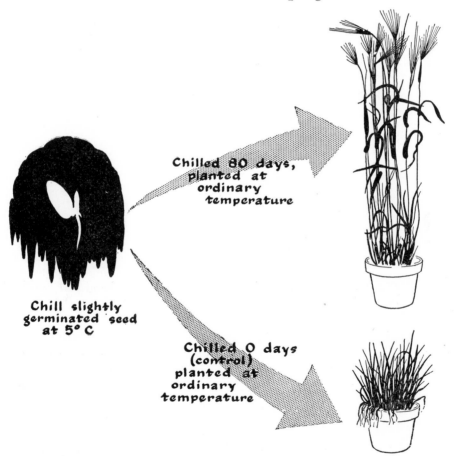

Chilled 80 days, planted at ordinary temperature

Chill slightly germinated seed at 5° C

Chilled 0 days (control) planted at ordinary temperature

Figure 17-15. *The cold requirement for flowering of cereals can be satisfied in the seedling stage. (After von Denffer, Jahrb. wiss. Botan., 88, 1939, p. 779.)*

Perception of the Cold Stimulus

It was early realized that the overwintering treatment commonly carried out in the field could be easily duplicated in the laboratory by chilling for an appropriate period of time. Treatments are effective if given to large vegetative plants or to seedlings; in the cereals, the very slightly germinated seeds are fully responsive, as shown in Figure 17-15. The temperatures required for effective cold treatment are relatively low, in general about 1 to 10° C. The optimum length of treatment

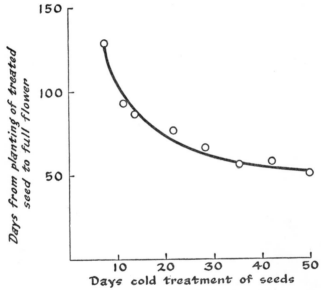

Figure 17-16. *The length of time between planting and flowering decreases as the period of cold treatment is lengthened. Data for rye. (After Purvis and Gregory, Ann. Botany, N.S., 1, 1937, p. 582.)*

varies among different varieties from a few days to many weeks. In general, as the length of chilling treatment is increased, the rate and intensity of the subsequent flowering response is increased, as shown in Figure 17-16 for rye. In this instance the number of days from planting to full bloom becomes progressively fewer with increasing length of chilling period.

In the flowering of temperature-limited plants, it is the apical bud which perceives the cold stimulus, rather than leaves, which perceive in photoperiodism. In biennial sugar beets it is possible to cold-treat the beet as effectively by cooling the bud alone as by treating the entire beet, bud and leaves. Similarly, for the cereals, successful cold treatment can be achieved by chilling the embryo alone rather than the entire seed. During the cold treatment no morphological changes occur which are recognizable as steps in the direction of the initiation of floral primordia. As a result of the cold treatment, however, the apical bud undergoes biochemical and physiological changes which enable the plant to respond with flowering when it is returned to temperatures suitable for growth. The application of cold treatment to buds or seedlings to effect subsequent flowering is known as *vernalization*.

Transmission of the Vernalization Stimulus

It is possible to conduct experiments on the transmission of the vernalization stimulus which parallel the experiments described earlier in relation to transmission of the floral stimulus induced by photoperiodic treatment. Thus, if a cold-treated and hence temperature-induced bud of a biennial henbane is grafted to a non-cold-treated henbane, flowering in the untreated individual is initiated by the temperature-induced scion, as shown in Figure 17-17. Similar experiments have been done with sugar beet. That the annual forms of sugar beet or henbane pro-

Cold-treated biennial henbane shoot grafted on non-cold-treated biennial henbane stock. Both shoots flower

Non-cold-treated biennial henbane shoot grafted on non-cold-treated biennial henbane stock. Both shoots vegetative

Figure 17-17. *The floral impulse initiated in henbane after cold treatment may be transmitted to a non-cold-treated plant by grafting. All plants grown under long days. (After Melchers, Biol. Zentr., 57, 1937, p. 594.)*

duce materials equivalent to those produced in biennial plants after cold treatment can also be shown by experiments in which annual scions are grafted to non-temperature-induced biennial stocks. Here, also, the buds of the biennial stock produce floral primordia. Transmission experiments cannot be readily conducted between spring and winter cereals, since it is difficult to make grafts between individuals of the grass family.

We may conclude that with the low-temperature-induced plants, cold treatment causes production of a flowering stimulus which is capable of movement through the plant or from plant to plant, just as is the photoperiodically produced flowering stimulus. The two stimuli are most probably chemical substances which act as hormones controlling floral differentiation.

Pollination and the Development of Flower and Fruit

With the initiation of floral primordia, the subsequent processes of reproduction depend upon the growth and development of floral parts. The floral primordium, once initiated, continues its growth with the differentiation and development of the individual floral organs—stamens, ovary and associated parts, petals, sepals, and so on. This development may or may not depend upon the continued presence of the environmental factors needed for floral initiation. With some species, once floral primordia have been laid down, further development of the flower proceeds regardless of the day length to which the plant is subjected. It is frequently found, however, that continuation of the photoperiodic treatment is required for full or optimal flower development. In biennial plants, where floral initiation is dependent upon low-temperature treatment, development of the floral parts proceeds, in general, under suitable day-length conditions without the further intervention of continued low-temperature treatment.

Most of our knowledge of flower growth is concerned with the development of the ovary. Even so, we know little about the factors which regulate growth prior to the pollination stage. Many experiments have shown that fruit growth after pollination depends intimately upon the number of leaves which supply nutrient to the developing fruit. The role of leaves in fruit development appears, however, to be primarily a quantitative regulation of fruit size. The intimate relation between the number of leaves which nourish a growing fruit and the size of the

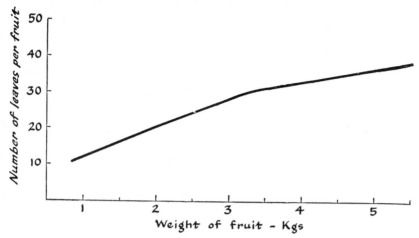

Figure 17-18. *Fruit size increases with the number of leaves nourishing the fruit. Data for pineapple.* (*After van Overbeek,* Botan. Gaz., *108, 1946, p. 69.*)

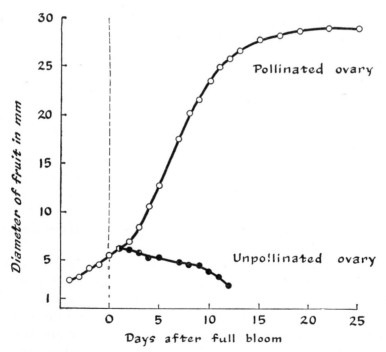

Figure 17-19. *Growth of pollinated and unpollinated ovaries of the gherkin.* (*After Nitsch, Thesis, California Institute of Technology, 1950.*)

fruit is shown for the pineapple in Figure 17-18. The role of pollination, on the other hand, is decisive in the development of the fruit. In most species, the ovary fails to grow without pollination; moreover, the un-pollinated ovary usually abscisses and falls from the plant. Figure 17-19 illustrates the growth of ovaries of the gherkin, a small cucumber, be-fore and after pollination. From this figure it may readily be seen that prior to pollination the ovaries develop at a rapid rate, and that with pollination, growth continues uninterruptedly. Ovaries which are

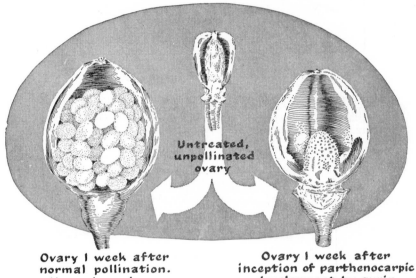

Ovary I week after normal pollination. Normal seeds

Untreated, unpollinated ovary

Ovary I week after inception of parthenocarpic development by auxin. No seeds

Figure 17-20. *Seeds fail to grow in Melandrium ovaries in which parthenocarpic development has been induced by chemical means. (After van Overbeek, Conklin, and Blakeslee, Am. J. Botany, 28, 1941, p. 648.)*

not pollinated cease growing, remain on the plant for a short period of time during which they decrease in size, and then drop off.

In Chapter 16 we discussed the discovery by Gustafson that growth of fruits of certain species may be induced by the application of auxin to the unpollinated ovary. The resultant fruits were seedless, however, because in the absence of pollination and fertilization of the ovules, normal development of seeds cannot take place. Fruit development of this type, shown in Figure 17-20, which is brought about by influences other than pollination, is known as *parthenocarpic development*, and the fruits are referred to as *parthenocarpic fruits*. There are many instances of parthenocarpic development of fruits known both in nature and particularly in horticulture, in which seedless varieties are selected by man. Seedless bananas, grapes, citrus, and other species are the result of naturally occurring parthenocarpy, in which fruit development occurs without pollination and without seed development. Such parthenocarpic development is, however, to be regarded as an exception to the general rule that the presence of developing seeds is essential to normal fruit development.

The fact that artificial application of auxin may substitute for pollination in the development of fruit suggests at once that pollination itself is influential in the normal supply of auxin. Qualitative evidence presented by various workers has suggested that in the normal develop-

Growth of receptacle induced by one achene

Growth of receptacle induced by three achenes

Normal growth of receptacle induced by many achenes

Figure 17-21. *The development of the fleshy receptacle of the strawberry is dependent on the achenes which occur on its surface. (After Nitsch, Am. J. Botany, 37, 1950, p. 212.)*

ment of pollinated fruit, auxin is in fact required by the developing fruit tissue, and that this auxin may be synthesized by the developing seeds.

The relation of seed development to fruit growth may be clearly demonstrated by the strawberry. The strawberry is, of course, a specialized fruit in that the tissues of the receptacle form the fleshy portion, while the true fruits are the achenes, which cover the surface of the receptacle. In its general characteristics, however, the development of the strawberry resembles the development of other fruits. The fruit of the strawberry does not ordinarily develop without pollination. If one achene is pollinated and allowed to develop, one region of the receptacle develops under this achene (Fig. 17-21). If several achenes, at widely separated locations on the receptacle, are pollinated, several separate areas of enlargement occur on the receptacle. A strawberry is, then, constituted by the juxtaposition of such areas, which are induced to develop by the individual developing achenes. The influence of the achenes on the development of the receptacle can be duplicated by the application of auxin. The data of Figure 17-22 show that in an achene-free strawberry fruit, application of auxin brings about completely

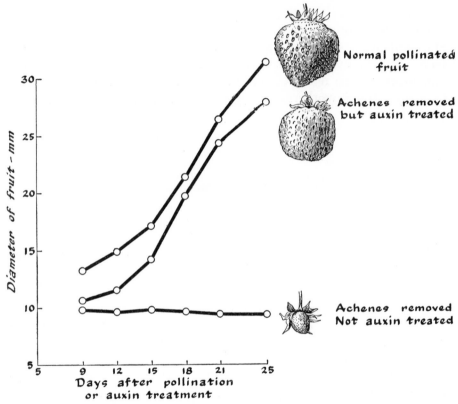

Figure 17-22. *The role of the achenes in inducing growth of the fleshy receptacle of the strawberry can be duplicated by the application of auxin to fruits from which the achenes have been removed.* (*After Nitsch,* Am. J. Botany, *37, 1950, p. 215.*)

normal development and an enlargement of the receptacle tissues. It may be further shown by analytical determination of auxin contained in developing strawberries that it is produced in the achenes and supplied to the enlarging tissues of the receptacle. Thus, every link in a chain of evidence has been developed to show that enlargement of the fruit tissue depends on auxin, and that this auxin is produced in the developing seeds and supplied to the fruit tissues by these seeds.

With the strawberry, as well as with many other fruits, there is a rapid increase in auxin content of the seeds after pollination of the ovary. Pollination gives to ovules the ability to produce the auxin needed for development of the fleshy tissues of the fruit. We may ask ourselves: What relation does pollination have to the production of auxin by the fertilized ovule? Pollen itself contains auxin. The amount contained in normal pollen grains is, however, much less than the amount which appears in the seed following pollination. More probably, pollination is concerned with the setting in motion of enzymatic systems for the production of auxin from substrates contained in the ovule itself. The exact mechanism by which auxin production is brought about by pollination remains obscure, despite many attempts to solve this problem.

Other Factors in Fruit Growth

Pollination has a hormonal relationship to the growth of fruit in that the auxin produced by the developing seeds moves into the adjoining tissues of the ovary and there brings about the specific response of fruit growth.

What substances other than auxin may be involved in the process of fruit development? Answers to this question have been sought in recent years by the methods of tissue culture, which have been discussed in Chapter 15. The general methods involved are the removal of the ovary from the plant, treatment to render it aseptic, and, finally, culture on a suitable nutrient medium. The general conclusions derived from the culture of excised ovaries have been that pollinated excised ovaries of tomato, gherkin, and currant tomato will grow very well in culture, provided that the medium contains a source of carbohydrate, such as sucrose, and mineral salts. Development occurs particularly rapidly if the ovary is excised from the plant a few days after pollination. Such excised ovaries, which are shown in Figure 15-6, will grow into mature fruits which develop pigments and ripen in a normal fashion. Unpollinated ovaries, on the contrary, do not grow in culture, even if supplied with auxin. It would seem, therefore, that pollination results in the production of materials other than auxin that are essential for fruit growth.

Although the growth of the gherkin and tomato in culture on a simple nutrient medium is considerable, these excised fruits grow at a slower rate and attain a smaller final size than do similar fruits on a normal plant. This is particularly true of the tomato. It would appear, therefore, that the parent plant supplies, in addition to sucrose and mineral salts, growth factors which are required for the development of the unpollinated fruit. These growth factors or their precursors, which are contained in the juice of the fruit (Chap. 15), must, under normal conditions, be obtained from leaves or other organs of the mother plant to which the fruit is connected. Also of considerable interest in relation to the nutrient requirements of excised fruits is the fact that seeds do not usually develop in fruits which have been allowed to grow *in vitro* after pollination. This indicates that the growth factor requirements of seeds must be different from those of other fruit tissues. A simple nutrient medium containing sugar and mineral salts more nearly supplies the requirements of the maternal tissues of the fruit than those of the developing seeds themselves.

Development of Seeds

The development of seeds normally contained within the tissues of the fruit parallels the development of the fruit itself. Thus, after normal pollination the mature fruit ordinarily contains mature seeds. Studies on the development of embryos and the factors which influence this development have most generally been carried out with the aid of tissue culture techniques. Frequently, these studies have been concerned with the development of the embryo or embryonic axis rather than with the development of the whole seeds, including the endosperm or cotyledons. Embryos isolated from mature seeds can be readily grown in a simple nutrient medium containing mineral salts and sugar. The culture of mature embryos from seeds of peach, rose, iris, and other commercially important plants has in fact been used on a large scale, since it provides a way of circumventing the long dormant period to which intact seeds of these species are subject. The immature embryos of developing seeds may also often be matured as excised embryos on simple nutrient media. This technique has therefore been used to obtain seedlings from species in which the embryos abort before full maturity.

In general, for each species of developing embryo there is some critical stage which must be attained on the parent plant before it can be excised and grown to maturity on simple nutrient media. The development of excised embryos of Zizania, a grass (Fig. 17-23), illustrates this point.

Embryos excised after they have attained roughly one-tenth of their final size continue to grow and mature, although they tend to germinate

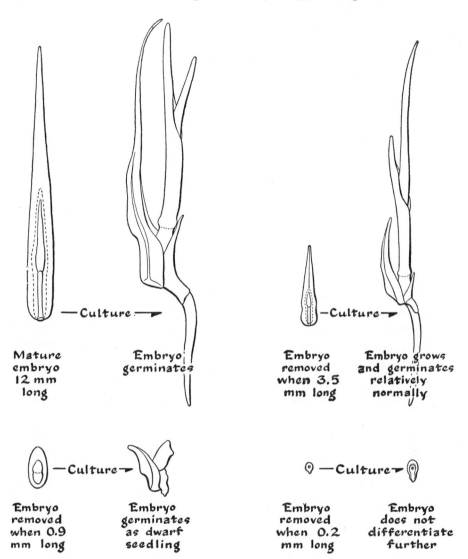

Mature
embryo
12 mm
long

—Culture—➤

Embryo
germinates

Embryo
removed
when 3.5
mm long

—Culture—➤

Embryo grows
and germinates
relatively
normally

Embryo
removed
when 0.9
mm long

—Culture—➤

Embryo
germinates
as dwarf
seedling

Embryo
removed
when 0.2
mm long

—Culture—➤

Embryo
does not
differentiate
further

Figure 17-23. *The growth of an embryo after its excision from the seed depends upon the stage of development which it has attained prior to excision.* (*After La Rue and Avery,* Bull. Torrey Botan. Club, **65**, *1938, pp. 14, 15.*)

and produce dwarf seedlings. Embryos excised at more immature stages do not, however, have the ability to continue independent development. The factors which influence the early development of the embryo will be considered in Chapter 19.

Fruit Ripening

The growth of the fruit is terminated in many species by a character-istic series of physiological processes which together are included under the term *fruit ripening*. Ripening includes such processes as change in fruit color, softening, production of soluble sugars and consequent sweetening, and many others. Rate of respiration characteristically rises to a maximum, the climacteric, only to fall again during senescence. With many species, such as the tomato, the processes of ripening may occur either while the fruit remains attached to the parent plant or when it is removed from the plant, provided only that it has been removed after having attained a suitable stage of development. With other species, such as the avocado, ripening occurs only after the re-moval of the fruit from the tree.

The processes of fruit ripening, and particularly the inhibition of fruit ripening, are of obvious interest in relation to commercial fruit storage and shipment, and a vast amount of both technological and basic investigation has been carried out. A considerable advance in our understanding of this process was marked by the discovery by Denny, in 1922, that the application of the simple organic substance ethylene to unripe fruit will cause simultaneous initiation of the characteristic group of ripening processes in many species of fruits, including such commercially valuable ones as the apple, pear, citrus, and banana. This suggests at once that ethylene or related substances may be involved in the normal spontaneous ripening of fruit. It has, in fact, been shown that ripening fruits of many species produce ethylene and that its pro-duction is initiated at the beginning of the ripening process. We do not, however, know the way in which ethylene acts to bring about fruit ripening.

Summary

With the initiation of floral primordia the growth of the plant is al-tered in direction and kind; a qualitative or developmental step has taken place. The internal and external factors which control this step act to insure that the cycle of reproductive development, once em-barked upon, will be completed under favorable environmental cir-cumstances. All plants must make a certain minimum amount of vege-tative growth before they reach the stage of ripeness-to-flower. The actual initiation of reproductive development may then in some species take place immediately and automatically, but in other plants the intervention of particular environmental conditions is essential for the onset of the reproductive process.

The two environmental factors most commonly involved in the regulation of reproduction are length of day and temperature. Flowering is initiated in certain species by exposure to days shorter than a particular critical day length. In other species, flowering is initiated by exposure to days longer than a particular critical day length. Still other species flower only after their buds have been chilled for weeks or months at temperatures in the range of 1–10° C. In many of these cold-requiring plants, exposure to low temperature is followed by flowering only if the plants are subjected to an appropriate length of day.

It is the leaves of the plant that respond to the photoperiodic stimulus. In the short-day plants this response is primarily to length of dark period. During the course of dark periods which are longer than the critical length, the leaves of the short-day plant become altered in such a way as to make possible the production and export of a substance or substances which travel through the plant and bring about the conversion of vegetative buds to floral primordia. Similarly, in the long-day plants the leaves are the organs of reception. During long dark periods the leaves of long-day plants appear, however, to produce materials antagonistic to flowering. Flowering in these species is therefore promoted by short nights. In the long-day plants, as well as in the short-day plants, processes essential to growth and flowering take place in the light, so that the dark periods, however long or short, must be interspersed by light periods in order for flowering to result. The photoperiodic response is, therefore, a response to the relative length of day and night.

The initiation of flowering is but the first stage in reproductive development. It is followed by growth of the flower, pollination and fertilization, growth of the fruit, and development of the mature seed. Although these developmental stages are all well known and have been described from a morphological and histological viewpoint, they are less well understood from the standpoint of physiology. One major contribution to our understanding of this field has been made, however, through the study of pollination and its relation to fruit development. Pollination and the subsequent fertilization of the egg nucleus within the ovules is a general requirement for fruit development of many species. Fruit development may also be brought about, however, by the artificial application of auxin to the unpollinated ovary. The experimental facts brought together in this chapter suggest that auxin is essential to fruit development and that this auxin is normally supplied by the developing ovules.

Our knowledge concerning the control of the plant's reproductive cycle, while extensive, is nevertheless primarily on the descriptive level. There is a great field for further investigation in the determination of the chemical processes which make up these intricate control mechanisms.

QUESTIONS

1. What evidence indicates that the onset of flowering in photoperiodically sensitive plants is due to the production of a specific floral hormone? What do we know concerning the nature of this hormone?

2. What is meant by each of the following terms: (a) short-day plant, (b) critical photoperiod, (c) photoperiodic induction, (d) vernalization?

3. Describe in some detail how you would proceed to classify a new plant as short-day, long-day, or photoperiodically neutral.

4. What kind of pigment is responsible for the absorption of light which leads to flowering? From what kind of evidence has this been deduced?

5. Describe several ways in which knowledge concerning photoperiodism has been put to practical use.

6. What regulates flowering in those species which are not sensitive to temperature or photoperiod? Is the mechanism of floral initiation in these species necessarily different from that in photoperiodically sensitive plants? Explain.

7. How is the dependence of floral initiation on low temperature different from its dependence on a photoperiodic stimulus?

8. The critical photoperiod of various races of range grasses has been found to vary with the latitude at which they grow. What is the ecological significance of such a finding?

9. What organ of a plant responds to (a) the photoperiodic stimulus, (b) the temperature stimulus? Give the evidence for your answer.

10. How could you most effectively prevent the flowering of a stand of Xanthium in an open field?

11. What specific chemical factors other than auxin are known to be involved in the growth or maturation of the fruit and its contents?

12. In some plants, such as Xanthium, the floral stimulus is mobile, but in others, such as Cosmos, it appears to be localized. How can this difference be satisfactorily explained?

GENERAL READING

Biale, J. B., "Postharvest Physiology and Biochemistry of Fruits." *Ann. Rev. Plant Physiol.,* 1: 183, 1950. A comprehensive survey of the fruit-ripening process.

Garner, W. W., and Allard, H. A., "Effect of Relative Length of Day and Night and Other Factors of the Environment on Growth and Reproduction in Plants." *J. Agr. Research,* 18: 553, 1920. This classic paper, which describes the discovery of photoperiodism, is widely available and should be read not only for its contribution to the physiology of flowering but also as a model of successful investigation of a new and complex problem.

Growth in Relation to Differentiation and Morphogenesis. New York: Academic Press, 1948. A symposium of the British Society for Experimental Biology. The chapters by Gregory, Hamner, and Harder are of great interest to plant physiologists.

Melchers, G., and Lang, A., "Die Physiologie der Blütenbildung." *Biol. Zentr.,* 67: 105, 1948. The most thorough and thought-provoking modern review of the subject. Written in German.

Murneek, A. E., and Whyte, R. O., eds., *Vernalization and Photoperiodism.* Waltham: Chronica Botanica, 1948. A series of essays on the internal factors involved in control of flowering, written by workers active in the field.

CHAPTER 18

Dormancy and Arrested Development

Introduction

We have thus far considered growth and development as continuous processes, processes which progress without interruption from the germination of the seed to complete maturity of the plant. With many species, however, growth is not necessarily continuous but may be suspended for longer or shorter intervals at various points in the cycle of growth and development. Thus, it is commonly found that mature seeds may be maintained for extensive periods of time without germination, provided only that they are kept in a dry condition. Still other species produce seeds which will not germinate until after the lapse of a particular period of time or until after exposure to particular environmental conditions. With many species of trees a yearly cycle of bud growth and inactivity accompanies the yearly cycle of climatic changes. Buds of tubers and similar storage organs may also show temporary suspension of growth, even under conditions where growth might reasonably be expected to take place. The temporary suspension of growth in healthy plant tissues or organs, even under conditions in which these tissues or organs are furnished with all of the chemical and physical prerequisites ordinarily considered as necessary for growth, is known as *dormancy*, and such tissues or organs are said to be *dormant*. A knowledge of the causes and nature of the varied kinds of dormancy is important to an understanding of the way in which the plant reacts to, and is adjusted with, the varied forces of its environment. Let us therefore consider the ways in which dormancy may be manifested and the mechanisms by which it is brought about.

424

Life Span of Seeds

Seeds of most species of plants may be preserved in an inactive condition after harvest merely by keeping them dry; they may be aroused to germination if placed under suitable conditions of moisture and temperature. Suspension of growth while the seed is maintained in the

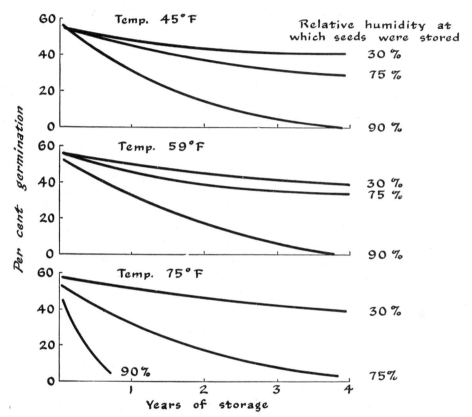

Figure 18-1. *The length of time seeds remain viable depends on both temperature and relative humidity of storage. Data refer to Tristania Conferta. (After Akamine, Pacific Sci., 5, 1951, p. 40.)*

dry condition is not to be considered as dormancy. It is rather a failure to grow because of the lack of an essential growth requirement, water. Although the seeds of some species, such as sugar cane, willow, tea, and others, are short-lived, in general the life span of seeds is measured in terms of years. In ordinary dry storage at room temperature, seeds of most crop plants appear to survive less than fifty years, many for less than ten years. The conditions of storage greatly influence the duration of seed vitality; low temperature and relatively low humidity, in particular, contribute to the increased life span of many seeds. Figure 18-1 shows the beneficial effect of low temperature and the deleterious effect of high moisture content on the vitality of Tristania seeds in storage.

Seed Dormancy

In contrast to the behavior of seeds which germinate if provided with suitable environmental conditions is the behavior of seeds which show true dormancy. Consider the seeds of such leguminous species as the black locust. If, after harvest, black locust seeds are placed under the moist, warm conditions ordinarily suitable for germination, only an occasional seed will germinate. If the seeds are first placed in a bottle, shaken vigorously for a few minutes, and then planted under suitable conditions, germination is greatly increased. The increased germination which results from this simple treatment has its basis in a simple mechanical effect. Because the seed coats of black locust are extraordinarily hard and normally impermeable to water, they do not absorb water from moist surroundings. However, the jarring of the seeds produces small cracks in the seed coats which make possible the entrance of water into the seed and subsequent germination.

Other methods are also effective in the production of small cracks in the seed coats of black locust or other seeds which possess water-impermeable seed coats. Such seeds may be shaken with sand or other sharp material; they may be nicked with a knife or rasped with a file. The breaking of the seed coats by such procedures is known as *scarification*. Chemical scarification is also possible; the partial dissolution of the seed coat can be achieved by sulfuric acid, by organic solvents such as acetone or alcohol, or even by momentary immersion in boiling water. In these treatments the principle is the same; all are designed to break open or weaken the hard seed coat so that water may enter more readily.

Water-impermeable seed coats are particularly common among the leguminous plants, although they are also found in the Cistaceae, Malvaceae, and others. When seeds of such species are planted without scarification, it is common for an occasional seed to germinate within a short period of time. The germination of other seeds may follow at intervals as the seed coats are weakened by the action of water or through oxidation by microorganisms present in the substrate. Germination of such seeds often continues over a period of many years. In

the water plant Nelumbo, which possesses an extraordinarily impermeable seed coat, seeds may remain in moist soil for two to four hundred
years and still retain fully their capacity to germinate.

Germination of hard-coated leguminous seeds under desert conditions may sometimes be accomplished by scarification caused by mechanical abrasion of the seed against sand. Thus it has been noted that
the seeds produced by such leguminous plants as the desert smoke tree,
Dalea spinosa, which grows in the ordinarily dry washes of the Southern California desert, do not germinate until they have been carried
for some distance by an occasional torrential rain. In the course of this
travel the seeds are abraded against sand and rock, and the normally
impermeable seed coats are ruptured.

Still another interesting example of impermeable seed coats is that
of the species of Rhus, which inhabit the chaparral region of the Pacific
Coast. Seeds of this species ordinarily germinate only after fires. It has
been shown that the seed coats are normally impermeable to water and
that the seeds may remain for many years without germination. During
the course of a brush fire, however, temperatures frequently rise to such
heights that the seed coat weakens and is cracked, leaving the embryo
itself unharmed. The seeds then germinate and produce regeneration
of the chaparral vegetation.

Hard seed coats may affect physiological properties of the seed other
than permeability to water. They may have a purely mechanical strait-
jacket effect upon the swelling and development of the seed or embryo.
Conversely, seed coats need not be mechanically hard in order to restrict the passage of water. The paper-thin integument resistant to the
passage of water may be as much a physical barrier as a hard seed coat
many times its thickness. Seed coats may be impermeable to oxygen as
well as to water. It has, for example, been shown that of the two seeds
produced in the fruit of cocklebur, one germinates readily in air while
the other requires a much higher oxygen concentration for germination.
This apparent high-oxygen requirement may be overcome very simply
by pricking the seed coat with a pin. The high-oxygen requirement of
the second seed is apparently nothing more than a low permeability
of the seed coat to oxygen.

Chemical Inhibitors of Germination

Still another kind of seed dormancy is that manifested by the seeds
of many desert plants, including the guayule, a rubber-producing desert
shrub of southwestern United States and Mexico. If seeds of the gua-

yule are placed on moist filter paper, they will germinate very slowly. If, however, they are first subjected to prolonged washing with water, they will germinate readily. Analysis of this phenomenon has shown that the chaff about the seeds contains a powerful chemical inhibitor of germination. Since the inhibitor is water soluble, it may be washed or leached from the seed and chaff, thus permitting germination. Such water-soluble inhibitors of germination appear to be common in desert species, and it is believed that they may be important ecologically. The seeds of these desert species lie upon the surface of the soil after they have been shed. Light rains do not leach sufficient inhibitor from the seeds to permit germination. Only in heavy soaking rains, which also insure adequate water for subsequent continued growth of the plant, does sufficient leaching take place to allow for germination. Chemical inhibition of germination is thus of considerable survival value for desert plants.

It is very generally found that fleshy fruits contain inhibitors which prevent germination of the seeds within them. An inhibitor of seed germination is present, for example, in the juice of the tomato fruit and in the fruit of citrus. The prevention of germination of the seeds within the fruit is evidently of considerable importance in that it insures that full development of the seed will occur prior to the inception of growth. Similar examples of inhibitors of germination within the fruit have been shown to be present in apples, pears, and other species.

Inhibitors also play a role in the development of those seeds which germinate only in light and fail to germinate in darkness, such as the seeds of certain lettuce varieties. In this case the action of light appears to be through the inactivation or suppression of germination inhibitors contained in the seed. Other species, for example the California poppy, germinate only in the dark. In this instance an inhibitor of germination is believed to be generated through the action of light.

Dormancy Broken by Cold Treatment

Still another type of dormancy of seeds is that caused by the requirement of the seed for certain subtle chemical changes which must occur before growth can take place. With many species, such changes, known collectively as *afterripening*, may be brought about by storage at low temperature for a period of time which varies from a few days to a few weeks or months. In *Sorbus aucuparia*, for example, the seed is surrounded by a hard pericarp and testa normally impermeable to water. If these are removed and the enclosed embryo explanted, it is found that this embryo is still dormant but will germinate after having been subjected to treatment for 6 weeks at 10° C (Fig. 18-2). Both pericarp and testa may be allowed to remain during treatment of the seed. Among other species whose seeds require cold treatment for germination are the roses and rosaceous fruits, such as peaches, apples and pears, as well as the linden, juniper species, dogwoods, and others. The

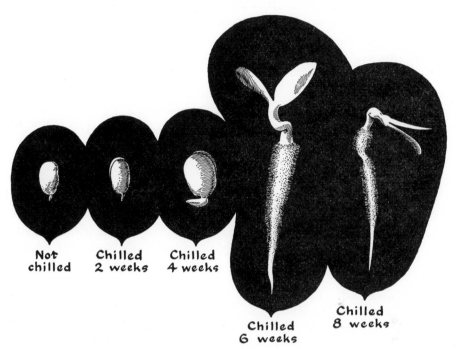

Not   Chilled   Chilled
chilled   2 weeks   4 weeks

Chilled
8 weeks

Chilled
6 weeks

Figure 18-2. *Dormancy of many seeds, including the Sorbus shown above, is broken by treatment with low temperature. Low-temperature treatment for six weeks gives optimal development. Prolongation of the treatment for an additional two weeks results in subsequent reduction of growth. The low temperature is effective only on moist seeds; dry seeds are unaffected. (After Crocker, Growth of Plants,* Reinhold Publ. Corp., 1948, p. 87.)

requirement for low-temperature treatment is evidently one which possesses survival value, since without it, seeds produced by a parent plant in fall would germinate at once and be killed by the low temperatures of winter. Because of the requirement for cold treatment, such seeds do not, however, germinate until the following spring.

It has been established that, in general, the most favorable condition of treatment for this type of dormancy is storage of the damp seeds at relatively low temperatures in the range from 0° to 10° C, a treatment known as *stratification*. The effect of stratification at varying temperatures in breaking the dormancy of rose seed is shown in Figure 18-3. Completely dry seeds are unaffected by such storage. During the course of the afterripening treatment, no general and readily detectable chemical alterations, such as changes in the several reserve constituents, take place. In general, morphological changes also fail to occur.

The fact that in many instances the entire embryo does not require afterripening gives us an insight into the possible nature of the afterripening process. Removal of the thin seed coat of the peach eliminates

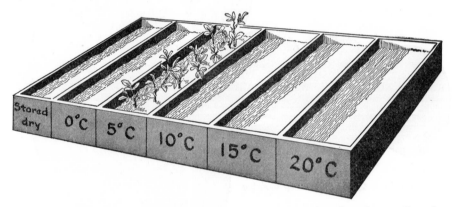

Figure 18-3. *The optimum temperature for breaking the dormancy of cold-requiring seeds such as those of rose is about 5° C. Seeds were treated for six months at temperatures noted and then returned to greenhouse temperatures for germination. (After Crocker,* Growth of Plants, *Reinhold Publ. Corp., 1948, p. 89.)*

the requirement for the afterripening cold treatment. It has been found also that the endosperm of dormant oak seeds contains a chemical inhibitor of growth whose presence may be demonstrated biologically by its ability to inhibit the growth of nondormant seeds. Stratification of the seeds depletes or destroys the inhibitor of the endosperm, making possible germination and growth of the embryo. Depletion of the inhibitor is, however, a curious reaction in that it proceeds more rapidly at low temperatures than at high. In Crataegus, the inhibitor may be related to auxin, for it has been shown that treatment of nondormant stratified seeds with auxin reinduces dormancy and that such dormancy may be broken by repeated cold treatment.

Biological Role of Dormancy

There are still other types of seed dormancy. In a few species the seed contains only a rudimentary embryo at the time of maturation of the fruit. The embryo develops to a stage where it is capable of germination and growth as a seedling only after weeks or months following its removal from the plant. This is true, for example, of Ginkgo, Gnetum, and other species.

In summary, seed dormancy may be thought of as an adjustment of the plant to its environment. This adjustment is one which helps to insure that germination will occur only under environmental circumstances suitable for the growth and establishment of the seedling. Of the mechanisms used for this purpose, Crocker, a long-time student of seed dormancy, has said: "In securing delayed germination, plants are not limited to the dead monotony of one method."

Dormancy of Buds

The buds of deciduous trees of the temperate region exhibit a regular cycle of growth and dormancy which is environmentally controlled. Buds of such familiar species as the apple and other deciduous fruits, or lilacs and similar deciduous ornamental shrubs, remain dormant through the winter, only to break forth in the spring with the production of new flowers and leaves. Growth of these buds, with the production of shoots, continues through the spring and summer, but with the advent of fall, leaves are shed. If a plant of such a species is removed from the out-of-doors, after the shedding of leaves and onset of bud quiescence, and placed in a warm greenhouse, growth of the buds will not occur. The buds are dormant. In general, the environmental factor needed for termination of bud dormancy is treatment with low temperature. The influence of low-temperature treatment in terminating dormancy in a typical case is shown in Figure 18-4. As with seeds, the exact temperature and duration of treatment required varies greatly with species and variety, but in general temperatures of 0° to 10° C and treatments of from a few days to several months are necessary to bring about reactivation of dormant buds.

The onset of the dormant condition is not wholly a response to the lowered temperatures of fall and winter. It has been noted in Chapter 17 that the abscission of leaves of deciduous plants in the autumn is a photoperiodic response to the shortening day length. If a deciduous tree is removed to a warm greenhouse and given supplementary light in such a way as to provide continued long photoperiods, the tree will remain in an actively growing vegetative condition, apparently indefinitely. Long photoperiods can similarly delay the onset of dormancy, even under outdoor conditions in which temperatures are relatively low. It is commonly noted that the shedding of leaves and the onset of bud dormancy are delayed in deciduous trees which are close to street lights.

Even though the onset of bud dormancy is conditioned primarily by

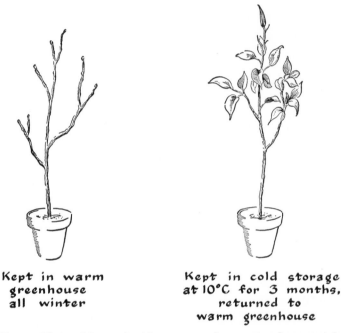

Kept in warm greenhouse all winter

Kept in cold storage at 10°C for 3 months, returned to warm greenhouse

Figure 18-4. *Many deciduous woody species become dormant in the fall. This dormancy is overcome by treatment at low temperature.*

the effects of short day length, dormancy cannot usually be broken by the application of long days. This is quite logical if we remember that the leaves respond to the photoperiodic stimulus. Once the leaves have been shed, in response to short days, it is not possible to affect the plant further by photoperiodic treatment. Breaking of bud dormancy must, therefore, be accomplished by low-temperature treatment. If the low-temperature treatment is not supplied or is insufficient, leafing out of the tree in the spring may be delayed or may fail altogether. This phenomenon, known as *delayed foliation,* is commonly observed when deciduous plants of the northern temperate regions are cultivated in the tropics or subtropics. Thus plants such as the apple, which require relatively long cold treatment for the breaking of dormancy, cannot survive in tropical regions. In subtropical regions, as in the low elevations in southern California, the winters are frequently so warm that the cold requirement of apple trees is not satisfied, and leafing out of the plant in the spring is greatly delayed.

Genetics of Bud Dormancy

The requirement of cold treatment for the breaking of bud dormancy varies among different varieties of a given species. Certain varieties of peach require only a very short exposure to low temperature for the breaking of bud dormancy. Such varieties leaf out in the spring and grow satisfactorily even in subtropical regions. Other varieties require much more cold treatment. Many genes are apparently concerned with the regulation of the amount of cold treatment required by a bud, the genes for a lesser cold requirement being, in general, recessive in the peach. By the crossing of various forms it is possible to obtain commercial varieties of peaches with a wide range of cold-treatment requirements. Similar relations hold in the lilac, in which species and varieties of greatly varying cold requirements are known.

Breaking of Dormancy

Unlike the responses to photoperiodism, the response to cold treatment is strictly localized. If a tree which has become dormant is subjected to cold treatment of one stem alone, the rest of the plant remaining under high-temperature conditions, it is found that the dormancy of only the treated stem is broken. This appears to indicate that the response of buds to low temperature is not hormonally controlled, at least not in the same sense as photoperiodic responses. The breaking of dormancy does not appear to travel from one portion of the plant to other portions (Fig. 18-5).

Chemical treatments of various kinds have been found useful in overcoming bud dormancy. The immersion of a branch in warm water is a classical method. Treatments with such chemicals as ethylene chlorohydrin and various nitrophenol sprays have been used in commercial practice to break dormancy in such plants as the peach. The mechanism by which these stimuli work is unknown.

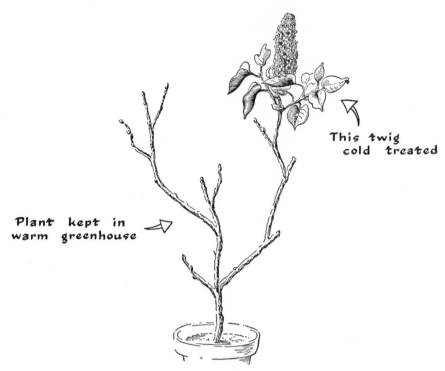

Figure 18-5. *The breaking of dormancy by low-temperature treatment is a local response and confined to the treated buds.* (*After Molisch,* Pflanzenphysiologie als Theorie der Gärtnerei, *Gustav Fischer* [*Jena*], *1930, p. 203.*)

Dormancy of the Potato

An interesting example of bud dormancy is found in the potato tuber. The potato is a modified and fleshy stem, the eyes of which contain buds. The tuber shows marked apical dominance, that is, the laterals fail to develop in the presence of the terminal bud. This is an expression of the auxin-mediated apical dominance and inhibition of lateral buds as discussed in Chapter 16. Superimposed upon this behavior is still another type of bud dormancy. When freshly dug potatoes are exposed to conditions suitable for growth or sprouting of the buds, sprouting does not take place. This is true even when the potato is cut into the so-called "seed pieces," each of which contains an individual bud. A period of storage is necessary before the buds of the potato tuber lose their dormancy and become capable of sprouting. Storage may be at either high or low temperatures. Dormancy may also be broken by the application of various chemicals, including ethylene chlorohydrin. The influence of this chemical on dormant potato buds is shown in Figure 18-6. Both the artificially broken dormancy and the sprouting of potatoes after breaking of dormancy by the normal process of storage may

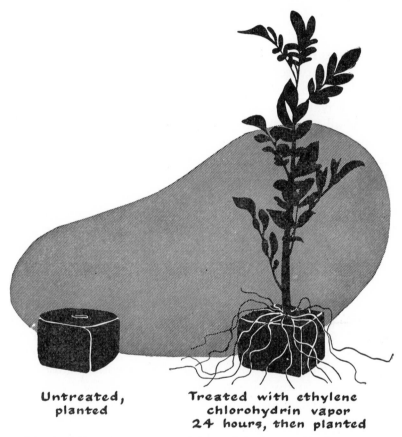

Untreated,   Treated with ethylene
planted   chlorohydrin vapor
                   24 hours, then planted

Figure 18-6. *Dormancy of the potato bud is broken by treatment with ethylene chlorohydrin.*

be interrupted by the application of auxin. The artificial application of auxins to potatoes in storage has, in fact, been used for prolonging their normal storage life.

We do not yet have a full insight into the physiological and chemical mechanisms which produce dormancy in either buds of trees or buds of potatoes. In general, however, it seems highly probable that both kinds of dormancy are due to the presence in the buds of growth-inhibiting substances. It is probable that this growth-inhibiting substance is destroyed or reduced in concentration by treatments which break dormancy. Such treatments would include low-temperature storage, as in buds of deciduous trees; storage at ordinary temperatures, as in the potato; or chemical treatment, such as that with ethylene chlorohydrin.

Summary

Dormancy, as it is found in many seeds and buds, is an inability to grow under otherwise favorable environmental circumstances. Dormancy is therefore an internal property. This property is one which possesses survival value for the plant in that the varied dormancy mechanisms all tend to restrict periods of active growth to favorable seasons and to limit or suppress growth under less favorable circumstances. Thus, on the desert, where water is in very short supply, the dormancy of seeds of many plants is terminated only by a soaking rain. Similarly, the dormancy of seeds of many of our temperate zone plants is terminated only by high temperatures following a long exposure to low temperature. Germination of such seeds cannot occur, therefore, until the spring following the year in which they are matured. Bud dormancy in woody species also insures that growth cannot occur during occasional warm periods in the winter but must await the advent of spring.

Dormancy, insofar as we now understand the process, most frequently invokes one of two general mechanisms. In the first type—that characteristic of the seed—hard, impermeable seed coats prevent the entry of an essential growth material. This essential material may be water or oxygen. In any case, termination of dormancy is achieved by the rupture or weakening of the seed coat, so that the necessary substance can penetrate to the embryo itself.

A second general mechanism by which dormancy is achieved involves the presence in the seed or bud of an inhibitor of growth. This inhibitor must be removed before germination or growth can occur, and the varied agents which can be shown to terminate dormancy of different species are often, perhaps generally, those which effect the removal or inactivation of such an inhibitor. In no instance has the responsible inhibiting substance been isolated in pure chemical form, and, although the principle of dormancy by inhibition would seem to be a general one, a detailed understanding of the mechanisms involved demands much further study.

QUESTIONS

1. Freshly harvested seeds of *Amaranthus retroflexus* require temperatures between 35–49° C for prompt germination. As the seeds age, they can do with progressively lower temperatures, finally germinating even at 10° C. Present a possible explanation.

2. Seed germination tests are frequently carried out on plaster or porous clay blocks which are slightly moistened. What dangers are inherent in the long-time use of such germinators?

3. What is the possible survival value of seed dormancy?

4. Certain seeds, which ordinarily require light for germination, will germinate in the dark provided they are placed in an atmosphere of 100 per cent oxygen. What might this indicate about the mechanism of the action of light on these seeds? In other seeds, nitrate will apparently substitute for light. How can this be interpreted?

5. How does the effect of low temperature on bud dormancy differ from its effect on flowering?

6. Barton found the seeds of *Trillium grandiflorum* to require two periods of low-temperature treatment interrupted by, and then followed by, warm periods. To what may such complex requirements be due?

7. Certain strains of corn and barley produce seeds which germinate and grow on the ear of the parent plant, undergoing no period of dormancy at all. How could these seeds be treated so as to render them dormant?

8. Discuss in some detail the specific factors involved in the dormancy of the eyes of a potato tuber.

9. How could one produce two successive crops of potato tubers in the same year?

GENERAL READING

Crocker, W., *Growth of Plants*. New York: Reinhold Publ. Corp., 1948. Contains excellent chapters on longevity of seeds, seed dormancy, and bud dormancy based on work carried out at the Boyce Thompson Institute for Plant Research.

Evenari, M., "Germination Inhibitors." *Botan. Rev.*, **15**: 153, 1949. The present status of knowledge concerning naturally occurring inhibitors in seeds.

CHAPTER 19

The Problem of Differentiation

Introduction

During the course of our discussion of plant growth and development we have described and repeatedly made use of the concept of differentiation—the production of new plant organs, the formation of leaves by the stem apex, the initiation of secondary or branch roots by primary roots, and the conversion of vegetative to reproductive growing points. We have also described the differentiation of meristematic cells into the many varied types of cells and tissues characteristic of the mature plant.

Even though the processes of differentiation are ubiquitous, and even though we ordinarily take these processes more or less for granted, differentiation confronts biology with one of its most complex and difficult problems. Let us consider one example which illustrates especially well the questions that must be answered if we are to understand differentiation. The fertilized ovule, a single cell, divides successively to form 2, 4, 8, etc., cells. Since these cells are the products of successive mitotic divisions, we may presume them to be identical so far as genetic composition is concerned. Despite their uniformity in hereditary complement, the cells produced by successive divisions of the zygote form a variety of tissues. Even the first cell division may, in many dicotyledonous plants, result in the formation of two distinguishably different cells, an apical and basal cell, respectively. The basal cell in many instances contributes only to the elongated suspensor, while from the apical cell or its products the proembryo ordinarily is formed. The apical cell of the proembryo may, in turn, typically divide to produce the embryo itself. By the time the embryo has attained the 8-cell stage, the differentiation of the cotyledonary and hypocotyledonary regions of the embryo may already be accomplished, and by the time a few hundred cells have been produced, the embryo may be clearly delineated into its several primordia and tissue-forming regions. From the primordia will grow the organs, the stem, leaves, and root of the mature plant, and from the tissue-forming regions will develop the characteristic tissues of the mature organs. These stages of embryonic development are recapitulated in Figure 19-1.

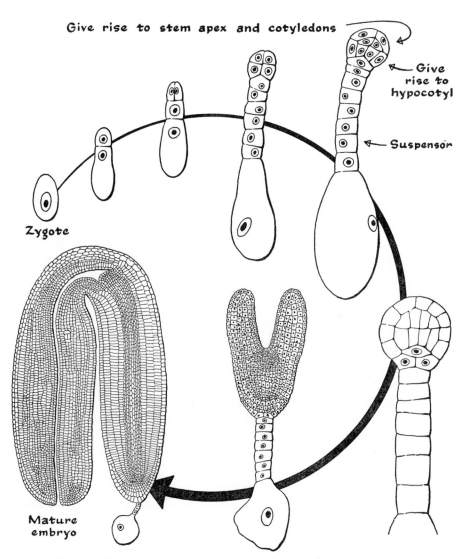

Give rise to stem apex and cotyledons

Give rise to hypocotyl

Suspensor

Zygote

Mature embryo

Figure 19-1. *Successive stages in the development of the embryo of Capsella. (After Johansen,* Plant Embryology, Chronica Botanica, *1950, p. 144.)*

We may now ask ourselves: What subtle influences bring about these metamorphoses of like cells into unlike cells? What forces determine the identity or nonidentity of the daughter cells of a single mitotic division? Biologists are still seeking satisfactory answers to these questions. We can, however, describe the processes of differentiation in detail, and discuss some of the methods used in the physiological study of them.

The processes of differentiation may be broadly subdivided into organ formation and tissue formation. We may consider as processes of organ formation those concerned with the organization of buds, root primordia, leaf primordia, and also of flower bud formation. The formation of root and shoot tip constitutes organ formation in the developing embryo. Tissue formation, the differentiation of meristematic cells into the characteristic tissues of the adult plant, usually occurs as a part of, and simultaneously with, organ formation. It is, however, a process distinct from organ formation and may proceed differently in similar organs.

Organ and Tissue Culture

The experimental study of differentiation has been greatly advanced by the application of the methods of organ culture referred to so extensively earlier. We have seen that it is possible to cultivate excised embryos, roots, leaves, stems, and fruits on appropriate nutrient media. By the technique of organ culture, it has been possible to identify certain of the factors which, by their movement within the plant, control and integrate plant growth. Each of these plant organs is, of course, complex and consists of many different tissues. It is also possible, however, to prepare some cultures in which reasonably homogeneous excised tissue is cultivated on an appropriate nutrient medium to the exclusion or near exclusion of other kinds of cells. Only meristematic cells, or parenchymatous cells which are still relatively meristematic, can be grown in this way, however, since continued production of new cells by cell division is essential to the continued growth of the tissue. With tissue cultures we may study not only the factors which bring about the production of new organs, such as buds or roots, but also the factors and influences which are required for differentiation of meristematic cells into vascular elements.

Embryo Growth

There have been many precise anatomical accounts of the pathways of embryo development in many different plant species. Such descriptive studies are, of course, accomplished by the removal and observation of embryos which have been allowed to develop normally *in situ* for measured periods of time. It is generally necessary to study the material after it has been fixed, sectioned, and stained. This method, while suited to the description of embryo development, is not applicable to the study of the causes of differentiation. It has, however, proved possible to study the development of embryos which have been aseptically excised from the ovary and transferred to a suitable nutrient medium.

As mentioned in Chapter 17, when mature or nearly mature embryos are cultured as excised embryos, they will develop into normal seedlings

Table 19-1. *Changing Nutritive Requirements of Excised Datura Embryos. (Mature Embryos Have the Simplest Requirements, Proembryos the Most Complex.)*

EMBRYONIC STAGE	GREATEST DIMENSION, MM	GROWTH OF EXCISED EMBRYOS ON:		
		SALTS AND SUGAR	SALTS, SUGAR, VITAMINS, AMINO ACIDS (BASAL MEDIUM)	BASAL MEDIUM PLUS COCONUT MILK
Mature embryo	ca. 5	Grows	Grows	Grows
Immature: cotyledons well developed	1–2	Little or no growth	Grows	Grows
Heart shaped	0.2	No growth	No growth	Grows
Proembryo	0.1	No growth	No growth	Rarely grows
Proembryo	less than 0.1	No growth	No growth	Occasionally grows to callus

even when maintained on a nutrient medium containing only mineral salts and sucrose. The nutrient requirements of younger embryos may, however, be more complex. The increasingly complex requirements of successively younger embryos of Datura are summarized in Table 19-1. Partly mature embryos of Datura must be cultured on a medium containing a variety of organic supplements, principally vitamins and amino acids, in addition to the mineral salts and sugar. Still smaller embryos of Datura require yet another growth factor if they are to continue their development—a factor of unknown nature which is contained in coconut milk or in malt extract. Datura embryos excised from the plant at still earlier stages do not, however, have the ability to grow in any nutrient medium yet discovered. Such a failure of normal growth and differentiation is characteristic of the behavior after excision of very young embryos of several plant species, and it has not, in fact, been possible to bring about normal development of excised zygotes or very young proembryos of any higher plant.

It appears, then, that with the excised embryo, growth, if it takes place at all, follows a more or less normal pathway. We do not know, therefore, whether the normal pathway of development is impressed on the developing embryo in some way by the surrounding tissues of the mother plant or whether it is inherent in the zygote. According to the first hypothesis it would be necessary to assume that once a certain degree of differentiation, a pattern, has been impressed on the embryo by association with the parent plant, normal development may continue even if the embryo is excised. If the second hypothesis is the correct one, plant embryos would resemble the embryos of certain animals in this character of their development.

The investigation of the development of embryos of such animals as frogs and salamanders has shown that during development particular areas of the embryo are centers for the organization of organ and tissue patterns. In the development of amphibian eggs, cell division of the zygote, coupled with the rearrangement of cells, leads to the formation of a hollow ball of cells. An indentation in the surface of this ball is formed, and through an opening in this depression, cells move inward to form the gastrula. The cells which form the upper or dorsal lip of this fold act as an organization center for much of the remaining embryonic development. If, for example, the dorsal lip tissue from one embryo is implanted in another locus on a second gastrula, a second embryo, more or less complete, will develop on this gastrula. We still have no complete picture of the way in which the dorsal lip induces differentiation in adjacent cells. The point to be stressed here, however, is that in the free-swimming amphibian embryo, in which there is no connection to mature tissue, successive cell divisions result in the formation of separate embryonic regions, one of which assumes the power of directing activity in other regions.

We shall see below that in the development of plant organs and tissues, differentiation may in some instances proceed in what appears to be a purely spontaneous manner, following patterns which are inherent in the developing tissue mass. In many other instances, on the contrary, differentiation appears to proceed, or perhaps to continue, as a result of influences exerted on meristematic tissues by more mature tissue, tissue which is already differentiated.

Root Formation

The formation of a root meristem constitutes one portion of the development of a plant embryo from a fertilized ovule. New root primordia also arise in other locations, however. The formation of branch roots requires the formation of new primordia on roots, while the formation of adventitious roots on leaves, petioles, stems, or at other unusual locations must, of course, be preceded by the development of organized root meristems.

It was noted in Chapter 16 that the application of an auxin, such as indoleacetic acid or a related compound, to stem cuttings of many species results in the formation of adventitious root primordia. Root primordia may also be formed on stems of intact plants as the result of auxin application. In all of these instances the primordia first appear as areas of meristematic activity, often in the pericycle of herbaceous stems or in the phloem parenchyma of woody stems. Accompanying continued cell division, this meristematic region becomes organized into a recognizable root meristem which finally protrudes through the surface of the stem.

We have seen that auxin applications to plant tissues evoke many kinds of responses in addition to root formation; the ability to form roots is by no means a specific property of auxin. How, then, does it come about that auxin application in a particular instance does result in the response of root formation? One hypothesis is that root formation results from the interaction of the applied auxin with a second material, rhizocaline, and that, although auxin brings about growth activity, it is the presence of rhizocaline which directs this activity along the specific pathway of root formation. Evidence for this view is the fact that auxin application to a stem cutting results in the loss by the cutting of the power to form additional roots in response to further auxin treatment. Thus, when the base of a cutting is treated with auxin, the treated base will ultimately form roots. If the treated base is excised and the remaining cutting treated basally with auxin a second time, as shown in Figure 19-2, few or no roots are produced. This is explained by saying that the hypothetical rhizocaline has been transported to and used in the first treated portion, so that after the excision of this portion there is none left for further root formation.

The hypothetical rhizocaline would appear also to be more or less equally distributed through the stems. In the stems of certain species,

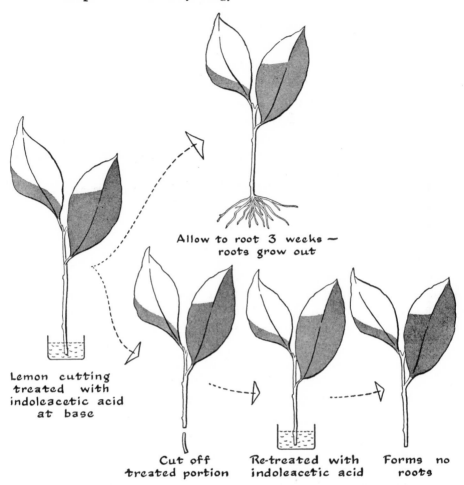

Allow to root 3 weeks — roots grow out

Lemon cutting treated with indoleacetic acid at base

Cut off treated portion

Re-treated with indoleacetic acid

Forms no roots

Figure 19-2. *The production of adventitious roots depends not only on auxin but on another factor or factors which are normally present in many stems and which may be mobilized to the site of auxin application.* (*Adapted from Cooper,* Plant Physiol., **10,** *1935, p. 791.*)

as the pea, for example, the number of roots formed per cutting is more or less proportional to the length of the cutting. Long cuttings form many roots, cuttings which are half as long form half as many roots per cutting, and so on. This result, which is depicted in Figure 19-3, may be interpreted on the basis that all of the rhizocaline in a long cutting is mobilized to, and available for, root formation at the base, while in a shorter cutting less rhizocaline is available for mobilization and fewer roots are formed. The stems of many species of plants lack entirely the ability to produce root primordia in response to auxin

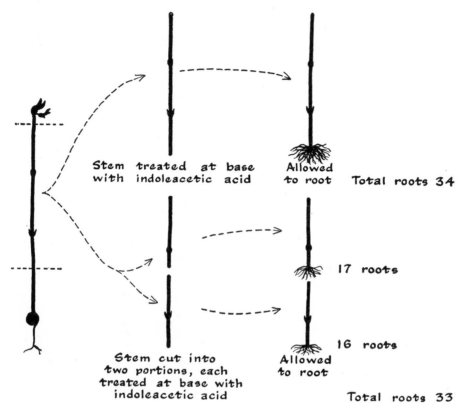

Figure 19-3. *The maximum number of adventitious roots formed by a cutting as the result of auxin treatment depends on the amount of other root growth factors which the cutting contains. This is determined in the pea by the size of the cutting. (Adapted from Went, Plant Physiol.,* **13,** *1938, p. 69.)*

treatment. According to the rhizocaline hypothesis, we would say that the stems of such plants lack rhizocaline.

The supposition that some second factor, rhizocaline, is essential for root formation even in the presence of applied auxin has not been verified by identification of any pure chemical with the property of directing growth along the pathway of root formation. Until this is done, we cannot be sure that such a material actually participates in organ formation, attractive though the possibility may be.

Tissue Differentiation in the Root Tip

A particularly elegant demonstration of the role of mature tissues in the differentiation of meristematic tissues is that provided by the growing root tip. We have seen in Chapter 15 that when excised root tips of any of several species are cultivated on an aseptic nutrient medium under appropriate physical conditions, they will develop into normal primary roots. The tips from which such excised roots are grown are ordinarily several millimeters in length and thus include not only the root cap and apical meristem but also well-defined tissue-forming regions, as well as differentiated regions of the root containing protoxylem and protophloem. Very extensive experiments have been conducted to determine exactly how much and what kinds of tissue must be

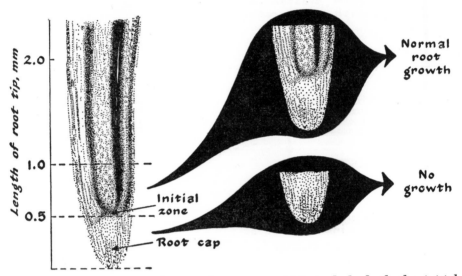

Figure 19-4. *Only root fragments which include both the initial zone and some differentiated tissue can develop into normal roots in culture.* (*Adapted from Addicott,* Botan. Gaz., **100**, *1939, p. 840; and Bonner and Addicott,* Botan. Gaz., 99, *1937, p. 144.*)

included in the initial tip to assure growth of this tip into a normal root. Apical fragments of pea roots, for example, which include only the root cap and the apical meristematic region, do not develop into roots but at most into a disorganized colony of parenchymatous cells. If, on the other hand, the apical portion, including root cap and meristematic region, is removed, the remaining elongating and differentiating tissues are incapable, generally, of regenerating a normal root. Only tips which contain both the meristematic region and a short section of the differentiating zone have proved capable of further development as a normal root. These relations are illustrated in Figure 19-4. The same behavior has been shown to occur with roots of corn and wheat, although these roots differ among themselves as to the exact amount of differentiating region which must remain in contact with the meristematic zone to effect normal development. The cells of the apical meristem of the root do not seem to be able, in and of themselves, to carry out the processes of normal tissue differentiation, but require the presence of other cells which are partly or completely differentiated.

The Formation of Buds

The most familiar example of the formation of new shoot primordia is offered by the development of lateral buds in the axils of the leaves cut off by a growing shoot apex. Shoot primordia may, however, be formed on leaves or even roots, as well as stems. Our body of information concerning the chemical control of bud initiation is, however, much smaller than that of adventitious root formation. The experimental control of bud formation is demonstrated by the culture of excised tissues derived from the stem of a particular hybrid tobacco. The stems of this

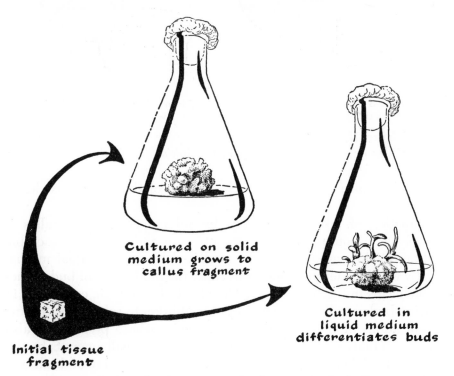

Cultured on solid
medium grows to
callus fragment

Cultured in
liquid medium
differentiates buds

Initial tissue
fragment

Figure 19-5. *The formation of adventitious buds by excised tobacco callus tissue is controlled by conditions of aeration.*

hybrid (*Nicotiana glauca*, crossed by *N. langsdorfii*) produce spontaneous gall-like outgrowths of callus. Fragments of the callus may be removed and grown as a tissue culture in a nutrient medium consisting only of mineral salts and carbohydrates, usually sucrose. The tissue consists of meristematic parenchymatous cells, essentially free of other types of cells, and may be maintained apparently indefinitely by subculture on a simple nutrient medium. When the medium is solidified by the addition of a small amount of agar, the tissue is able to grow upon the surface, obtaining nutrients from the medium yet remaining under highly aerobic conditions. If, however, a growing piece of callus is placed in liquid nutrient medium, it sinks to the bottom of the culture vessel, and, under these conditions of limited oxygen supply, adventi-

Excised tobacco stem
tissue untreated

Stem tissue treated
with adenine

Figure 19-6. *The application of adenine to excised tobacco stem tissue or stem callus results in the initiation of adventitious buds.*

tious buds appear scattered over the surface of the culture, as shown in Figure 19-5.

Production of adventitious buds by submerged tobacco callus is probably a response to low-oxygen pressure and partially anaerobic conditions. This response may be mediated by some internal mechanism by which anaerobic conditions cause the production of bud-inducing chemicals in the tissue itself. The effect of anaerobic conditions in inducing buds can be duplicated by the addition to solid media of low concentrations of the purine adenine. Auxin, whose presence is also necessary if buds are to be formed, is produced in small amounts by the tissue itself. Adenine applications evoke the formation of buds not only in tobacco callus but also in segments of tobacco stem, a response shown in Figure 19-6.

Although bud formation in tobacco callus may be promoted by supplying adenine to the tissue, it seems probable that adenine evokes activity in plant tissue in general (Chap. 15) and that, as with root formation, a more specific bud-forming material must somehow direct the activity along the pathway of bud formation. The nature of this factor of bud formation is unknown.

The Formation of Flower Buds

Another instance of organ differentiation is the transformation of vegetative stem primordia into floral primordia. In plants with determinate growth, the shoot apex grows vegetatively, producing leaf primordia and lateral buds until such time as conditions become appropriate for flowering. At this time the structure of the apical meristem itself alters, becoming broader and, in many cases, large and swollen relative to the vegetative apex. This altered apical meristem now produces primordia which become floral parts rather than leaves. The process of floral initiation involves primarily an alteration in arrangement and functioning of the initial cells in the shoot apex itself. Secondarily, the differentiation of the primordia produced by the shoot apex is also effected. We have seen in Chapter 17 that in species whose flowering is controlled by photoperiodism, it can be shown that alteration of the vegetative apex into a floral apex is brought about by a substance or condition produced in the leaves and transported to the vegetative buds where it manifests its effects. In the flowering factor we have a clear instance of a differentiation-inducing material, and elucidation of its nature could conceivably contribute to our understanding of differentiation in general.

Tissue Differentiation in the Shoot Apex

The apical meristem of the shoot appears to be much more autonomous in its pattern of differentiation than the apical meristem of the root. Even when exceedingly small sections of shoot apex, containing not over a few thousand cells, are excised from Tropaeolum or lupine and cultured *in vitro*, normally differentiated vascular tissue is produced, and an entire plant may result, as shown in Figure 19-7. The relative independence of the shoot apex is also shown by the fact that such apices may be divided longitudinally into two or even four segments, with complete recovery of the segments and production of normal shoots. These observations signify that the meristematic cells

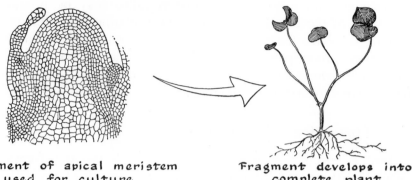

Fragment of apical meristem
used for culture

Fragment develops into
complete plant

Figure 19-7. *The cells of the initial zone and closely adjacent meristematic portions of the shoot apex of Tropaeolum are capable of regeneration into an entire plant.* (*After Ball, Am. J. Botany, 33, 1946, p. 302.*)

of the extreme shoot apex are somehow determined, so that they produce the appropriate stem structure independent of the nature of the subtending tissue. Whether this is a property determined purely genetically or whether the early determination of the cells of the apical shoot meristem is achieved by contact with more mature tissue, as it is with root meristems, is very difficult to decide on a purely experimental basis.

Induction of Tissue Differentiation Patterns

A typical meristem gives rise to many cells, all of which, so far as we know, possess the capacity for developing into any of the specialized cells which make up the plant. The exact fate of each of these cells depends partly on its geographical position relative to other cells, and partly on the chemical influences which may be brought to bear upon it by surrounding mature cells.

A growing cell in the interior of an organ is subjected symmetrically to the pressures of other expanding cells, and tends to become isodiametric. Epidermal cells, on the other hand, lacking neighbors on one surface, are subjected to unequal pressures, which results in their flattened form. The relationship of cell shape to the pressures and tensions to which the cell is subject can be demonstrated experimentally. If a potato tuber is sliced open, the new cells produced at the cut surfaces assume the flattened form typical of epidermal layers, rather than the isodiametric form typical of internal parenchyma. Similarly, the flattened elongate cells of the cambium and its derivatives may owe their form to the forces with which these tissues are compressed between the rigid wood and the restricting bark.

Only in a very few cases has it proved experimentally possible to cause undifferentiated plant cells to assume a particular pathway of differentiation. The relatively undifferentiated parenchymatous cells of some kinds of callus tissue can, however, be caused to differentiate into vascular elements, and the agent capable of bringing about such tissue differentiation is nothing less than a developing bud. The influence of

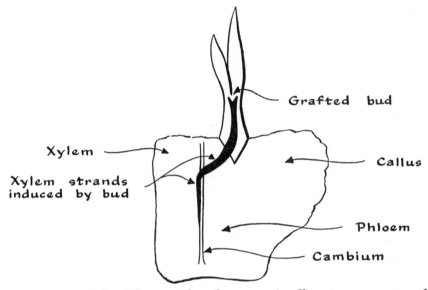

Figure 19-8. *The vascular elements of callus tissue occur as disorganized whorls. The presence of a grafted bud, containing organized vascular elements, induces organized vascular patterns in the callus. (After Camus,* Rev. Cytol. et Biol. végét., *11, 1949, p. 119.)*

buds on tissue differentiation has been studied with callus tissue of roots, especially of endive and Scorzonera. The production of the callus tissue occurs when short segments of root are cut from the plant and placed aseptically in a nutrient medium. With many species of roots, including those named above, as well as with stem segments of many species, the cultured segments frequently respond by the formation of basal and apical swellings composed principally of callus tissue containing parenchymatous, relatively meristematic cells. The callus tissue is derived primarily from the cambium of the excised stem fragment, although parenchymatous cells of superficial regions of the xylem and phloem parenchyma may return to meristematic activity and contribute to callus production.

The callus tissues are composed chiefly of cells which are undifferentiated or at most only slightly differentiated as parenchyma. Isolated and unorganized vascular elements may be scattered throughout the meristematic mass of callus tissue. Differentiation into organized vascular elements may, however, be experimentally induced by grafting young buds of the same species into these undifferentiated calluses. After the graft union has become established, vascular elements appear in the callus across the graft line. They are formed in continuity with the vascular elements of the bud itself and, as time elapses, progress downward into the host tissue, a result depicted in Figure 19-8. We see here that the differentiated cells, in this case those of the bud, are capable of effecting differentiation in adjacent undifferentiated cells. This implies that cellular differentiation, like so many other processes of plant growth and development, may be mediated by differentiation-inducing chemical substances which move about through plant tissues.

Effect of Auxin on Tissue Differentiation

The formation of callus tissue on stems or roots is greatly increased by the application of indoleacetic acid, and a great deal of attention has been paid not only to the induction of callus on intact plants but also to the tissue differentiation in such auxin-induced callus. The callus tissue, so formed, may be excised from the stem or root which has produced it and may, in many instances, be cultured through repeated passages as an isolated tissue. Continued growth of the isolated callus tissue, whether from stem or root, requires a nutrient medium which contains not only the usual minerals and sugar but also an auxin, such as IAA, which is apparently not produced by the callus. Both callus tissue induced by the application of IAA to the stem and callus maintained in tissue culture on a medium containing IAA exhibit extensive differentiation of xylem and phloem elements. These elements are scattered through the meristematic parenchymatous cells and are not ordinarily organized into regular vascular bundles as they would be in a normal stem.

The promotion of callus growth by IAA consists, then, of at least two separate kinds of activity. On the one hand, IAA causes the resumption of meristematic activity in cells which otherwise would not show such activity. On the other hand, IAA evokes tissue differentiation in certain of these cells. A fact which may be of great value in the further study of tissue differentiation is that certain substances chemically related to IAA possess the ability to cause cell division but do not appear to evoke tissue differentiation. This is said to be true of the compound 2,5-dimethylphenoxypropionic acid. The compound 2,4-dichlorophenoxyacetic acid (2,4-D), although it causes cell division in the cambium and in xylem parenchyma, as well as in callus tissue, may not cause cell division in the phloem parenchyma, for instance, in endive. It appears that we may have in these observations material on which to base a chemical approach to the study of tissue differentiation.

Tumor Tissue

One class of plant tissues is usually marked by a low degree of differentiation, by certain chemical properties, and by the fact that production of this type of tissue may spread through the plant and from plant to plant as a disease. These tissues are the plant tumors. Tumors may result from a variety of causes, one of which is infection of the plant with the crown-gall organism *Agrobacterium tumefaciens*. In our discussion of crown-gall tumors in Chapter 16, we have seen that the bacterium enters the plant through a wound, and that at the site of the infection a massive growth of meristematic parenchymatous tissue takes place. After a time, secondary tumors may appear at varied locations some distance from the original primary tumor. These secondary tumors, although they are in general free of the original bacteria, resemble the primary tumor in their growth.

Secondary crown-gall tumors may be excised from the plant, divided aseptically into fragments, and these fragments grown in culture. They may be maintained in culture apparently indefinitely through repeated transfers. If at any time a fragment of cultured tumor is grafted back onto a piece of normal stem tissue, it acts as a center for the induction of additional secondary tumors (Fig. 19-9).

Tumor tissues such as those induced by the crown-gall bacterium differ from the callus tissues mentioned above in two important respects. In the first place, callus tissue does not possess the ability to induce new callus at a distance. It is meristematic tissue which may be maintained as such but which does not have the power of inducing other cells to grow as undifferentiated tissue. Secondly, tumor tissues, insofar as they have been investigated, differ from callus tissues in their nutrient requirements; they do not require the presence of IAA or other auxins in their nutrient media. Moreover, it is known that, in certain instances at least, tumor tissues possess the ability to produce auxin themselves. Since tumor tissues do not require auxin or other growth factors from their host plant, they are relatively autonomous; that is, they are emancipated to a considerable extent from the hormonal controls which integrate normal growth. They are therefore free to grow as rapidly and as extensively as is possible on the basis of the sugars, minerals, water, and similar nutrients which they can obtain from their host plant. The relatively autonomous physiological nature of the tumor may also be disseminated through the plant, so that fresh centers of

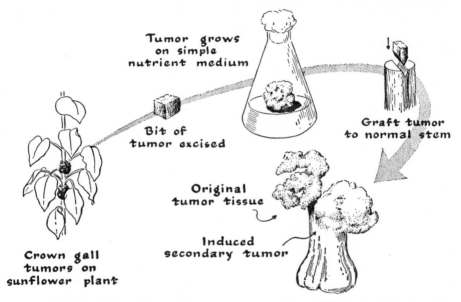

Figure 19-9. *Tumor tissues possess the ability of inducing the tumorous state in adjacent normal tissues. This effect can be propagated across a graft union. (Adapted from de Ropp, Am. J. Botany, 35, 1948, p. 372.)*

tumor activity are induced. In some instances at least, the tumefacient agent which spreads the tumorous conditions through the host plant is a virus. This is true, for example, of the so-called "wound tumor," a plant virus disease in which the virus is spread from plant to plant by a particular insect. The virus, once introduced within a particular plant, causes a disease, the symptom of which is the production of tumors.

We might regard the production of tumor tissue as a particular kind of chemical differentiation in which the characteristic features are: (1) ability to form growth substances and (2) meristematic activity. This kind of differentiation, like certain of the others discussed earlier, can be induced in nontumorous tissue through the influence of tumor tissue. The agent responsible for mediating the induction of their differentiation is, in some instances at least, a virus. We do not know whether normal differentiation in cases other than that of tumors may be mediated by viruslike materials. This is, however, a possibility to be considered.

Summary

The evolution of like cells into unlike cells constitutes differentiation. We may divide the study of this process into two separate phases: the study of organ formation and the study of tissue formation. The formation of organs such as root and bud primordia may be induced experimentally in certain plants by the use of particular chemical substances. Root primordia are evoked in many instances by application of auxin, while bud primordia in tobacco stem or callus may be evoked by adenine. Both indoleacetic acid and adenine fill many different functions in the plant; both are compounds which appear to be generally essential to plant activity. The channeling of activity evoked by indoleacetic acid or adenine along the pathway of root or bud initiation may, therefore, be a result of the interaction of these substances with still other, unknown, specific agents.

The differentiation of meristematic cells into the component tissues characteristic of such mature organs as the root appears to depend on influences exerted on the meristematic tissue by more mature tissues, tissues which have already differentiated. We might say that so far as these tissues are concerned, differentiation begets differentiation. In other instances, as in the shoot apex, meristematic cells appear capable of normal differentiation in the absence of more mature tissues. Here, the mere position of the cell relative to other cells and to the forces of the external environment may determine the course of differentiation.

QUESTIONS

1. A root tip removed from a plant and cultured on a synthetic medium continues to grow as an organized entity with normal anatomy. A fragment of stem similarly cultured usually gives rise to a more or less disorganized callus. What does this indicate about the nature of the plant's control over differentiation patterns?

2. We have described an experiment in which an organized bud grafted onto an unorganized tissue mass of Scorzonera elicits certain definite patterns of vascular organization. Through what mechanism may the bud be affecting the previously unorganized tissue?

3. The production of adventitious buds by submerged hybrid tobacco callus is generally attributed to anaerobiosis. Present an alternative explanation, and design an experiment to decide between the two alternatives.

4. From the facts presented concerning crown-gall, propose a hypothesis to explain the nature of the influence transmitted from crown-gall to normal cells. How could you test this hypothesis?

5. Schaffner, studying the physiology of sex expression in dioecious Cannabis, found the ratio of male to female plants to be altered according to the level of nitrogen supplied. What might this indicate concerning the nature of the difference between maleness and femaleness in this plant?

6. May differentiated cells de-differentiate and resume active growth?

7. How may various chemical influences be used to control differentiation patterns in plants? Can the substances themselves be said to produce specific tissue and organ patterns?

8. In the germinating zygote of the marine alga Fucus, the rhizoid develops (a) on the side away from the light, (b) on the side which is in a warmer environment, (c) toward neighboring developing eggs, (d) toward more acid media, (e) at the centrifugal pole of a centrifuged egg. On the basis of these facts, propose a theory accounting for the origin of a rhizoidal and nonrhizoidal pole.

9. How would you proceed in a research program designed to study differentiation?

GENERAL READING

Camus, G., "Recherches sur le Role des Bourgeons dans les Phenomènes de Morphogénèse." *Rev. Cytol. et Biol. Veg.*, 11: 1, 1949. A comprehensive account of the use of tissue culture in the study of tissue differentiation. In French. Some of this work is reviewed very briefly in the article of Gautheret, cited below.

Gautheret, R. J., "Plant Tissue Culture." *Growth*, supplement to 10: 21, 1946. An English summary of some of the extensive French work on differentiation in tissue culture.

Growth in Relation to Differentiation and Morphogenesis. New York: Academic Press, 1948. A symposium of the British Society for Experimental Biology. Many chapters grapple authoritatively and in a modern manner with the problem of differentiation.

Skoog, F., ed., *Plant Growth Substances.* Madison: University of Wisconsin Press, 1951. Includes articles on growth of plant embryos, bud formation, and tumor growth.

White, P. R., "Plant Tissue Cultures," Parts I and II. *Botan. Rev.,* **2**: 419, 1936; *ibid.,* **12**: 521, 1946. General survey of the accomplishments of tissue culture in the study of differentiation.

CHAPTER 20

Plant and Environment

Introduction

Through their effects on plant growth and development the various factors of the environment control not only the distribution of plants in nature but also the pattern of the world's agriculture, crop yields, and the success or failure of certain crops in particular regions. The identification of the environmental influences which are of consequence to the plant and the study of the ways in which these influences are expressed in terms of plant responses constitute an important aspect of plant physiology.

Temperature, light, and water supply are probably the most important climatic influences so far as plants are concerned. These factors regulate plant growth in many different and subtle ways, as is evident from the fact that plants respond to daily changes, seasonal changes, and other fluctuations of climatic components. Other environmental factors influencing plant growth are the characteristics of the soil and, finally, the biological elements.

Of these biological factors, only the influence of neighboring plants will be discussed here, but it should be mentioned that the bacteria and other microorganisms of the soil, and even the animals which graze on plants and disseminate seeds, are also environmental factors of significance to the plant.

Genetic Constitution and Plant Response

The growth and development of a plant are results of the interaction between the genetic constitution of the plant and the factors of the environment. The genetic constitution of the plant determines both the nature of the individual and how this individual will react to the influences of the environment.

We have seen in Chapter 17 how the low-temperature requirement for vernalization of buds or seeds may be determined by a single gene. Resistance to injury by excessive cold, as well as optimal temperatures for plant growth, are also genetically controlled, although in a more complicated fashion. Among the many other responses of the plant which are affected in an important way by genetic constitution are those of resistance or susceptibility to attack by predatory microorganisms. Thus the resistance of wheat to attack by wheat rust, *Puccinia graminis*, depends upon particular genes which have been incorporated into our present commercial varieties. Since the wheat rust organism can also produce new genetic types, it is necessary to maintain a continuing program of wheat breeding for rust resistance. The breeding of crop plants for increased yield is, then, in part a matter of breeding for resistance to disease. It is also partly a matter of selecting plants whose genetic constitution fits them to their physical environment. An outstanding example of the breeding of plants to fit them for a specific environment is the production of deciduous fruit trees capable of growing in subtropical climates. This has been achieved by incorporating genes for low-chilling requirement into existing horticultural varieties.

We saw in Chapter 17 how such vegetative characteristics as tuberization and bulb formation may be controlled by the length of the photoperiod. Thus with onions, bulb formation occurs in response to long days, different varieties having different critical photoperiods. The variety Yellow Bermuda, for instance, will produce bulbs if the photoperiod exceeds 12 hours per day, whereas the variety Ebenezer requires a minimum of 13 hours, and Italian Red 14 hours. In many cases, these photoperiodic characteristics are controlled by one or a few genes. Thus, in selecting and producing new varieties adaptable to specific localities, the geneticist perpetuates those genes which will permit bulbing at a favorable period of the growing season. Here also, the manner in which the plant responds to a given environmental influence is genetically determined.

Temperature

We have discussed in earlier chapters the influence of temperature on individual processes and reactions within the plant. The effect of temperature on all of these individual processes is finally expressed in the effect of temperature on growth of the plant as a whole. From this standpoint, temperature is of interest as an environmental factor influencing plant growth and crop yields. Temperature is influential also as an ecological factor and is, in many ways, the most important of the climatic factors which divide the world into its varied vegetational zones.

The experimental study of the temperature relationships of plant growth goes back to Sachs, who found that seedlings respond to tem-

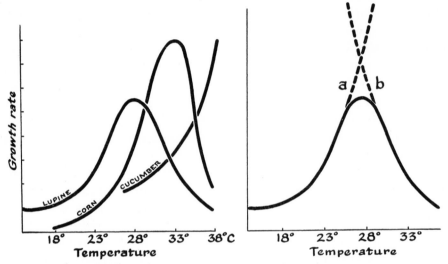

Figure 20-1. Left, *growth of seedlings as related to temperature. Lupine and corn have an optimum in the range studied, whereas cucumber has an optimum higher than 38° C. Right, interpretation of the lupine curve on the left. The increase in growth rate with increasing temperature (a) is ultimately obscured by the increasing rate of growth-deleterious processes (b). (From Sachs' original data, redrawn after Thompson,* On Growth and Form, *new ed., Cambridge University Press, 1942, p. 218.)*

perature variations as shown in Figure 20-1. As the temperature is increased, the rate of growth also increases, until an optimum value is reached. Above this optimum, a further increase in temperature leads to a decrease in growth rate. Why should the relation of temperature to growth be expressed by this type of optimum curve? The reasons are probably somewhat as follows: Chemical reactions, in general, increase in rate as temperature is increased. The ascending portions, designated as *a*, of the curves of Figure 20-1 may therefore be thought of as representing the influence of temperature on the processes leading to growth of the plant. As temperature is still further increased, other reactions, designated as *b*, become of importance. These reactions, such as the heat denaturation and inactivation of proteins of the plant, retard growth. It is the composite effect of these two counteracting processes which results in optimum temperature curves.

Sachs introduced a system for the characterization of the effects of temperature on plant growth by designating three temperatures: the minimum, optimum, and maximum. Thus for corn, Sachs found that seed germinations would not take place below 9.5° C or above 46° C, while the optimum temperature for germination under his conditions was 34° C. The temperature requirements of a great many seedlings have been described in these terms, and we know that different species vary greatly not only in their optimum, but also in their minimum and maximum temperatures for germination. Alpine and arctic plants, for example, may germinate at temperatures close to 0° C and may have maxima as low as 10° C, whereas many tropical species may have their entire range above 10° C.

The maximum and minimum temperatures for seed germination determine not only the geographic distribution of plant species but also the season of the year at which particular species appear in a given region. There are in the deserts of the southwestern United States, for example, well-defined and distinct summer and winter floras of annual plants. Combined laboratory and field experimentation has shown that the seeds of winter annual species are typically able to germinate only at relatively low temperatures. The seeds of summer annual species, on the contrary, are restricted to germination at high temperatures. Thus, temperature determines which seeds of the mixture on the desert floor germinate at a particular season of the year.

After the seed germinates, and as the plant progresses toward reproductive maturity, the optimal temperatures and even the minimal and maximal temperatures required for growth frequently shift. In the tomato, the optimum temperature (night temperature) for vegetative growth gradually decreases from 30° C, in the seedling plant, to 13°–18° C (depending on the variety) as the plant matures. The processes of flower initiation and fruit set may have temperature requirements quite different from those necessary for vegetative growth. Biennial plants require a period of low temperature followed by a return to high temperature before reproductive development may commence (Chap. 17). Even with the annual plants, where a discontinuity is not introduced into the cycle of growth by the yearly temperature cycle, it is nevertheless commonly found that the particular temperatures required for reproductive development may not coincide with those optimal for vegetative growth. For example, spring flowering species such as stocks require a lower temperature for flowering than for vegetative growth, whereas the reverse may be true of summer flowering species.

Thermoperiodicity

Under natural conditions and in most climates, the day temperatures are higher than the night temperatures, so that there is a regular diurnal temperature cycle. These diurnal changes in temperature are important in their influence on plant growth. The optimum day temperatures for growth and development of many plants are higher than the optimum night temperatures. Plant growth is therefore greater in an appropri-

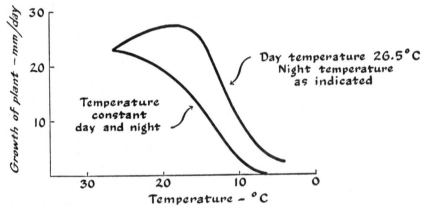

Figure 20-2. *Thermoperiodicity as exhibited by the tomato plant. Growth is, in general, more rapid under conditions of diurnal temperature variation than at constant temperature. (After Went, Am. J. Botany, 31, 1944, p. 140.)*

ately fluctuating temperature than in any single constant temperature. To this fact the name *thermoperiodicity* has been applied.

The concept of thermoperiodic response is illustrated in Figure 20-2, which refers to tomato plants grown in an air-conditioned greenhouse under controlled temperature conditions. Plants were grown at a series of temperatures from 5° to 26.5° C. These plants remained night and day at their respective temperatures. Other plants were grown in the same series of temperatures during the night but were removed to a temperature of 26.5° C during the day. It is clear that with the

26.5° C day temperature, the optimum night temperature for growth of the tomato is considerably lower than 26.5° C, being approximately 18° C. On the other hand, the growth of plants subjected to an 18° C night temperature was greater when the day temperature was higher than 18° C. Both the optimum day and particularly the optimum night temperature decrease as the tomato plant progresses toward maturity,

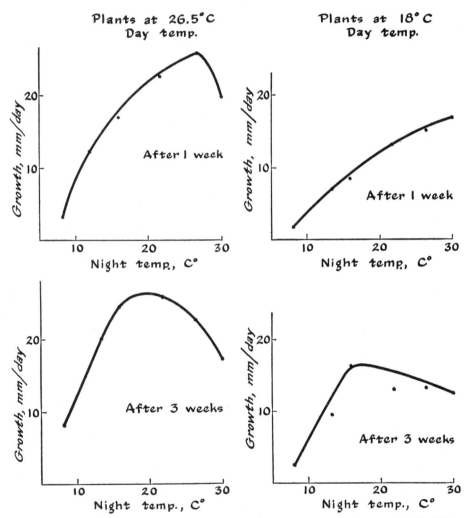

Figure 20-3. *The temperature optimum for plant growth shifts downward with increasing age.* Left, *tomato plants grown at varied night temperatures with a day temperature of 26.5° C.* Right, *tomato plants grown at varied night temperatures with a day temperature of 18° C.* (*Data after Went, Am. J. Botany, 32, 1945, p. 469.*)

as has been noted earlier. Figure 20-3 gives a composite picture of the effects of temperature on the growth of the tomato plant and shows how growth at different day temperatures varies with night temperature and with age of plant.

Thermoperiodicity is clearly an important aspect of the relation of temperature to plant growth. Typical thermoperiodic responses are shown by many different species of plants, particularly those which are native to the temperate regions, where diurnal temperature fluctuations are a characteristic feature of climate. Tropical plants, which grow normally in regions of little diurnal temperature change, frequently show little or no increase in growth in response to fluctuating day and night temperatures, but grow best at constant temperatures.

How may we visualize the basis of the thermoperiodic behavior of those species which grow best in fluctuating temperatures? The growth of the plant over a period of time is the result of many different reactions, reactions which presumably respond differently to temperature. Some of these reactions may proceed both day and night, while others may be confined to the light or to the dark periods. Thermoperiodic behavior implies that the growth-limiting reactions of the daytime are different and have different temperature characteristics from those of the dark period. It is evident that one important process, photosynthesis, takes place in the plant during the day and does not occur at night. On the other hand, certain processes take place in the plant only during the dark period. Growth in height is such a process in the tomato plant, which elongates only at night. We have also seen (Chap. 17) that the photoperiodic responses of plants are based upon the fact that physiological processes occur in the dark which are different from those which take place in the light. It seems probable that in many species of plants the photosynthetic accumulation of carbohydrates and other products may be the most notable daytime activity from the standpoint of long-term growth. Direct measurements such as those given for pine seedlings in Figure 20-4 have shown that under the usual outdoor conditions of high light intensity and low CO_2 concentration (0.03 per cent of air), rate of photosynthesis increases relatively little with temperature over the range of 20° to 30° C, and may even decrease above 30° C. This is in qualitative agreement with the interpretation of photosynthesis as the growth-limiting process during the light period, since, as we have seen, growth does not vary greatly with day temperature, or is at least much less sensitive to day temperature than to night temperature. It is true, however, that, in the tomato, growth as measured over a period of time is quite considerably greater with day temperatures of 26.5° C than with lower day temperatures. This indicates that other unidentified photochemical reactions, perhaps involving the synthesis of specific growth factors, contribute to the response of the tomato to day temperature.

For those species in which stem elongation is confined to the nighttime, as in the tomato, the elongation process itself may be an important element of the night temperature-sensitive growth system. The growth

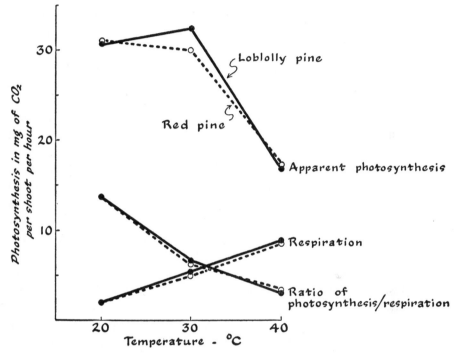

Figure 20-4. *Rate of respiration and photosynthesis with increasing temperatures in two species of pine. (After Decker,* Plant Physiol., **19,** *1944, p. 685.)*

process as a whole, measured, for example with germinating seedlings, has a relatively high temperature optimum. It is probable that still another important aspect of the thermoperiodic response may be the maintenance of a favorable balance between the photosynthetic production of plant material during the day and the respiratory loss of plant material at night. Respiratory rate, in contrast to photosynthesis, is greatly influenced by temperature and proceeds in most species several times as rapidly at 30° as at 15° C. The data for pine in Figure 20-4 show that in this species respiration is more than twice as rapid at

30° as at 20° C. High night temperatures lead to the loss of a very considerable portion of the day's photosynthate as respiratory carbon dioxide, and even under field conditions one-tenth to one-half of the total carbon dioxide fixed photosynthetically during the day may be again released by plant respiration at night. The higher the night temperature, the larger will be the loss of the day's photosynthetic gain. Low night temperature leads, therefore, to diminution of this respiratory loss. In the pine seedlings of Figure 20-4, for example, the respiratory loss during a night at 20° C would be only half that which would occur during a night at 30° C.

The night temperature optimum for the long-term growth of the tomato, and perhaps of other species, may, therefore, represent the result of the combination of favorable effects of high night temperature on elongation and the unfavorable effect of loss of the previous day's photosynthate. Much remains to be done, however, before the effects of temperature on the growth of the intact plant can be interpreted in terms of temperature effects on individual chemical processes.

Low Temperature Damage to Plants

One of the important aspects of temperature in determining plant distribution is the damage caused by excessive cold. Tropical species are, of course, unable to tolerate low temperatures, and for this reason are excluded from temperate climates. Temperate zone species, on the other hand, accommodate themselves to cold either by producing cold-resistant seeds, as do many annual species, or by actually being or becoming resistant to low temperature. Although tropical plants may be damaged by temperatures well above freezing, plant damage by cold generally results from actual freezing of tissue, and hence is associated with temperatures below the freezing point of water.

It is well established that tissue damage due to freezing is caused by the formation of ice crystals within the plant. Crystallization may occur either within the cells of the tissue or in the intercellular spaces. The formation of ice within the cell, which appears to be the most usual cause of freezing injury, may take place in the protoplasm as well as in the vacuole. This can be observed *in situ* in the frozen cell under the microscope. As long as the cell remains frozen it is not possible to discern any visible damage, but when the cell is thawed it loses its semipermeability and no longer retains its turgor. This type of damage is thought to result from purely mechanical effects of the ice crystals within the protoplast that disrupt the physical structure of the protoplasm and protoplasmic membrane.

The formation of ice crystals in the intercellular spaces results in the withdrawal of water from, and the consequent drying out of, the cells themselves. The injury caused by this type of freezing seems to be quite comparable to that which results from the drying of tissue at ordinary temperatures. Here, also, death of the cell is probably brought about by the mechanical stresses on the protoplasm and protoplasmic membrane resulting from the severe deformation inherent in the drying and shrinking process.

The rate at which ice crystals form and grow depends on temperature, and it is greatest at temperatures close to the freezing point. If living tissues are frozen in such a way that their temperature is decreased very rapidly to an extremely low level (as by plunging into liquid air), supercooling occurs, and ice crystal formation is slowed or prevented altogether. If, now, the temperature of the tissue can be brought rapidly back through the danger zone close to the freezing point, then ice crystal formation during thawing may also be avoided. Under these conditions, living cells may be frozen and thawed without damage, and this has in fact been accomplished in the cells of certain microorganisms. The necessary conditions are difficult to achieve except with very small pieces of tissue, since with larger pieces the rate of heat conduction out of and into the center of the piece usually limits the rate of freezing or thawing and permits some portion of the tissue to remain at temperatures suitable for ice crystal formation for appreciable periods of time. Quick-frozen fruits and vegetables are ordinarily frozen slowly enough to permit ice crystal formation, and the tissues are always killed by the freezing and subsequent thawing.

Resistance to Freezing Injury

Frost-hardiness is a property common to many of the biennial and perennial plants of the temperate regions. Even so, the individuals of any particular species may exhibit great differences in frost-hardiness, depending on their condition and previous treatment. A plant which is very resistant to freezing injury in the winter may be readily damaged if subjected to freezing during a period of active growth. Such plants acquire frost-hardiness with the advent of fall. The climatic factors which induce frost-hardiness are primarily low temperatures and short photoperiods. Thus, alfalfa, cabbage, and other species may be experimentally hardened by placing them at temperatures slightly above freezing for several days. The low-temperature treatment need not be continuous; a few hours of each 24 hours at 0° C have proved sufficient to increase markedly frost-hardiness in both cabbage and alfalfa. It would seem probable, therefore, that in nature it is the intermittent periods of minimum night temperature which are responsible for the induction of frost-hardiness.

What physiological changes accompany the induction of frost-hardiness in the plant? To what quality of the plant is frost-hardiness due? We have seen that freezing injury is most frequently caused by ice crystal formation within the cell, less frequently by dehydration of tissue by extracellular ice crystal formation. Hence resistance to freezing injury could either take the form of an inhibition or lessening of ice crystal formation and growth, or it could take the form of increased resistance of the protoplasm to the deformations occasioned by ice crystal formation. Present information, especially that gathered by the Canadian Scarth, indicates that hardening is linked primarily with mechanical properties of the protoplasm. It has been found that as tissues are hardened they also become more resistant to the mechanical damage caused by plasmolysis and deplasmolysis. This effect is also associated with increased permeability of the plasma membrane. These physiological changes during hardening are accompanied by two major changes in chemical composition of the plant. The osmotic pressure of the cells of the hardened tissues increases, in some tissues by as much as a factor of two or more. This, of course, is a factor in the frost-hardiness of the tissue, since through the increase in osmotic pressure the freezing point of the tissue is lowered. At the same time, the concentration of tissue protein increases sharply to a value two or more times that found in nonhardened plants. These changes in tissue protein content in particular would seem to be matters of importance for further study in connection with the future elucidation of the mechanism by which frost-hardiness is induced and maintained.

Light as an Environmental Factor

The maximum intensity of sunlight at noon on a clear, cloudless day is 10,000–12,000 foot-candles. During the course of a daily cycle, then, light intensity rises from a predawn minimum to the noon maximum, only to approach zero again at some time after sunset. The plant is therefore exposed during the day to a continuously varying light intensity, and spends a large part of even a cloudless day at intensities less than the theoretical maximum. It is not surprising, therefore, that most plants are capable of carrying out full growth and development at intensities much lower than 10,000 foot-candles. Sunflower and tomato, both typical sun-loving species, are capable of normal growth even if they are shaded to the extent that the light does not exceed 2000 foot-candles. Species which characteristically grow in shaded locations are able to remain alive at exceedingly low intensities, sometimes not over a few foot-candles, and redwood seedlings, which normally grow in the deep shade of the forest floor, are able to grow at intensities of as little as 100 foot-candles.

The effects of light intensity on the growth of plants are related mainly to the role of light in photosynthesis. For a plant to remain alive over a prolonged period of time, light intensity must be sufficient to cause photosynthetic carbon dioxide fixation during the day in an amount which will balance the twenty-four hour respiratory loss. Thus, the minimal light intensity for plant survival must slightly exceed the compensation point (Chap. 2), at which photosynthesis and respiration are balanced during the day. The amount of light intensity adequate for survival varies greatly among different plants. Shade plants, such as the redwood seedlings mentioned above, may survive at intensities of only 2–3 foot-candles, whereas for sun plants, intensities as high as 400–500 foot-candles may be required. These minimal intensities, although they provide for maintenance of the plant, are not sufficient for plant growth.

The way in which the photosynthetic rate changes with increasing light intensity not only is an important aspect of the relationship between each plant and its environment, but it also contributes to the interactions of plants as they grow together. Figure 20-5 gives data on the photosynthetic rate as a function of light intensity for an oak and a pine, both of which grow in the southern piedmont area of the United States. The photosynthetic rate of the oak is not further increased by light intensities above about 2000 foot-candles. The pine is much less efficient in photosynthesis than the oak and is not light saturated even at intensities approaching full sunlight. These relations enable the oak, which becomes established in the shade of the pine, to grow vigorously and ultimately to eliminate the pine, which is unable to photosynthesize effectively in the shade.

Thus far we have discussed light intensity as a quantitative factor in plant growth and have had reference only to sunlight. Sunlight is of course made up of a continuous spectrum, containing all wave lengths from the ultraviolet through the visible region to the infrared.

In Chapter 2 it was noted that either red or blue light alone is suitable for the process of photosynthesis, the only requirement being that the incident light be appropriate for absorption by chlorophyll. The normal development of most plants requires, however, not only the wave lengths of light necessary for photosynthesis but also other portions of the spectrum. Thus normal plants cannot be grown in either red light alone or blue light alone. Plants grown in red light, light from which the short wave-length region of the spectrum has been removed, are generally weak and spindly and show poor development. More nearly

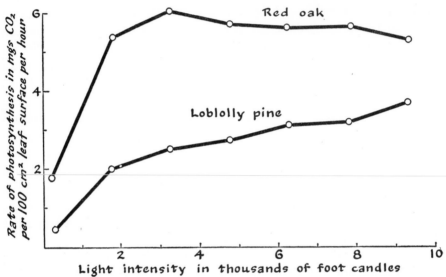

Figure 20-5. *Photosynthesis of lobolly pine and of red oak seedlings with increasing light intensity. Temperature maintained at approximately 30° C. (After Kramer and Decker, Plant Physiol., 19, 1944, p. 352.)*

normal growth has been obtained with plants grown in light from which the longer wave-length regions of the spectrum have been removed, although such plants tend to be abnormally small in stature.

Light regulates the growth of the plant in still other ways. We have already seen that light is required for the processes of photoperiodism, phototropism, and the formation of chlorophyll. Seedlings grown in darkness, etiolated seedlings, not only lack chlorophyll but also exhibit morphological abnormalities, as shown in Figure 20-6. The internodes of such seedlings are unusually long, and in general almost no leaf development takes place. Shortening of the internodes and the growth

Plant and Water

The supply of water is still another environmental factor of importance in delimiting the distribution of native plant species as well as in determining the success or failure of agriculture in a particular region. Although a few plants obtain water directly from water vapor contained in the air, precipitation in the form of rain is certainly the chief source of water available to land plants. This water penetrates into the soil, from which it is taken up by the roots. The effectiveness of a given amount of precipitation or of a given supply of soil moisture in supporting plant growth depends in turn on the water losses from plant and soil through evaporation. The characterization of a climate with regard to the water factor must, therefore, include consideration of not only the amount of precipitation but the amount of evaporative

Table 20-1. *Relation of Vegetation Type to Precipitation/Evaporation Ratio. (Modified after Jenny,* Factors of Soil Formation, *McGraw-Hill Book Co., 1941, p. 109.)*

VEGETATION TYPE	GEOGRAPHICAL REGION	PRECIPITATION/EVAPORATION
Slash pine	Atlantic plain	0.9–1.2
Oak, hickory	Central lowlands	0.5–0.9
Shrub, grass	High plains	0.3–0.6
Desert shrub	Great Basin and Southwestern desert	0.1–0.2

water loss as well. One measure of the evaporative loss used for the characterization of climate is the annual evaporative loss from a free water surface. The ratio of precipitation to evaporation can be correlated, roughly, with the type of vegetation in a particular physiographic region. Table 20-1 shows that the climates of the forest regions of the eastern and central United States are characterized by a precipitation-evaporation ratio of approximately 1. For the short-grass region of the high plains this ratio drops to 0.3–0.6, while for the true deserts of the Southwest it may be as low as 0.1.

The annual precipitation and its relation to the annual evaporation is therefore one important measure of the water factor in relation to plant distribution. Of equal importance, however, is the way in which the annual precipitation is distributed during the year. Generally speaking, regions with evenly distributed rainfall support vegetation

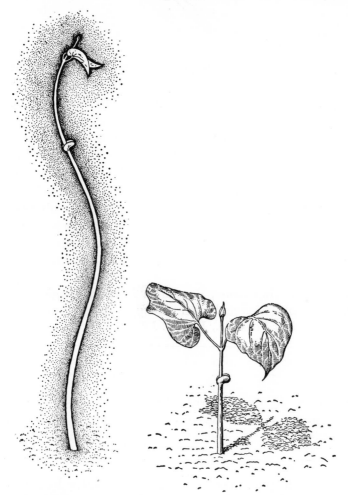

Figure 20-6. *Etiolated plants (grown in darkness) differ from plants grown in the light by their greatly elongated internodes and minute leaves. Left, bean seedlings grown in the dark; right, in the light.*

of leaves can be brought about by illumination of the seedlings with as little as a few minutes of light per day. The amounts of light energy needed to bring about these morphogenetic effects are thus smaller than those needed to cause significant amounts of photosynthesis. Since the growth and development of the plant depend both on photosynthesis and on other light-controlled processes, it is not surprising that a wide range of wave lengths of light is required for the production of a normal plant.

which is more luxuriant than and quite different from that of regions where a similar total rainfall is concentrated in wet seasons separated by long dry seasons. The shrubby chaparral of the Pacific Coast and the corresponding flora of the regions bounding the Mediterranean are extreme examples of vegetation adapted to torrential winter rainfall followed by a long dry summer and fall. In spite of the relatively abundant annual rainfall, these areas are characterized by drought-resistant, leathery-leaved evergreen shrubs not unlike the shrubs of the desert.

We have noted earlier (Chap. 4) that when water is supplied to soil, it first raises the water content of the surface soil to field capacity. Additional water then passes down through the soil as a moving front. Heavy rains, therefore, wet the soil to field capacity to very great depths, whereas light rains, although they wet the soil to field capacity, wet only a thinner layer of surface soil, leaving dry soil below. One can readily see that the distribution of precipitation in individual storms has a great influence on the distribution of roots in the soil. Thus, in desert regions characterized by light rains, it is common to find plants with widespread root systems which are close to the surface. Those desert shrubs which have deep root systems are frequently found to draw their water from a low-lying water table.

The water relations of desert plants have attracted much attention and much study because these species persevere under extreme conditions of drought. Plants of dry regions, the xerophytes, cope with drought in one of three general ways: (1) Many of the desert species are annuals which germinate and grow to maturity in the brief desert rainy season; in fact the entire cycle of growth and reproduction may be completed after a single heavy rain. These species, then, evade, rather than tolerate, the effects of drought. (2) The succulents, of which the Cactaceae are the most familiar examples, are equipped with an extraordinarily extensive root system close to the soil surface through which they rapidly absorb water after even a light shower. This water is then stored in the fleshy organs from which it is lost only slowly, in part because of the small transpiring surface. This small transpiring surface presents, of course, a relatively small photosynthetic surface, which accounts for the characteristic low growth rate of succulent species. (3) The most characteristic of the xerophytes are the drought-enduring perennial shrubs. Although certain of the desert shrubs shed their leaves with the onset of the dry season, others, exemplified by Larrea, the creosote bush, retain their leaves and possess the ability to dry out to a remarkable degree without injury.

Plant and Soil

Not only vegetation but the soil also is dependent on climate. Of the climatic factors which determine soil development and soil type, temperature and water are the most significant. It follows, then, that particular vegetation types are associated in nature with particular soil types, and that this association is due not so much to any cause-and-effect relation but rather to dependence on common climatic influences.

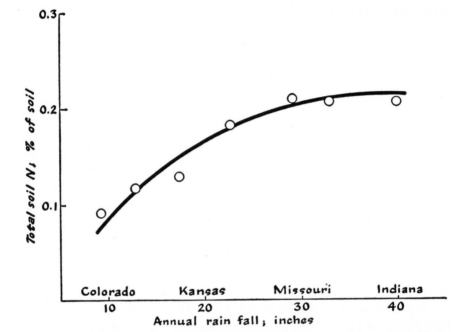

Figure 20-7. *The relation of soil nitrogen content to rainfall along a west-east transect through the central United States (annual isotherm of 11° C). (By permission, from* Factors of Soil Formation *by Jenny, Copyright, 1941, McGraw-Hill Book Co., p. 115.)*

There are, nevertheless, important ways in which climate, through its effect on vegetation, influences soil properties, and other ways in which climate, through its effect on soil, influences plant growth.

The nitrogen content of a given soil tends to remain constant at a level which is characteristic for any particular set of environmental conditions and particular type of vegetation. This equilibrium level of soil nitrogen content varies with certain climatic factors, tending, for example, to increase with increasing rainfall, provided that the comparison is based on regions of similar temperature. Such a relation is evident in a comparison of soils taken along a west-east transect through the grasslands of Colorado, Kansas, Missouri, and Indiana, a comparison summarized in Figure 20-7. On the dry western edge of this region, the nitrogen level is roughly 0.1 per cent of the weight of soil, while on the more humid eastern edge, soil nitrogen values may reach as high as 0.25 per cent. This relation is probably due primarily to the much greater annual production of organic matter by the plants of the more humid region, with a consequent larger return to the soil each year of nitrogen-containing organic matter. The higher level of soil organic matter may also result in a greater activity of nitrogen-fixing soil microorganisms. The relation of soil nitrogen to rainfall is, then, a very indirect one.

Soil nitrogen level is influenced also by temperature. The relation of nitrogen level to temperature can be deduced from comparison of soil samples taken along a north-south transect through the United States along a line of equal rainfall. The data of Figure 20-8, which refers again to grassland regions, show that in the extreme north, soil nitrogen levels may be as high as 0.5 per cent (of soil dry weight), while in the more southern regions, levels drop to less than 0.1 per cent. This relation can be accounted for by a greatly accelerated rate of decomposition of organic matter in the warmer regions by microorganisms which do not fix nitrogen. This results in less microbial fixation of nitrogen and in a lower equilibrium level of nitrogen-containing plant residues in the soil.

The relations of climate to soil and plant include, of course, many other aspects. In regions of heavy rainfall, the exchangeable cations, such as calcium, potassium, and magnesium, tend to be leached from the soil and to be replaced by hydrogen ions. Soils of moist regions, therefore, tend to be more acid than soils of drier climates. Layers of calcium carbonate or lime, if present in a soil, tend to be much closer to the surface in dry than in moist regions. Both of these features of the soil influence plant growth. Thus the short-grass vegetation of the high plains occupies a region distinguished not only by low rainfall and low soil nitrogen level but also by accumulations of calcium carbonate relatively close to the surface. The tall grasses of the true prairie occupy soils characterized by higher rainfall, higher nitrogen level, and much deeper strata of calcium carbonate.

These are some of the ways in which climate influences soil through the intermediary of the plant and the ways in which climate influences the plant through the intermediary of the soil. In spite of the many

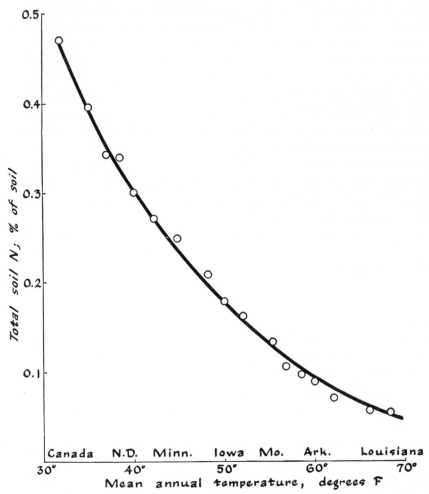

Figure 20-8. *Relationship of soil nitrogen content to mean annual temperature in semi-humid regions. In hot climates there is a greater decomposition of organic matter by nonnitrogen-fixing bacteria, thus reducing total soil nitrogen content.* (*By permission, from* Factors of Soil Formation *by Jenny, Copyright, 1941, McGraw-Hill Book Co., p. 147.*)

interactions between plant and soil, it would appear that the effects of climate on plant distribution are determined primarily by effects on the plant itself. This may be due to the differing natures of the responses of plant and soil to climate. Broadly speaking, the properties of a well-developed soil are determined by the mean of each climatic factor, the average rainfall or temperature. The distribution of plants, on the other hand, is determined to a much greater extent by the extremes of temperature and moisture supply which prevail in a particular climate.

Extremes of soil condition may also play a significant role in the determination of plant distribution. Among such conditions are, for example, extremes of acidity or alkalinity. Particular species, such as Rhododendron and others of the Ericaceae, may be confined to highly acid soils, whereas other species, such as greasewood (Sarcobatus), are confined to alkaline soils high in calcium carbonate. Marked deficiencies or excesses of mineral elements similarly exert an influence on the distribution of particular plant species. Many plants cannot tolerate the high concentrations of magnesium characteristic of soils recently derived from the mineral serpentine, so that serpentine soils support their own characteristic floras. The high concentrations of soluble salts present in the soils of the interior basins of the western United States are not tolerated by most plants, and such saline regions have their own salt-tolerant vegetation, the various species known collectively as the halophytes (Chap. 7). The aquatic plants make up another group limited in their distribution to an extreme condition. Aquatic forms are not only able to satisfy their nutrient requirements from the low concentrations of mineral elements present in the water about them but are also adapted to conditions of relatively poor aeration.

The nature of the soil, then, imposes limits on plant distribution. These limits are most clearly recognizable in locally extreme soil conditions. Under less extreme conditions the interactions of vegetation and soil are of significance for the development and properties of the soil, but, in general, they are not limiting factors in plant distribution.

The Plant Community

Only rarely does a plant live as an isolated individual. More generally, a plant grows in association with other individuals of the same and different species. The individuals affect one another and are in turn affected by the interaction. A group of plants living together and mutually interacting with one another is known as a *plant community*.

The simplest interaction between individual plants of the same or different species is that of competition for some essential growth requirement, such as water, light, or mineral nutrients. Those plants which grow crowded together are individually smaller than similar plants growing widely separated from one another. Reduction in growth of plants in crowded conditions may be due to mutual shading (competition for light), to exhaustion of the water supply (competition for water), or to depletion of mineral nutrients. Exactly which factor is most important can be determined by experiments in which plants are grown at different densities and supplied with excess water or nutrients. The results of such an experiment with wheat are shown in Fig. 20-9.

In this experiment wheat plants were grown at the rate of 8, 16, 32, or 64 plants per container. As the plants grew, they shaded one another, so that competition for light became a factor in all instances. In one series, water was added in nonlimiting amounts to all pots, in

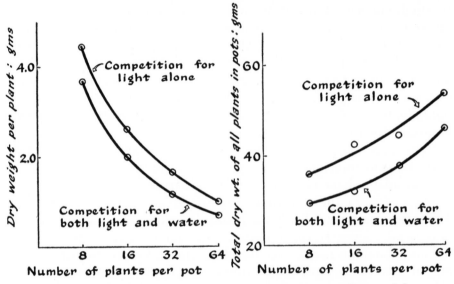

Figure 20-9. *The growth of wheat plants as influenced by competition induced by the presence of varied numbers of plants per container. (Data after Weaver and Clements,* Plant Ecology, *2nd ed., McGraw-Hill Book Co., 1938, p. 161.)*

a second series, nutrients were added in nonlimiting amounts, while in a third series, both water and nutrients were allowed to become limiting. The results of Figure 20-9 show that competition for light is apparently the most important factor in this experiment, although competition for water is also quite significant. It should be noted also that as the number of plants per container is increased, the total weight of plants produced per container is increased in all instances, even though the size of the individual plants is decreased.

An extreme form of competition between higher plants is the parasitic dependence of such forms as mistletoe and dodder on the water and nutrients of their host plants. In such a relationship, the parasite may absorb enough materials to result in greatly decreased growth, and even death, of the host. Less serious for the host is the epiphytism of such flowering plants as Spanish moss or bindweed. Spanish moss, a member of the pineapple family, grows over and may completely envelop branches of the host, thus interfering with photosynthesis by its shading effect. Bindweed, a relative of the morning glory, grows around and physically constricts its herbaceous host stems, thus effecting a partial girdle. In both cases, the epiphytic association leads to decreased growth of the host.

Much has been learned concerning competition as a factor in plant distribution, and this information forms one important aspect of our knowledge concerning plant ecology. There is no doubt that competition is an exceedingly important element in determining the ability of different species to grow together in a plant community.

The influence of one plant on another is not restricted to competition, however, for plants influence one another in many chemical ways also. For many centuries, legumes and nonlegumes have been grown together in cultivation, as grass and clover, or beans and corn, and so on. This has been done because early agriculturalists found that the nonlegume partner profited by association with the legume. We now know that a portion of the nitrogen fixed by the legume becomes available to the nonlegume partner, perhaps in part by the decomposition of legume roots and in part by actual loss of nitrogenous compounds from the living roots of the legume. In general, however, the promotion of the growth of one species of plant by another is found only in rare cases such as those mentioned above. This is because higher plants do not usually need or benefit by organic materials contained in the soil, so that organic substances given off by one plant probably have but little direct beneficial effect on the vegetative growth of others. It is true, however, that the association of two plants may be mediated by chemical substances which specifically influence the process of seed germination. A simple example of this kind of plant interaction is the following: A root parasite, Striga, produces seeds which do not germinate until the root of a susceptible host plant, such as corn, comes in close proximity to the seed. The Striga seed then germinates and is able to attach itself to the root of the host. It has been shown that the induction of germination of Striga seed is due to a particular chemical substance, a rare ketopentose sugar, which is continuously given off by the root of the host plant, regardless of whether seeds of Striga are present or not.

Interaction may also take the form of inhibition of one individual by particular chemical substances given off by a different species. Several examples of this type of interaction have been described, such as the inhibition of tomato and alfalfa by the black walnut and the inhibition of many species by the wormwood *Artemisia absinthium*. In the latter case, it was first noticed that the growth of other plants was inhibited by the presence of wormwood. This effect was found to be caused by a substance, absinthin, which is produced in the glandular hairs of the leaves of the wormwood and washed off onto the surrounding ground by rain. Although many species are greatly inhibited in their growth by absinthin, others are not, and the plants which grow as weeds in fields of wormwood are solely of these absinthin-resistant species.

The influence of chemical inhibitors on the interaction of plants is an aspect of plant ecology which has as yet received little detailed study. Because of its apparent relation to the compatibility of individuals or species in a plant community, however, further investigation in this field would seem to offer an opportunity for deepening our understanding of the interaction between plant and plant.

Summary: The Environmental Complex

The factors of temperature, light, water, nutrition, and neighboring plants together constitute perhaps the most important part of the environmental complex in which plant growth occurs. These factors are in turn made up of many individual facets, each of which may have its own particular significance for plant survival and growth. Thus, intensity is but one of the aspects of light which are of importance in the complex. The seasonal cycle of changing day length, which affects the photoperiodic responses of plants, is another. Temperature has its own roles in the environmental complex. The yearly temperature cycle determines the survival of plants injured by heat or cold. The low temperature of winter determines the degree of the fulfillment of the cold requirements for vernalization or for the breaking of dormancy. Because of the thermoperiodic aspect of plant growth, the daily temperature cycle also has its significance.

Each species of plant has its own requirements and its own tolerance, its own cardinal points for each of these environmental factors. These requirements may not be independent by any means. The factors of the environment may be related to one another, as are high light intensity, high temperature, and other dependent factors of, say, a desert climate. Since light, temperature, and water supply vary not only with geography but also with time of day and season, each species has its own requirements and tolerance for daily and seasonal variation of the environmental complex. The growth and development of the individual plant are, then, determined by the many and interlocking factors of the environmental complex which the individual plant inhabits. Few, if any, species of higher plants have a sufficiently wide tolerance for variation in the environmental complex to enable them to live over all or over even a major part of the earth's surface. We have, rather, a great number of species of plants, each of which has become genetically adapted to grow in its own relatively narrow range of habitats. For this reason, the determination of the exact elements of the environmental complex which are of significance for each species of plant, the experimental study of the relation of plant to environment, is an important part of plant physiology.

QUESTIONS

1. Which of the following is probably most important in limiting the geographical range of a particular plant species? (a) average annual temperature, (b) lowest night temperature, (c) highest daily temperature, (d) highest night temperature, (e) total number of days with temperatures below freezing.

2. A producer of high-grade, out-of-season cut flowers installs several controlled-condition chambers containing panels of fluorescent lights. He finds that, although the light intensity at the growing surface approximates 2000 foot-candles, his plants are weak, spindly, and semi-etiolated. What would you recommend to correct this condition?

3. What characteristics of desert plants particularly fit them for life in an arid region?

4. Why does the light requirement for maximum photosynthesis of a tree differ from that of an individual leaf? How do you account for the fact that "shade" plants are much more efficient in the utilization of light energy than are "sun" plants?

5. Climate may influence plant distribution not only through effects on the plant itself but also indirectly through effects on the soil. Illustrate this with specific reference to soil nitrogen.

6. Why should plants have a different temperature optimum for growth during the light and dark periods of the day?

7. Discuss the relative roles of gene and environment in the bulbing response of onions. Of the three varieties Ebenezer, Yellow Bermuda, and Italian Red, which would be best suited for production in Louisiana? In Minnesota?

8. What is the primary cause of frost damage to plants? How may the plant be made more resistant to low temperature? To what is this increased resistance probably due?

9. Describe several ways in which the members of a plant community may affect each other's growth.

10. It is a common experience that weeds will often grow vigorously in environments where desirable cultivated plants can barely maintain themselves. To what factors may this difference in behavior be due?

GENERAL READING

Bonner, J., "The Role of Toxic Substances in the Interactions of Higher Plants." *Botan. Rev.*, **16**: 51, 1950. The relation of chemical substances to interaction of plants in a community.

Climate and Man. U. S. Dept. of Agriculture Yearbook, 1941. Popularly written, yet accurate.

Crocker, W., *Growth of Plants.* New York: Reinhold Publ. Corp., 1948. Includes sections on the growth of plants in light of varying intensities and colors.

Daubenmire, R. F., *Plant and Environment.* New York: John Wiley & Sons, 1947. Stresses the climatic and nutritional aspects of plant ecology.

Klages, K. H. W., *Ecological Crop Geography.* New York: Macmillan Co., 1942. Environmental factors in relation to the distribution of crop plants.

Levitt, J., *Frost Killing and Hardiness of Plants.* Minneapolis: Burgess Publ. Co., 1941. A fine review of the knowledge on the subject.

Oosting, H. J., *The Study of Plant Communities*. San Francisco: W. H. Freeman and Co., 1948. A general introduction to plant ecology, with emphasis on the communal aspects of plant life.

Went, F. W., "Thermoperiodicity," in Murneek, A. E., and Whyte, R. O., eds., *Vernalization and Photoperiodism*. Waltham: Chronica Botanica, 1948. A detailed statement by the discoverer of the phenomenon.

Whyte, R. O., *Crop Production and Environment*. London: Faber & Faber Ltd., 1946. An extensive rambling account of environmental factors in relation to crop growth.

INDEX

A

Abscission
auxin delay of, 379ff
day length and, 406
pollination and, 380
Absinthin, 480
Absorption
of ions, 89ff
of nonionized materials, 76ff
of solutes, 74ff
Accumulation, of solutes, 89ff
Acetaldehyde, 232, 240
Acetate,
in fat metabolism, 292f
in respiration. 227, 241ff
Acetyl phosphate,
in fat metabolism, 292ff, 298f
in respiration, 227, 241f
Achene, strawberry, 415f
Acidity,
plant growth and, 67ff
soil, 137, 477
Acids,
fatty, 287ff
plant, 240f
Aconitase, 241f
cis-Aconitic acid, 240, 242
Action spectrum,
of photoperiodism, 400
of photosynthesis, 27
of phototropism, 366f
Activation energy, 181f
Addicott, F. T., 446
Adenase, 302
Adenine, 236, 247, 301f
nucleotides and, 268, 269
as leaf growth hormone, 343
as bud factor, 448
Adenosine, 247, 268
Adenosine diphosphate, 228, 230f, 247ff
Adenosine triphosphate, 228, 230f, 247ff, 293, 301
Adenylic acid, 247, 268
ADP, see Adenosine Diphosphate
Adventitious roots, 443ff
Aeration,
bud formation and, 447ff
and root growth, 50ff
After-ripening, 428ff
Aglycon, 310
Agrobacterium tumefaciens, 377, 453
Akamine, E. K., 425
Alanine, 256ff
Albino plants, 31

Albumins, 263ff
Alcoholic fermentation, 231ff
Alcohols, long chain, in waxes, 285, 294
Algae,
nitrogen fixation in, 277
permeability relations of, 76ff
photosynthesis in, 14ff
solute accumulation by, 90
Aldolase, 229
Aleurone, proteins in, 264
Alkalinity, soil, 138, 477
Alkaloids, 300ff
Allard, H. A., 393f, 423
Alpine plants,
germination of, 461
Aluminum,
in plant nutrition, 69
in soil, 131
Amino acids, 256ff
formation of, 258f
as growth factors, 254, 338ff
metabolism of, 258ff
in plant nutrition, 254
structures of, 256
Ammonia,
amide accumulation and, 273
amino acid formation and, 258f
free in plant, 254f, 259
as intermediate in nitrogen fixation, 278
nitrate reduction and, 254ff
nitrification and, 254
Ammonium salts,
as fertilizers, 281
as nitrogen source, 57, 254
in protein separation, 262f
α-Amylase, 202
β-Amylase, 200f
Amylopectin, 197f
Amylose, 197f
Anderson, D. B., 98
Annual,
vs. biennial habit, 407
desert, germination of, 461
Annual-biennial grafts, 412
Anthocyanidins, 310
Anthocyanins, 310ff
effect of nitrogen deficiency on, 57
Apical dominance, 373
Aquatic plants, 477
Arabans, in cell wall, 210
L-Arabinose, 190
Arctic plants, germination of, 461
Arginine, 257ff
Arnon, D. I., 56, 68
Ascorbic acid, 179

485